GENERAL COLLEGE MATHEMATICS

GENERAL COLLEGE MATHEMATICS

W. L. AYRES, CLEOTA G. FRY, H. F. S. JONAH

Department of Mathematics, Purdue University

McGraw-Hill Book Company, Inc.

New York Toronto London

1952

General College Mathematics

Library of Congress Catalog Card Number: 52-5327

IV

THE MAPLE PRESS COMPANY, YORK, PA.

What and Why

All scientific education which does not commence with mathematics is, of necessity, defective at its foundation. COMTE

Most first-year courses in mathematics are planned to provide the foundation for the calculus and other advanced mathematics. They do not fit the large group of students who will major in the humanities and in the biological and social sciences and who do not expect to study mathematics beyond the one-year course. This book has been planned for this group and every topic has been chosen to fit their needs.

In the course of the year, we shall study some topics that may be slightly familiar, as well as some quite new ideas. We shall dip back into arithmetic for another look at ratios and percentages. These are used in many different places in college courses, in newspapers and magazines, in the world of business and finance, and every intelligent person must understand them and their uses. We shall examine closely the properties of linear and quadratic relations, since here are found most of the laws of the physical world about us. Because a bit of trigonometry is needed in physics and some other college courses, we shall learn the necessary parts.

Most of the topics mentioned above are familiar and occur in most freshman courses. In addition, we shall study some subjects not often found in the traditional courses. We shall examine interest and its application to installment buying. We shall learn the laws of growth as applied to population studies, growth of bacteria, and decay of radioactive substances. We shall spend considerable time on probability and statistics, since some knowledge of these is necessary to every educated person. Any study of social problems, economic situations, market possibilities, or scientific investigation usually employs the language of statistics. Finally, at the end of the book we shall examine briefly a few topics from logic and modern mathematics. These may prove interesting and certainly will upset any idea that mathematics was all done before the time of Columbus. We shall even talk about a few problems that seem quite simple but which mathematicians have not yet been able to solve.

Throughout the year the emphasis will be on thinking things out rather than on memory, on understanding rather than on drill or technique, and on problems from life rather than on mathematical equations and formulas. It is assumed that the students have had a year of high-school algebra and know a little about plane geometry. Even if the student has forgotten some of this, it will not be too serious, for he is expected to reason rather than to remember.

Finally, the authors will have failed unless the student finds something of interest and of fun, too, in this year's course. Believe it or not, there is fun in mathematics! This book even contains a series of problems "Just for Fun!" Some of these are quite simple and others will require some careful reasoning. In most cases they require little or no formal mathematics but will require a thinking cap. It is hoped that they will add some spice and excitement to the course. They are not expected to be part of the regular class assignments but will challenge and amuse the thinking student.

The authors have found that the material of this book can be covered in two semesters with classes meeting three times a week, although it would be preferable to devote a bit more time on some topics. With a few exceptions the chapters are independent. Chapters 4, 5, and 6 form a unit on algebra, chapters 7 to 13 form a unit on trigonometry, chapter 15 leads naturally into growth (chapter 16), and probability (chapter 17) is a necessary introduction to statistics (chapters 18, 19, 20). These units and other chapters may be taken in any order, and some of the earlier more elementary chapters may be omitted, if desired.

The authors are indebted to their colleagues K. W. Crain, John Dyer-Bennet, P. E. Irick, M. W. Keller, Marian Moore, A. H. Smith, E. A. Trabant, and M. S. Webster, who have taught the material of this book in mimeographed form and have been generous with suggestions and criticisms.

W. L. Ayres
Cleota G. Fry
H. F. S. Jonah

Lafayette, Indiana
June, 1952

Contents

CHAPTER

1

Charts and Graphs

(*Seeing Is Believing*)

Order and regularity are more clearly recognized when exhibited to the eye in a picture than they are when presented to the eye in any other manner.

DR. WHEWELL

1. Charts and graphs

Psychologists have discovered that we are less likely to forget a fact if we have seen it in picture form in addition to hearing it. We have also been told that one good picture is worth a thousand words. For these reasons, we try to exhibit our work and problems pictorially. By so doing, we are often able to solve difficult problems or at least get a better understanding of the problem at hand. "Always draw a picture" is a very good piece of advice.

A chart or graph is a diagrammatic representation of facts which enables us to grasp quickly the information. Scientists use graphs as a convenient method for recording and studying the results of experiments. Businessmen who desire to know at a glance the condition and trend of their sales, cost, profits, etc., resort to graphs. A very important use of graphs in practical work is in making approximate calculations rapidly.

We shall discuss some of the common types of charts and graphs. The student will recall having seen many examples of these in newspapers, magazines, and advertising literature. The main types of graphs used to illustrate data are bar graphs, line graphs, and circle graphs.

2. Bar graphs

In constructing a bar graph, the quantities are represented by heavy lines or bars with lengths proportional to the number. Sometimes the bars are placed side by side, and sometimes they are separated by a small distance. If there is to be a close comparison made between two or more of the variables, the bars are placed side by side. If we are clever, we may use different colors or shadings and other devices to bring out the points that we are trying to show.

As an example of a bar graph, consider Table 1, showing data taken from the U.S. Public Roads Administration, SMB Tables.

TABLE 1. Surfaced Roads Built by State Highway Departments

Year	*Portland cement concrete*	*Bituminous type*	*Gravel, stone, and stabilized soil*	*Total*
1928	6,171	3,583	10,823	20,577
1929	7,091	3,398	14,582	25,071
1930	8,814	3,344	15,306	27,464
1931	9,825	4,141	20,573	34,539
1932	7,067	4,284	18,226	29,577
1933	4,797	4,180	18,236	27,213
1934	3,790	21,687	10,336	35,813
1935	2,350	10,768	10,412	23,530
1936	2,610	14,774	11,529	28,913
1937	3,717	17,046	6,354	27,117
1938	3,120	20,366	9,931	33,417
1939	2,443	18,525	7,983	28,951
1940	1,956	20,358	5,958	28,272
1941	2,203	20,151	6,857	29,211
1942	1,416	10,931	4,696	17,043
1943	1,071	9,880	3,283	14,234
1944	591	11,403	1,641	13,635
1945	423	12,001	2,153	14,577
1946	779	15,830	3,832	20,441

Most people would take one look at this table and quit in disgust, because there are too many figures to be comprehended. Let us concentrate on only one column, for example, the last. We note that there is an increase in the number of miles of roads built between 1928 and 1931, and then there is a decrease until 1934. Then there is another large increase, which is followed by a large decrease, etc. On the whole, the figures appear dull and uninteresting, and most of us do not see at a single glance or in several glances the relation between the numbers.

On the other hand, let us choose a suitable scale and use a bar graph to picture the last column of this table, and the dull table of data comes to life (Fig. 1).

We get at once a means of comparing the number of miles of roads constructed in the United States during these years. We see that the construction in 1939, 1940, and 1941 was about the same. Then there

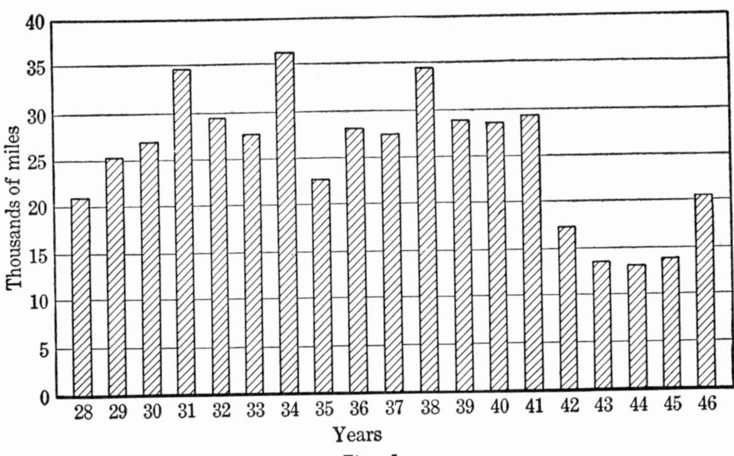

Fig. 1

was a big drop in 1942, a smaller drop in 1943 and 1944, etc. A moment's consideration of the economic state of this country during the years from 1928 to 1947 will furnish some of the reasons for the wide variation in the mileage of roads built.

If we wonder just how many miles of each total were concrete, bituminous, or gravel, we can easily show these various parts of the whole by using different colors or shadings (Fig. 2).

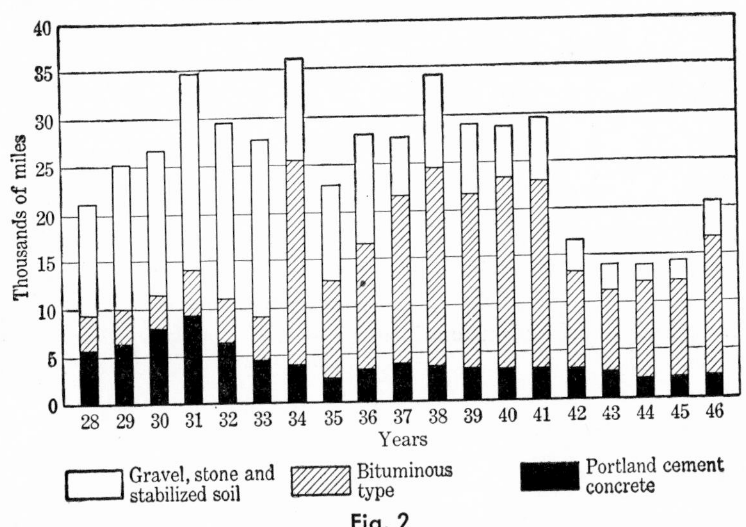

Fig. 2

If you drive a car and have been complaining about the condition of the roads in this country, this chart should give you an insight into the reasons for such road conditions.

3. Percentage

The chart in Fig. 2 does not show clearly the trend in the proportion of different types of road construction. We might ask whether the proportion of concrete construction was increasing between 1928 and 1946. Such questions are answered by graphing the percentages of the three types of construction.

The word "percentage" or "per cent" is derived from the Latin words *per centum*, meaning "out of a hundred," and in everyday language means a hundredth part of a quantity. If an organization had 100 members and 90 attended a meeting, the attendance would have been 90 out of 100, or 90 per cent, for that meeting. If a student answers 8 questions correctly out of 10 questions, his per cent score is 80 per cent. The symbol % is used to denote per cent. One per cent is written as 1%, and 20 per cent is written as 20%.

Per cent is a ratio of something. For purposes of calculation, per cent must be changed into either decimal or fraction ratios. If there were 30 questions on a test and a student answered 70% of them correctly, he would have answered $\frac{70}{100}(30) = 21$ questions. We could have obtained this answer by multiplying 30 by 0.7, since $70\% = 0.7$.

Common fraction ratios may be changed into per cents. For example,

$$\frac{1}{8} = 0.125 = \frac{12.5}{100} = 12.5\%$$

$$\frac{3}{4} = 0.75 = \frac{75}{100} = 75\%$$

EXERCISES

1. Change the following to fractions and decimals:

a. 62½% *b.* 33.3%
c. 125% *d.* 37.5%
e. 12.5% *f.* 200%

2. Change the following fractions into per cent:

a. ⅞ *b.* ⅚
c. ⅔ *d.* ⅗
e. ⅙ *f.* ¼

3. For the data in Table 1 (page 2), determine the percentage of concrete, bituminous, and gravel road constructed in the years 1930, 1935, 1940, and 1945.

4. Choose a suitable scale and construct a bar graph similar to that in Fig. 2 for the percentages obtained in Prob. 3.

5. Does this chart for Prob. 4 give as much information as the chart shown in Fig. 2 for the same years? Discuss.

6. Which chart do you prefer? Discuss.

??????????? PROBLEM JUST FOR FUN ???????????

The eight digits are arranged in two columns as shown.

3	6
2	4
7	5
9	8

Can you rearrange the numbers, moving as few as possible, so that the two columns will add to the same number?

??????????????? JUST FOR FUN ???????????????

4. Another example of a bar graph

Table 2 gives the percentage of new businesses, current business population, and commercial failures in each of the nine geographical regions in the United States. These percentages are based on totals for

TABLE 2

Region	*New businesses, %*	*Total number of businesses, %*	*Business failures, %*
New England	5.5	6.8	11.5
Middle Atlantic	19.2	22.4	28.0
East North Central	19.3	20.9	16.8
West North Central	11.2	11.0	4.3
South Atlantic	11.4	11.0	7.1
East South Central	6.7	5.7	2.0
West South Central	10.5	9.1	3.3
Mountain	3.9	3.3	3.0
Pacific	12.3	9.8	24.0
	100.0	100.0	100.0

the entire country. The data of Table 2 are taken from "Current Business Trends in the Nine Geographical Regions of the U.S.," a 1948 release by Dun and Bradstreet.

We shall use a bar graph to represent this table. We shall use three bars placed side by side to represent the data for each of the nine regions, and we shall separate the groups by a small space (Fig. 3). This chart

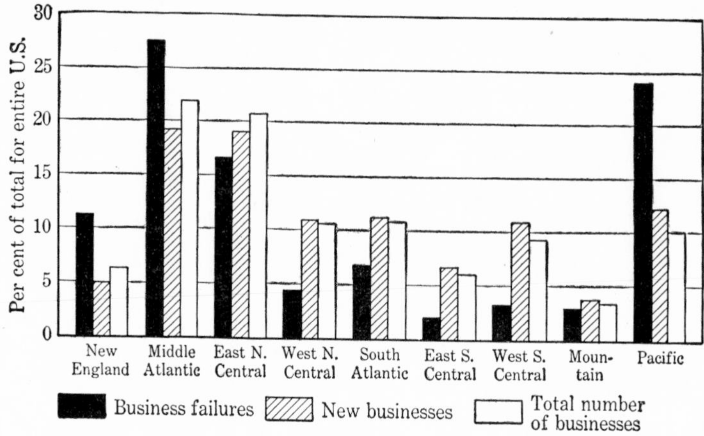

Fig. 3

enables us to compare the number of businesses in each region and, at the same time, compare the business health as expressed in new businesses and failures.

EXERCISES

1. Table 3 gives the enrollment in Purdue University between 1930 and 1940. Use a bar graph to represent this table.

TABLE 3

Year	1930	1931	1932	1933	1934	1935	1936	1937	1938	1939	1940
Enrollment	4,781	4,877	4,242	3,903	4,121	3,945	4,546	5,153	5,575	5,878	5,802

2. Table 4 from the U.S. Bureau of the Census figures and estimates gives the per cent of distribution of United States population by age. Use a bar graph to represent this table.

TABLE 4

Year	*Under 20, %*	*20–44, %*	*45–64, %*	*65 and over, %*
1850	52.5	35.1	9.8	2.6
1900	44.4	37.8	13.7	4.1
1930	38.8	38.3	17.5	5.4
1950	33.0	38.2	21.1	7.7
1990	27.2	34.6	25.1	13.1

3. Table 5 gives the maximum and minimum temperatures in St. Louis, Mo., for the week of Jan. 20 to 26, 1948. Make a chart for this table. Use a bar to represent the temperature range for each day. Your graph will show both the maximum and minimum variation in temperature.

TABLE 5

Day	*Maximum temperature, °F.*	*Minimum temperature, °F.*
20	44	26
21	40	17
22	18	10
23	9	1
24	21	6
25	31	17
26	24	16

??????????? PROBLEM JUST FOR FUN ???????????

When do 10 and 4 make 2?

???????????????? JUST FOR FUN ????????????????

5. Circle or pie charts

Circle charts, commonly called *pie charts,* are useful for comparing the different parts of a whole. In order to construct these charts, we need a compass to draw circles and a protractor for measuring angles. Radii are drawn at such angles to each other so as to divide the total area of the circle into pieces of pie proportional to the quantities represented. The following example will illustrate the pie chart.

For the fall semester of the 1948–1949 year, the enrollment at Purdue University was 11,261 students. These students were divided into the classifications shown in Table 6.

TABLE 6

School	*Students*
Agriculture	1,148
Engineering	4,994
Pharmacy	423
Science	1,847
Home Economics	1,046
Trade and Industrial Education	135
Physical Education	300
Graduate	1,368

Since there are 360° in a circle, we let 360° represent the 11,261 stu-

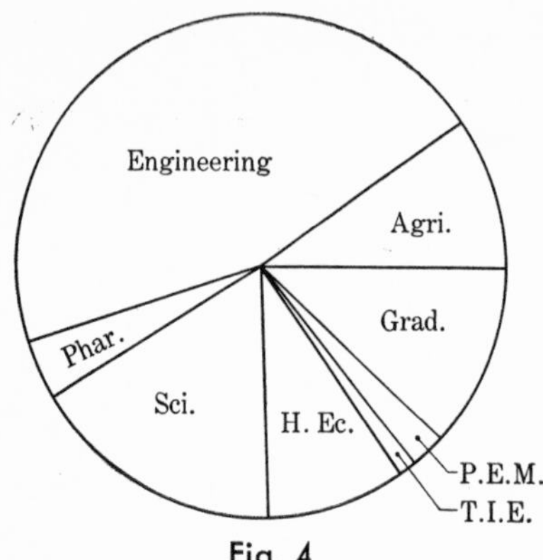

Fig. 4

dents. Then each student is represented by $\frac{360}{11,261}$ degrees. Hence the 1,847 students in the School of Science would be represented by $\frac{360 \times 1,847}{11,261} = 59°$. Continuing in this way, we construct the chart as in Fig. 4.

EXERCISES

1. Make a pie chart for the data in Table 1 (page 2) for the year 1946. Do you like this chart as well as the bar chart? From which type of chart is it quicker to get information? Easier?

2. Make a pie chart for the data in Table 4 (page 6) for the year 1950.

3. The assets of a small community bank are

Cash balances with other banks.	$249,000
U.S. government obligations.	528,000
Loans and discounts.	176,000
Bank premises.	3,000
	$956,000

Make a pie chart showing this bank's assets.

??????????? PROBLEM JUST FOR FUN ???????????

Find two numbers which contain only 1's and whose sum is equal to their product.

???????????????? JUST FOR FUN ????????????????

6. Line graphs

Another type of chart used to show growth or change of quantities is the *line graph.* It differs from the bar graph in that the tops of the plotted data are joined by a curve or lines. It is most commonly used to exhibit quantities which change continuously, such as temperature of a room, atmospheric pressure, etc. In addition, it is used to chart data which do not vary continuously when we are particularly interested in detecting trends. Examples are the daily sales of a department store or month-by-month reports on building construction. Such data might also be plotted in bar graphs, and we should choose the type of graph which gives the best picture of the data.

Example 1. Galileo was the first to discover how the distance a stone falls when dropped from a high building depends upon the time of fall. Table 7 shows the distance d in feet a stone falls in t seconds.

TABLE 7

t	0	½	1	1½	2	2½
d	0	4	16	36	64	100

Solution. We shall draw the distances as vertical lines on our graph. Since we are interested in how these distances change with time, we shall join their tops by a smooth curve, as in Fig. 5.

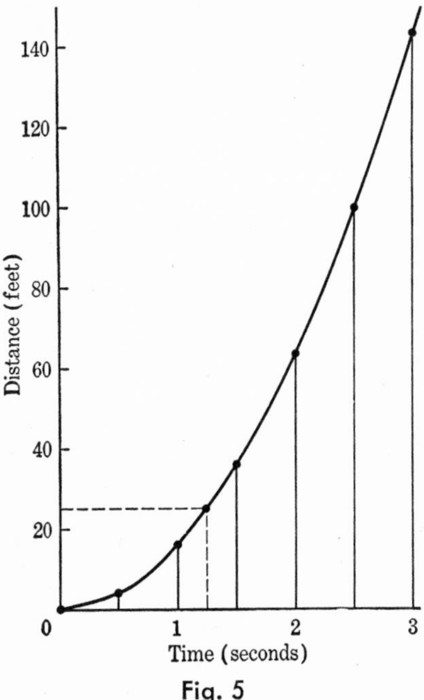

Fig. 5

Example 2. Table 8 is the monthly record of the number of ice-cream cones sold by a drugstore.

TABLE 8

Month	*Number of cones*	*Month*	*Number of cones*
January	302	July	983
February	248	August	2160
March	405	September	1576
April	420	October	603
May	495	November	253
June	764	December	171

Solution. We shall use a graph similar to Fig. 5 to exhibit these data. In order to aid the eye in tracing the up-and-down fluctuations, we join the tops of the vertical lines by straight lines (Fig. 6).

Notice that we used a smooth curve to join the tops of the vertical lines in Fig. 5 and straight lines to join the tops of the vertical lines in Fig. 6. In the first example, we know that a stone will fall a certain distance in any given time. For example, we see from the table that a stone will fall in $1\frac{1}{4}$ seconds some distance between 16 and 36 feet. If we erect a vertical line at a point $t = 1\frac{1}{4}$ (see dotted line in Fig. 5), its end lies on the curve, and its height is approximately 25 feet. We can draw a smooth curve whenever we know that the change from one value of the table to another is a smooth process.

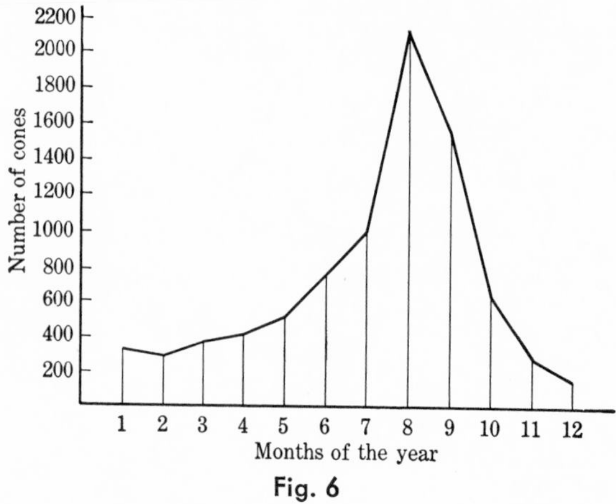

Fig. 6

In Example 2, from the nature of the data we know that the change from one month to the next was not a gradual change. Also, no meaning can be attached to any vertical line that might be drawn between two lines of the data. For example, the merchant may have sold all his cones for the month of February during a two-day period when it was warm. We might observe the graph rising during June and conclude that daily sales were increasing. This would not be a valid conclusion, because we have no knowledge of how the 764 cones are distributed over the month. This merchant would have had a more informative study had he kept a record of his daily sales and the daily mean temperatures.

In plotting values of a quantity which we have no reason to suppose varies regularly, or where no meaning can be attached to the vertical lines drawn between the given lines, we join the ends of the plotted data by straight lines. Where we know that the quantity graphed varies smoothly, we join the lines by a curve.

The graph exhibits the actual variation of a quantity more clearly than tables. For this reason, experimental data are usually graphed and the graph carefully studied to observe the character of the variation. In this way the scientific law behind the data can be discovered.

Example 3. When weights are hung on a spring, it is found that the spring is stretched by different amounts. Table 9 gives the observed stretch of a spring for different weights.

TABLE 9

W (weight in pounds)	0	1	2	3	4	5	6
S (stretch in inches)	0.0	0.5	1.0	1.5	2.0	2.5	3.0

When a line graph is used to show this data graphically, it is seen that the ends of the vertical lines all lie on a straight line. We conclude that the stretch of a spring is obeying a scientific law which graphs into a straight line. With this conclusion, we may read from the graph the stretch for any other weight. For example, for $3\frac{1}{2}$ pounds we read off a stretch of 1.75 inches, and if we wish, we may check this by experiment.

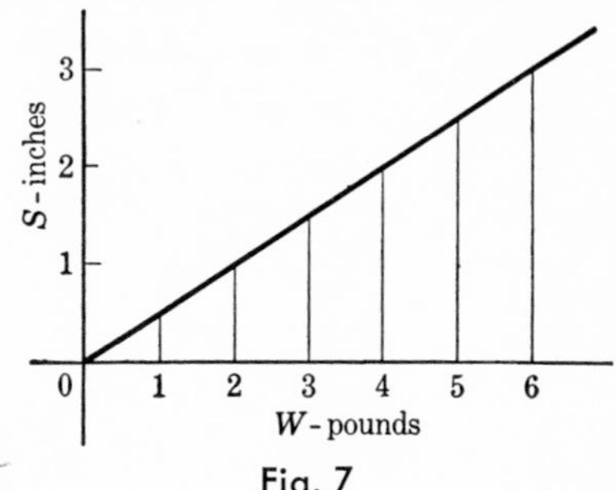

Fig. 7

Example 4. Another type of line graph is illustrated by the following example. The United States Postal Regulations state that the postage on each ounce or fraction of an ounce of first class mail is 3 cents, when the destination is in the United States or its possessions.

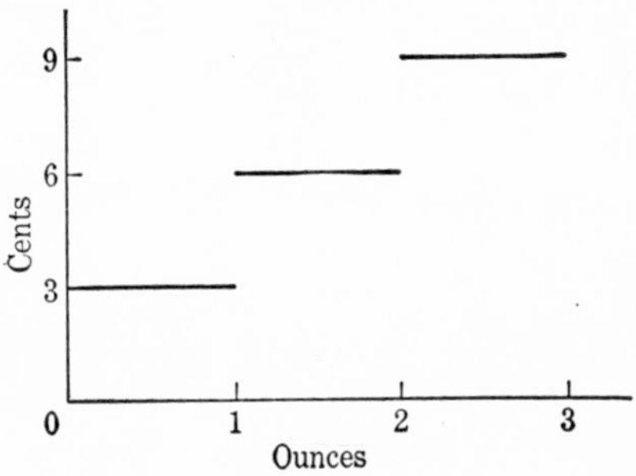

Fig. 8

Solution. The graph in Fig. 8 is a series of horizontal lines which have breaks or "jumps" between them. Mail weighing 1 ounce pays 3 cents and not 6 cents, but mail weighing 1.1 ounces pays 6 cents.

7. Pointers on drawing graphs

The following example will be used to illustrate the method of drawing line graphs.

Example. The atmospheric pressure depends upon the altitude above sea level, and Table 10 gives the pressure for various altitudes above sea level.

TABLE 10

Elevation, miles	0	5	10	15	20	25
Pressure, centimeters of mercury	76	27	8	2.4	0.7	0.2

Solution. First mark off on a horizontal line six equally spaced points, the distance between them chosen to fit the paper. Label them to represent the heights shown in the table. The pressure at sea level (0 miles) is 76 centimeters of mercury, and we erect a vertical line 76 units tall at the point $h = 0$. Any convenient size may be chosen for

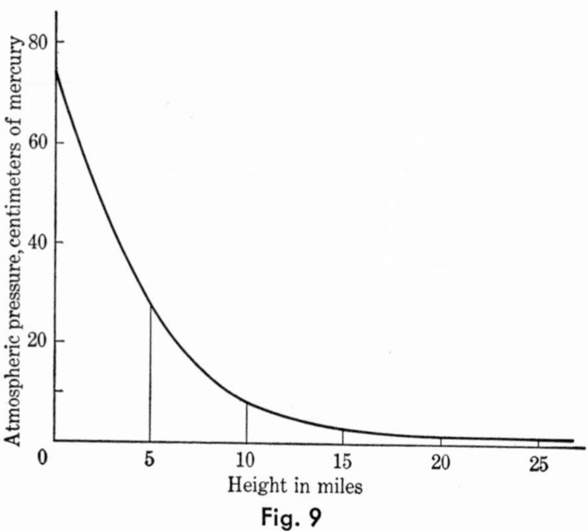

Fig. 9

the unit in the vertical direction. Common sense tells us that the unit should be so chosen that the vertical line representing the largest number in the table will fit onto the paper. Erect vertical lines of the proper length at all other points. These vertical lines show the comparison between the pressure and the height above sea level. We use a smooth curve and not a series of straight lines to join the ends of the vertical lines because we know from the nature of our problem that the change of pressure with altitude is a smooth change and not an abrupt change.

Usually we use graph paper for plotting. This paper is ruled for us and saves considerable time. Study your data and mark off suitable scales. Make your graph as large as possible, since variation is better exhibited by large graphs.

Let the horizontal scale increase toward the right and the vertical scale increase upward. The negative values are plotted to the left and downward.

Make the graph as smooth as possible. Draw the curve lightly until you are satisfied with it, then make it heavier. You will find that you will draw curves better if you turn the paper so that your hand is on the inner, or concave, side of the curve. If one line does not seem to fit in smoothly with the other values, check to see if the line was drawn correctly.

If you are plotting the values of a quantity which you know to vary regularly, join the ends of the vertical lines by a smooth curve. Otherwise, connect the ends of the vertical lines by straight lines.

8. Summary

I. General directions for graph construction
  A. Accuracy
    1. All calculations and measurements should be made carefully.
    2. All lines should be drawn with a good ruler; all circles with a compass.
    3. For most graphs use graph paper.
  B. Completeness
    1. Every graph should have a title.
    2. All parts of a graph should be properly labeled.
    3. Any scale used should be clearly marked.
  C. Presentability
    1. A graph should be scaled to the space to be used.
    2. The page should give a balanced appearance.
    3. Labeling should be neat.

II. Bar graphs
  A. Quantities are represented by heavy lines or bars.
  B. Bars may be either horizontal or vertical.
  C. Bars are drawn to scale—only one scale is used.
  D. Scale units are usually shown at the left and below the graph, but sometimes a right vertical scale is shown also.
  E. Width and spacing of the bars should be such as to produce a pleasing appearance.
  F. Usually the scale will begin with zero, but an exception should be made whenever it makes the variation of the data clearer.

III. Circle graphs
  A. Convert all data into degrees.
  B. Transfer to circle by means of a protractor.
  C. If the data does not exactly fill the circle, recheck your work.
  D. In labeling the sectors of the circle, avoid upside-down writing.
  E. Do not write the number of degrees on the graph.

IV. Line graphs

A. Graph should consist of line segments if the values between those represented have no meaning.

B. Graph should consist of a smooth curve if the intermediate values do have meaning.

C. The line should go *across* the page, *not* from top to bottom.

D. The graph should extend the entire width of the paper.

EXERCISES

1. See what examples of the types of chart we have been studying you can find in the daily papers, especially the Sunday edition, and in magazines. Study them to see what information you can get from them. From your point of view, decide whether a particular chart is the best way to illustrate the material. Could you think of other ways of showing the same material?

Do you think that the average person learns more from graphs than he does from a table of numbers? Do you think that the average person knows how to read a graph and get all the information possible from it?

2. Table 11 gives the number of kilograms equivalent to various numbers of pounds. Make a chart for this table. Read off the equivalent of 18 pounds and of 3.80 kilograms.

TABLE 11

Pounds	0	5	10	15	20	25	30
Kilograms	0	2.268	4.536	6.804	9.072	11.340	13.608

3. Table 12 gives the 1948 estimates of the population in the seven geographical regions of the United States. What type of chart would you use to show this data? Construct the chart.

TABLE 12

Region	*Population*
New England	9,000,000
Middle Atlantic	35,000,000
South	25,000,000
North Central	39,000,000
Plains and Mountains	8,000,000
Southwest	15,000,000
Pacific Coast	14,000,000

??????????? PROBLEM JUST FOR FUN ???????????

Mary selected three bananas and two oranges from a fruit peddler's cart. After she paid the peddler 23 cents for the fruit, she changed her mind and exchanged an orange for a banana. "That'll cost you another penny," said the peddler. Can you help Mary figure out the price of oranges and bananas?

???????????????? JUST FOR FUN ????????????????

4. Table 13 shows the temperatures read on the hour at a weather station for a 24-hour period. Construct a graph to show this temperature variation.

TABLE 13

Hour	*Temperature*	*Hour*	*Temperature*
12	27	12 M	37
1 AM	24	1 PM	41
2	23	2	41
3	21	3	40
4	21	4	38
5	20	5	32
6	19.5	6	27
7	20	7	23
8	22	8	18
9	28	9	12
10	32	10	11
11	36	11	10
		12	9

5. The right fielder throws a ball in to the second baseman, who is 128 feet away. The heights h in feet of the ball above the ground at different distances d in feet from the right fielder, which were obtained from observations, are given in Table 14. Construct the graph.

TABLE 14

d	0	16	32	48	64	80	96	112	128
h	6	20	30	36	38	36	30	20	6

CHAPTER

The Concept of Functions

(*The Mathematician's Shorthand*)

. . . that flower of modern mathematical thought—the notion of a function.

THOMAS J. McCORMACK

1. Functions

It frequently happens that two variables are so related that for each value of the first variable a corresponding value of the second is determined. Then we say that the second variable is a *function* of the first and that there is a *functional relation* between the variables. To make the meaning clearer, consider these examples:

1. The cost of shipping freight between two points is a function of the weight.
2. The area of a circle is a function of the radius.
3. The height of the mercury in a thermometer is a function of the temperature.
4. If $y = x^2$, the value of y is a function of the value of x.

It often happens that one variable is a function of more than one variable. For example, the cost of manufacturing an article is a function of the cost of the material used, the cost of the labor required, and the overhead. The cost of any object depends upon the cost of production, transportation, handling, etc. On the other hand, the price of an object depends upon profit, supply, and demand, as well as cost. The rate at which the population of a country changes is a function of the birth and death rate, immigration, and emigration.

2. Symbols for functions

In mathematics, it is found convenient to invent a symbolic way of indicating a functional relationship between two variables. Consider the first example above: it states that the cost C of shipping freight is a function of the weight W. That is, C is a function of W, and we abbreviate the statement still further by writing

$$C = f(W)$$

The symbol $f(W)$ stands for the phrase, "function of W." If we wish to speak of a second function, we use the symbol $F(W)$, $g(W)$, or $\phi(W)$, etc. If, in the second example, we let A be the area and r the radius, then the statement, "The area of a circle is a function of the radius," can be replaced by

$$A = F(r)$$

The number of miles m that an automobile can travel without stopping is a function of the number of gallons g of gasoline in the tank at the start of the trip. That is, $m = f(g)$. The height h to which a ball will rise when thrown upward is a function of the speed v with which it is thrown, or $h = g(v)$.

3. Definition of a function

We are led in this way to formulate the following definition: *One variable is said to be a function of a second variable if to each possible value of the second variable there corresponds a value of the first variable.* The second variable is called the *independent* variable, and the first variable which depends on the second is called the *dependent* variable. Thus, in the last example above, v is the independent variable and h is the dependent variable.

The serious student may object to this definition because it does not say that one variable *causes* the other variable to change. However there are many functional relations in which a change in the independent variable may leave the other variable unchanged. For example, the postage on each ounce or fraction of an ounce of first-class mail is 3 cents. The dependent variable is the amount of postage, and the independent variable is the weight of the letter. If we change the independent variable (weight of the letter), we do not necessarily produce a change in the dependent variable (cost of postage).

It is sometimes a matter of choice which variable is called the independent variable and which the dependent variable. For example, the area A of a circle is given by the expression

$$A = \pi r^2 \qquad \text{where } A = f(r)$$

but the radius r may be a function of the area, that is,

$$r = g(A) \qquad \text{or} \qquad r = \sqrt{\frac{A}{\pi}}$$

If we know the area of the circle, we can calculate the radius, and conversely. However, there are many cases in which one variable is expressed in terms of another variable, but we cannot reverse this situation. For example, if we know the weight of first-class mail, we can calculate the postage. But the postage does not determine the weight.

EXERCISE

Think up three more examples of functional relations between two or more quantities.

??????????? PROBLEM JUST FOR FUN ???????????

Show that the sum of the numbers from 1 to 100 inclusive is 50×101.

???????????????? JUST FOR FUN ????????????????

4. The important mathematical problem

The important problem for us will be to discover when one variable is a function of one or more other variables and then to express this relation in such a way as to make its character apparent. It is usually a simple matter to observe the existence of a functional relation between two variables, but it may be a much harder problem to discover precisely what the character of the relation between the variables is. For example, it is easy to see that the area of a circle is a function of the radius. But it was no easy job to discover that the area of a circle is precisely $A = \pi r^2$. Indeed, it is sometimes not possible to find any satisfactory relation between the variables. That is, we know that the temperature of a room is a function of time, but we cannot state this relationship precisely. There are many ways of expressing precisely the functional relation between two variables. The most important ways are by

A table of values
A graph
An equation, theoretically or empirically obtained
A precise verbal statement

5. Expression of a functional relation by tables

By actual measurement, the distance D in miles that a man can see on a desert is found to vary with the height h in feet of the observer's eye above the ground, according to Table 15. It is hard to draw any definite conclusions about the functional relation between h and D

TABLE 15

h, feet	0	10	50	100	150	200	300	400
D, miles	0	3.9	8.7	12.3	15.1	17.4	21.3	24.3

simply by studying Table 15. We can conclude that D increases as h increases, but we cannot answer such questions as, "How far can one see if $h = 250$ feet?" To study the functional relation between D and h we resort to graphing, because we have learned that a graph pictures one quantity as a function of another quantity.

The graph in Fig. 10 is constructed as before from the given table of values. The independent variable h is plotted along the base line, and the dependent variable D is plotted along the vertical line.

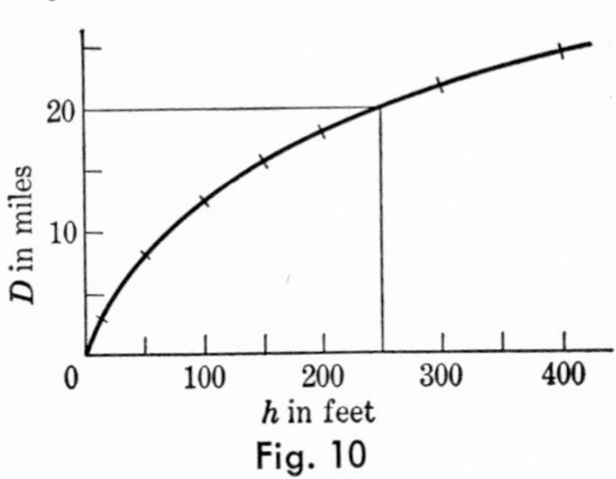

Fig. 10

Although we do not know the exact relationship between h and D (later we will determine this relationship), this graph can be used to answer many questions regarding the behavior of D relative to h. For example, when $h = 250$ feet, D is equal to approximately 20 miles. How much farther can one see at a height of 270 feet than at 70 feet?

In drawing a graph it is important to explain carefully the meaning of the symbols used and to explain the scale. In the following problems, take particular care to label the figure in such a way that a perfect stranger could pick up your paper and make sense out of it.

EXERCISES

1. Which quantities would you plot vertically and which horizontally if you wished to show the relation between the death rate of bacteria and the amount of sunshine to which they are exposed? Between the pressure on a submarine and its depth below the surface of the water?

2. The area A of a wound in square centimeters decreased with the time t in days as shown in Table 16. Plot the curve of healing. Find the area A after 10 days.

TABLE 16

t	0	4	8	12	16	20	24
A	16.3	10.8	6.6	3.9	2.2	1.1	0.4

3. Table 17 gives the boiling point of water in T degrees centigrade at various

pressures in P millimeters of mercury. Plot the pressure-temperature curve. Find T when $P = 825$, also P when $T = 100.8$.

TABLE 17

P	760	787.7	816	845
T	100	101	102	103

4. The amount of water, or weight of water vapor, that a cubic meter of air can hold depends upon the temperature of the air. Table 18 shows the amount of water vapor W that a cubic meter of air can hold at the various temperatures T. Plot the data in Table 18. What is the amount of water vapor in a cubic meter of air when the temperature is 28°? When it is 12°? What is the temperature of the air if a cubic meter of air holds 16.2 grams of water vapor?

TABLE 18

T, °C	W, *grams*	T, °C	W, *grams*
−20	1.0	15	12.8
−15	1.5	20	17.2
−10	2.3	25	22.9
−5	3.4	30	30.1
0	4.9	35	39.3
5	6.8	40	50.9
10	9.3	45	64.3

??????????? PROBLEM JUST FOR FUN ???????????

Mr. Smith had to pay 75 cents a square foot for glass to replace a broken window which was square and measured 4 feet from top to bottom. Yet Mr. Smith paid $6 for the single sheet of glass required to fix the window. Account for this total.

???????????????? JUST FOR FUN ????????????????

CHAPTER

Ratio, Proportion, and Variation

(*This Is to That*)

Mathematical language is not only the simplest and most easily understood of any, but the shortest also. H. L. BROUGHAM

We have seen that the functional relation between two variables can be given by a table or a graph. The next problem, a very important one, is to discover the exact relation which exists between two variables whose functional relation is exhibited by a table of values or a graph. That is, we want to determine the formula or the equation which gives the exact relation between the dependent variable and independent variable. The discovery of such relations is a difficult mathematical study, and we cannot go into this question in any great detail. We shall, however, determine the formula for a few special functional relations which are exhibited by tables or graphs. The procedure will be discussed in later sections.

Before attempting to determine the exact functional relations between varying quantities, we must know the meaning of certain common statements, and we must be able to express these statements by equations.

1. Ratio

When we want to compare two magnitudes, we first decide if they are equal or unequal. If the two magnitudes are unequal, we immediately want to know which one is the larger and by how much. We may compare the sizes by a difference method, that is, subtract the smaller from the larger. For example, if one book contains 486 pages and another book contains 162 pages, we may compare the size of the two books and find that the first book has 324 pages more than the second book. We may also compare the two books by saying that the first book has three times as many pages as the second. This second method of comparison allows us to use smaller numbers and is usually the more useful of the two methods. It enables us to perform computations that cannot be performed by means of the method of differences and is used in making maps, blueprints, and house plans. It is also useful in the fields of science and engineering.

When the relation between two quantities is expressed by forming the quotient of the two quantities, the quotient is called the *ratio* of one quantity to the other quantity. Thus the ratio of A to B is written A/B. If, in the example above, we divide the number of pages in one book by the number of pages in the other book, we get

$$\frac{486}{162} = \frac{3}{1} \qquad \text{or} \qquad \frac{162}{486} = \frac{1}{3}$$

The quantities compared in this way must represent measures of the same kind and dimensions. We cannot compare weight and area, time and distance, or length expressed in feet and length expressed in yards. However, we can compare the two lengths if we convert both to feet or both to yards.

The ratio of two quantities is a pure number. For example, the areas of two circles whose radii are 4 inches and 9 inches are 16π square inches and 81π square inches. The ratio of the smaller area to the larger area is

$$\frac{16\pi \text{ square inches}}{81\pi \text{ square inches}} = \frac{16}{81}$$

As another example, the difference between the freezing point and the boiling point of water is $212° - 32° = 180°$ on the Fahrenheit scale and $100° - 0° = 100°$ on the centigrade scale. Then, between any two temperatures there are $^{180}\!/_{100} = {}^{9}\!/_{5}$ as many degrees Fahrenheit as degrees centigrade. That is, the ratio of the number of degrees Fahrenheit to degrees centigrade is $^{9}\!/_{5}$.

For computational work, ratios should be reduced to the simplest form.

2. Proportion

A proportional equation is formed by joining two equal ratios by an equality sign. For example,

$$\frac{2}{3} = \frac{12}{18} \qquad \text{and} \qquad \frac{3}{5} = \frac{24}{40}$$

When two ratios a/b and c/d are set equal to each other, a proportion is formed which states that a divided by b is equal to c divided by d. The proportions determined by the ratios found in the problems in the preceding section are

$$\frac{\text{Number of pages in large book}}{\text{Number of pages in small book}} = \frac{3}{1}$$

$$\frac{\text{Area of the small circle}}{\text{Area of the large circle}} = \frac{16}{81}$$

$$\frac{\text{Number of degrees Fahrenheit}}{\text{Number of degrees centigrade}} = \frac{9}{5}$$

There are many ways in which proportions may be arranged. It is sufficient to notice that the proportion is simply an equation, and as such, we can deal with it as we would with any other equation in algebra.

Example. Find the area of a room if the length is 15 feet and the ratio of the length to the width is $4/3$.

Solution.

$$\frac{\text{Length of room}}{\text{Width of room}} = \frac{4}{3} = \frac{15}{\text{width of room}}$$

Solving, we find that the width of the room $= 45/4 = 11\frac{1}{4}$ feet, and the area of the room is $15 \times 11\frac{1}{4}$ square feet.

There are many types of problems that lead to proportions. For instance, the cost of a number of objects increases in proportion to the number of objects, so that if the number is doubled, the cost is doubled, and so on. Sometimes a quantity depends simultaneously on two different things. For example, the quantity of work done is in proportion to the number of workmen and the number of hours each man works per day.

3. A word of warning

Particular attention should be called to the fact that the theory of proportion applies only to constants and to things that increase or decrease in *constant* ratio. Careful consideration must be given to this fact. A few examples will illustrate this. If one man can do a certain amount of work in one day, will two men working together do twice the amount in one day? It depends on the job. In some jobs the two men would get in each other's way. If a tank contains 10 gallons of water and it all runs out through a hole in the bottom in 1 hour, would it require double that time to empty the tank if the tank contained 20 gallons? The answer is that it would require less than double the time. If 1 horse can pull a load of 1 ton, could 10 horses pull 10 tons? Only if all horses pull alike in amount and manner. We turn our attention now to problems which involve constant ratios.

4. Problems in proportion

In order to write the correct proportion for a problem, we must fully understand the problem. Read the problem slowly and be certain you understand it.

Example. If 36 grams of water yields 32 grams of oxygen, how many grams of water will be required to yield 10 grams of oxygen?

Solution. We assume that the amounts of oxygen produced are proportional to the number of grams of water. Hence twice as much water should yield twice as much oxygen. That is, 72 grams of water should yield 64 grams of oxygen. Half of 36, or 18, grams of water should yield 16 grams of oxygen. Notice that

$$\frac{72}{64} = \frac{18}{16} = \frac{36}{32}$$

i.e., all the ratios are equal to the ratio $36/32$. In fact, to say that the amount of oxygen produced is proportional to the amount of water is equivalent to saying that the ratio

$$\frac{\text{Amount of water}}{\text{Amount of oxygen produced}} = \frac{36}{32}$$

Now in our problem, let x be the number of grams of water which will yield 10 grams of oxygen. The previous proportion then gives at once

$$\frac{x}{10} = \frac{36}{32}$$

so that

$$x = 10 \cdot \frac{36}{32} = \frac{45}{4} = 11\frac{1}{4} \text{ grams of water}$$

We can solve this problem in another way. Since 36 grams of water yields 32 grams of oxygen, then it takes $36/32$ grams of water to yield 1 gram of oxygen, so it will take 10 times this much to yield 10 grams of oxygen, i.e.,

$$10 \cdot \frac{36}{32} = 11\frac{1}{4} \text{ grams of water}$$

EXERCISES

1. At the time a vertical pole 5 feet tall casts a shadow 7.5 feet long, a tree casts a shadow 30 feet long. How tall is the tree?

2. If 180,000 calories of heat is obtained from 25 pounds of a certain grade of coal, how many calories of heat will be released from 2 tons of this coal?

3. The ratio of the weight of zinc to copper in brass is $2/3$. What is the weight of copper in a piece of brass which weighs 7.82 pounds?

4. When decomposed by an electric current, 18 grams of water yields 2 grams of hydrogen. How much hydrogen could be obtained from 25 grams of water?

5. A piece of alloy contains 3.72 pounds of copper and 2.52 pounds of zinc. How much zinc and copper make up a piece of alloy five times as heavy?

6. Neglecting friction in pushing a weight up an inclined plane, the ratio of the weight to the required force is equal to the ratio of distance to the height the weight is moved and lifted. Find the force required to move a weight of 2,000 pounds 60 feet up an incline to a height of 12 feet.

7. Divide the number 720 into two parts which will be in the ratio of $7/5$.

8. If soft solder is composed of two parts of tin and one part of lead, how much lead and how much tin is needed to make 40 pounds of solder?

9. On a farm, the area of land in cultivation exceeds the area of the grazing land by 150 acres. If the ratio of cultivated land to grazing land is $7/2$, how many acres make up this farm?

10. The scale of a map is 1 to 10,000. What is the actual area in square miles of a section shown on a map as a rectangle 1.5 by 3 inches?

??????????? PROBLEM JUST FOR FUN ???????????

Find the number which when divided by 4 more than itself has a quotient of $\frac{3}{4}$.

???????????????? JUST FOR FUN ????????????????

5. Variation

We continue to try to solve the fundamental problem, that is, to find a way to express the exact functional relation that exists between two or more quantities. On studying the statements expressing the dependence or relation between the dependent and independent variables, we discover that these statements often contain the words "is proportional to," "varies directly," "varies inversely," "varies jointly," etc. For example, the distance that a person can see on a desert is found to change with the height of the observer above the ground; the stretch of a spring changes with the weight placed on the spring; the circumference of a circle is proportional to the diameter; the volume of an enclosed gas varies inversely with the pressure if the temperature of the gas is kept constant; the height to which a liquid rises in a capillary tube is inversely proportional to the radius of the tube and directly proportional to the surface tension of the liquid.

The above remarks with respect to the variation between elements suggest that we discuss the topic of variation, which has a language of its own. We need to understand and translate this language into mathematical equations. Variation is usually classed as *direct*, *inverse*, *joint*, and *combined*. *Each of the four types of variation is described by standardized characterizing phrases, and each type has a standard equation.*

6. Direct variation

The phrases that characterize direct variation are "varies as," "varies directly as," "is proportional to," and "is directly proportional to."

The statement that one quantity A is proportional to or varies as another quantity B means that the ratio of the two quantities is a constant k. That is,

$$\frac{A}{B} = k, \text{ or } A = kB$$

The equation $A = kB$ is the *standard equation* for direct variation. The constant k is called the constant of *proportionality*, or *variation*.

The constant of proportionality k is very important. Even though the value of k is constant, it has the units of the quantity A divided by the quantity B. For example, if the distance in feet that a car travels is proportional to the time in seconds, we have

$$\frac{\text{Distance}}{\text{Time}} = k$$

and the constant k has units of feet per second. On the other hand, if the time is measured in minutes, the constant k will be in units of feet per minute and will be 60 times larger.

We leave out the constant of proportionality only when the variable A is equal to the variable B, or $A = B$. This is rarely possible, as the following examples will illustrate.

Example 1. The cost of a beef roast varies as the weight of the roast. The cost of the roast does not equal the weight, but

$$\frac{\text{Cost}}{\text{Weight}} = k \qquad \text{or} \qquad \text{cost} = k \text{ times weight}$$

In this case, the constant of proportionality k is the price per unit of weight of beef roast.

Example 2. The weight of gold nuggets is proportional to the volume. The weight of the nuggets does not equal the volume, but

$$\frac{\text{Weight}}{\text{Volume}} = k \qquad \text{or} \qquad \text{weight} = k \text{ times volume}$$

Here k, the constant of proportionality, is the density or weight per unit volume of gold.

Example 3. The distance d in feet that a body falls from rest varies directly with the square of the time of fall t in seconds. The exact relation between d and t is given by

$$\frac{d}{t^2} = k \qquad \text{or} \qquad d = kt^2$$

The constant k has units of feet per second per second, or feet per second^2.

Never leave out the constant of proportionality. You may on a few rare occasions find that it is numerically equal to 1.

7. Inverse variation

The phrases that characterize inverse variation are "varies inversely as" and "is inversely proportional to."

The statement that one quantity A varies inversely or is inversely proportional to another quantity B means that A varies with the reciprocal of B, which is $1/B$. Then we may write

$$\frac{A}{1/B} = k \qquad \text{or} \qquad AB = k$$

k is again the constant of proportionality. The equation $AB = k$ is the standard equation for inverse variation.

The equation $AB = k$ states that if A gets larger B must become smaller in the same ratio in order that the product AB remain a constant. In this case, if we triple A, we must reduce B to one-third its original value.

Example. The illumination I is inversely proportional to the square of the distance d from the source of light. The exact relation between I and d is given by

$$Id^2 = k \qquad \text{or} \qquad I = \frac{k}{d^2}$$

We can always find the value of k, the constant of proportionality, if we know the value of one quantity A corresponding to any value of the other quantity B.

8. Problems involving direct and inverse variation

Example 1. Under constant temperature, the density of a gas D in a container varies as its pressure P. By actual measurement it was found that when the density of the gas was 0.075 pound per cubic foot, the pressure was 2,000 pounds per square foot. Find the density when the pressure is 1,500 pounds per square foot.

Solution. Since the pressure P varies as the density D, we can write

$$\frac{P}{D} = k \qquad \text{or} \qquad P = kD$$

But $P = 2{,}000$ pounds per square foot when $D = 0.075$ pound per cubic foot, therefore

$$k = \frac{2{,}000}{0.075}$$

Then the relation between pressure P and density D becomes

$$P = \frac{2{,}000}{0.075} D$$

To find D when $P = 1{,}500$, substitute this value into the equation above.

$$1500 = \frac{2{,}000}{0.075} D$$

Solving for D we get

$$D = 1500 \cdot \frac{0.075}{2{,}000} = 0.05625 \text{ pound per cubic foot}$$

Therefore the density is 0.05625 pound per cubic foot when the pressure is 1,500 pounds per square foot.

There is another way to solve this problem without finding the exact value of the constant of proportionality.

We know from the statement of the problem that

$$P = kD$$

But

$$P = 2{,}000 \text{ pounds per square foot}$$

when

$$D = 0.075 \text{ pound per cubic foot}$$

Therefore

$$2{,}000 = k(0.075)$$

We want to find the value of D when $P = 1{,}500$ pounds per square foot, or

$$1{,}500 = kD$$

If we divide the last two equations, we get

$$\frac{1{,}500}{2{,}000} = \frac{kD}{k(0.075)} = \frac{D}{0.075}$$

We can solve at once for D, getting

$$D = \frac{1{,}500}{2{,}000}(0.075) = 0.05625 \text{ pound per cubic foot}$$

Note. *The student should pay particular attention to the units to be attached to his final answer when he has solved practical problems such as the example discussed above.*

Example 2. Since the distance d in feet that a body falls from rest is directly proportional to the square of the time of fall t in seconds, we write

$$d = kt^2$$

Find the distance fallen in 4 seconds if a body falls 16 feet in 1 second.

Solution. Since the body falls 16 feet in 1 second, we can write

$$16 = k(1)^2$$

The distance the body falls in 4 seconds is given by

$$d = k(4)^2$$

If we divide these two equations, we get

$$\frac{d}{16} = \frac{k(4)^2}{k(1)^2} = 16$$

Then

$$d = 16(16) = 256 \text{ feet}$$

In a problem dealing with variation between two quantities, A and B, in which we know the value of A corresponding to a particular value of B and desire to find the value of A for another value of B, it is not necessary to find the constant of variation. It is quicker to set up the equations for each case and solve for the unknown by dividing the two equations.

EXERCISES

In the following examples, set up the equations for the functional relations involved and evaluate the constant of proportionality when enough information is given.

1. The area of a circle is proportional to the square of the diameter.

2. The circumference of a circle is proportional to the diameter.

3. The intensity of sound is inversely proportional to the square of the distance from the source of sound.

4. The daily wage is proportional to the number of hours worked.

5. The volume of an enclosed gas is inversely proportional to the pressure if the temperature of the gas is kept constant. If a tank contains 8,000 cubic feet of gas at a pressure of 18 pounds per square inch, what is the volume if the pressure is increased to 22 pounds per square inch?

6. The pressure on a submarine is proportional to its depth below the surface of the ocean. Find the pressure at a depth of 1 mile if the pressure at 100 feet is 64 pounds per square foot.

7. A body which is dropped from a height strikes the ground with a speed which is proportional to the square root of the height. An object falling from 16 feet strikes the ground with a speed of 32 feet per second. How far must an object fall to hit the ground with a speed of 80 feet per second?

8. The pressure P in pounds per square foot exerted by a wind against a wall varies as the square of the wind velocity V in miles per hour. If $P = 30$ pounds per square foot when $V = 90$ miles per hour, find the pressure when the wind velocity is 50 miles per hour

9. The amount A in grams of a substance digested in Q grams of pepsin in 1 hour varies as the square root of Q. If $A = 7$ grams when $Q = 100$ grams, find the amount digested in 150 grams of pepsin in 1 hour.

10. A current flowing in an electric circuit varies inversely as the resistance of the circuit. If the current I is 10 amperes when the resistance R is 11 ohms, write an equation for the variation. Find the current when the resistance is 5 ohms.

11. The distance required to stop a certain car varies as the square of the velocity. If the car with a speed of 35 miles per hour can stop in 45 feet, how many feet are necessary to stop a car traveling at 50 miles per hour? At 60 miles per hour?

12. The horsepower required to drive an airplane varies with the fourth power of the plane's velocity. If two 150-horsepower motors will drive a plane at a speed of 75 miles per hour, how much horsepower is necessary to drive this plane at 100 miles per hour? At 120 miles per hour?

??????????? PROBLEM JUST FOR FUN ???????????

'Tis the time for the annual Freshman Hop! The guys are backward and the gals are bashful. The person delegated to see that everyone dances finds three girls and three boys who just can't get together. Trying to remedy this situation, the well meaning get-gals-and-guys-together person arranges the six people

as shown, with a space between the boys and girls. "Let's pair off!" he calls. The plaid couple, the polka-dot couple, and the white couple are to get together. *But it must be done according to the rules.* At each call, one person moves into an empty space by stepping into it or leapfrogging over one person. Boys move to the left and girls move to the right. Can do in six moves. You call 'em!

???????????????? JUST FOR FUN ????????????????

9. Joint variation

The phrases that characterize joint variation are "varies jointly as" and "is directly proportional to." The statement that one quantity A varies jointly as, or is directly proportional to, B and C means that the ratio of A to the product of B and C is a constant. That is,

$$\frac{A}{BC} = k \qquad \text{or} \qquad A = kBC$$

The equation $A = kBC$ is the *standard equation for joint variation*, where k is the constant of variation.

For example, the area A of a triangle varies jointly with the height h and the base b. The functional relation between the area, height, and base of the triangle is given by the equation

$$A = kbh$$

The volume V of a cylinder varies jointly as the height h and the square of the radius r of the cylinder. The exact relation between V, h, and r is given by

$$V = khr^2$$

10. Combined variation

The phrase that characterizes combined variation is "varies directly as ——— and inversely as." If the quantity A varies directly as the quantity B and inversely as the square of the quantity C, the *standard equation for this combined variation* is

$$A = \frac{kB}{C^2}$$

The amount of illumination I on a table varies directly as the brightness c of the light source and inversely as the square of the distance d from the light. The equation relating I, c, and d is

$$I = \frac{kc}{d^2}$$

From the equation, we notice that the stronger the light source the greater the amount of illumination, but the farther away the light, the less the illumination.

EXERCISES

In the following examples, set up the equations for the functional relations involved and evaluate the constant of variation when enough information is given.

1. The area of a rectangle varies jointly as the length and width of the rectangle.

2. The intensity of sound varies directly as the strength of the source and inversely as the square of the distance from the source of the sound.

3. The force of wind on a sail is directly proportional to the area of the sail in square feet and the square of the wind's velocity in miles per hour. If the force on 1 square foot of sail is 1 pound when the wind velocity is 15 miles per hour, find the pressure on 1 square foot of sail when the wind velocity is 10 miles per hour.

4. Using the data of Prob. 3, what must be the value of velocity to exert a force of 20 pounds on 1 square foot of sail?

5. The mass of metal deposited by passing a current of I amperes through an electrolytic solution varies jointly as the atomic weight of the metal deposited, the current, and the time. If a current of 10 amperes deposits 1.08 grams of silver from a silver chloride solution in 96.5 seconds, how long will it take a current of 2 amperes to deposit 0.56 gram of silver?

6. The heat lost per hour through a glass window of a house on a cold day varies jointly as the difference between the inside and outside temperature and the area of the window, and also varies inversely as the thickness of the window. If 6,000 calories of heat is conducted through a window 100 by 150 centimeters, ¼ centimeter thick, in 1 hour when the temperature difference is 40°C., how many calories is conducted in 1 hour through a glass window ⅓ centimeter thick having the same area, when the temperature difference is 20°C.?

??????????? PROBLEM JUST FOR FUN ???????????

Something is wrong!

$$1 \quad 2 \quad 3 \quad 4 \quad 5 \quad 6 \quad 7 \quad 8 \quad 9 = 100$$

The typist left out two plus signs and two minus signs because they didn't look important! Can you insert them in the equation in order to make it correct?

???????????????? JUST FOR FUN ????????????????

CHAPTER

Linear Equations and Relations

(*A Straight Line Is the Shortest Distance between Two Points*)

The human mind has never invented a labor-saving machine equal to algebra. *The Nation*, vol. 33, p. 237

1. The Cartesian rectangular coordinate system

Before proceeding to a more general discussion of graphing, let us pause for a brief look at the framework involved. Let us draw a horizontal line and a vertical line which intersect at right angles at the point O. These two lines form the coordinate axes of the reference system. The horizontal line is called the x axis and the vertical line is called the y axis. The two axes divide the plane into four pieces which are called *quadrants*. For easy reference these are named by numbers, first quadrant, second quadrant, etc., as shown in Fig. 11. The point of intersection of the two axes is called the origin. Scales are marked along the x and y axes. By convention, positive numbers are attached to the points to the right of the origin on the x axis and upward from the origin on the y axis. Likewise, negative numbers are assigned to the points to the left of the origin on the x axis and downward from the origin on the y axis. This reference system is known as the *Cartesian rectangular coordinate system.*

2. Locating a point in a plane

Now, the position of any point P in the xy plane can be specified conveniently by referring it to the Cartesian coordinate system. Through a point P draw a line PN parallel to the x axis. The distance ON is called the y coordinate, or ordinate, of the point P and is designated by y. Likewise, the line PM drawn parallel to the y axis determines the distance OM, which is called the x coordinate, or abscissa, of P. It is convenient to indicate the coordinates of P on the graph near the point by the symbol $P(x,y)$ or just (x,y). In the figure the point P shown has coordinates $OM = x = 3.6$ and $ON = y = 2.2$ or $(3.6,2.2)$. Similarly we may find the coordinates of any other point in the plane or locate the point when its coordinates are given.

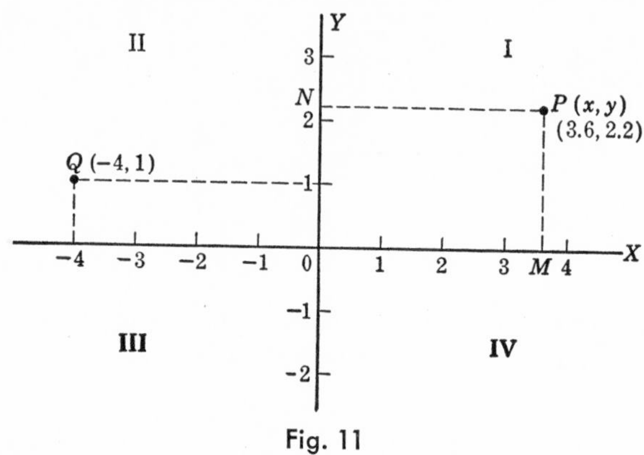

Fig. 11

Let us practice a bit. Let us locate the point Q that has coordinates $(-4,1)$. The x coordinate of Q is -4, so we must go 4 units along the x axis to the left of the origin. Since the y coordinate of Q is 1, we move one unit upward from the x axis. *Remember the x coordinate is always written first.*

The scale on the y axis need not be the same as that on the x axis. We choose suitable scales to make the graph as large as possible. This point will be discussed again in the following sections. It is obvious that graph paper with vertical and horizontal lines was made especially for work with the rectangular coordinate system.

3. Historical notes

The coordinate system described in Sec. 2 above was introduced by the French mathematician and philosopher René Descartes, (1596–1650). This coordinate system joined the fields of algebra and geometry together into the field of analytical geometry. This new field of analytical geometry gave the mathematicians new techniques for solving problems that had defied solution.

Before the time of Descartes the existence and use of negative numbers was a highly controversial subject among mathematicians. With the advent of the theory of analytical geometry, which united the concepts of direction and of numerical distances, it was found that the negative numbers had meaning and a definite place in the number system. The negative numbers were accepted by mathematicians without further argument.

EXERCISES

1. Use graph paper and take the vertical scale equal to the horizontal scale. Plot the following points:

a. (1,2) *b.* (6,2)
c. (−1,3) *d.* (4,−3)
e. (−2,−5) *f.* (−3,7)
g. (2,−4) *h.* (3,7)
i. (−3,−3) *j.* (−1,−6)

??????????? PROBLEM JUST FOR FUN ???????????

Miss Swank, Miss Social, and Miss Highhat descended upon the hatter and demanded the latest creations in chapeaux. The hatter asked the three ladies to take three chairs. He had, however, arranged the chairs in such manner that Miss Highhat could see the hats that Miss Swank and Miss Social tried on, and

Miss Swank could see Miss Social's hat, but Miss Social could not observe the other two ladies' hats. The hatter showed the ladies five hats, three of which were green and two of which were pink. He mixed the hats and from the rear placed a hat upon each lady's head. He asked Miss Highhat the color of her hat. She replied that she did not know. He asked Miss Swank the color of her hat. She replied that she did not know. When Miss Social was asked the color of her hat, she could tell the hatter the correct color. What was the color of Miss Social's hat?

???????????????? JUST FOR FUN ????????????????

2. Take the vertical scale twice the horizontal scale and plot the points in Prob. 1.

4. The graph of the equation $y = kx$

In Sec. 5, Chap. 2, we learned that a table giving the functional relation between two quantities does not picture this relation as well as a graph does. In Secs. 5, 6, 7, 9, and 10, Chap. 3, we learned that we could write an equation for the functional relation between two or more quantities whenever this relation was stated in a definite way. We now ask whether a graph shows better than an equation or statement the dependence of one quantity upon another quantity. The answer to this question is that, although a graph may not be better than the equation or the statement, it will give a picture of the functional relation under consideration, and the student will be better able to visualize the variation under discussion.

What type of curve or graph represents the statement that the quantity y is proportional to the quantity x? Since we can write the equation $y = kx$ for this relation, we must find the graph of the equation $y = kx$. Of course, the curve will depend upon the value of k, the constant of proportionality. In order to get some knowledge of the shape of the curve represented by the equation $y = kx$ and the effect that k has on the curve, let us plot the curve for $y = kx$ when $k = \frac{1}{2}$, 1, 2, -1, and -2. That is, we will plot the curves for the equations $y = x/2$, $y = x$, $y = 2x$, $y = -x$, $y = -2x$.

In order to plot the equation $y = x$, we observe that y is a function of x, and if we change the value of x, we change the value of y. Let x take on different values (both positive and negative), and find the corresponding value for y. For example, when $x = 2$, $y = 2$. We tabulate our results in Table 19.

TABLE 19

x	0	1	2	-1	-2
y	0	1	2	-1	-2

In order to plot the values in Table 19, we treat the pairs of values, (0,0), (1,1), (2,2), . . . , as the coordinates (x,y) of points in the plane. We locate these points on a Cartesian graph and join the points by a smooth curve. The graph of the equation $y = x$ is a straight line passing through the origin.

We plot on the same coordinate system the curves for the equations $y = x/2$, $y = 2x$, $y = -x$, and $y = -2x$ in the same way. We see that the graph of each equation is a straight line which passes through the point (0,0). Changing the value of the constant k in the equation $y = kx$ changes the steepness or the slope of the lines.

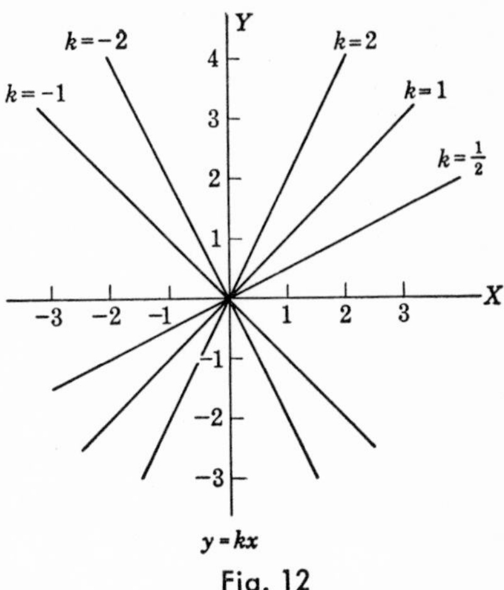

Fig. 12

We can conclude that the equation $y = kx$ represents a straight line that passes through the point (0,0). In the future, when we find a graph which is a straight line passing through the origin, we will know that the equation of the functional relation between the variables is of the form $y = kx$. We can determine the value of the constant k and have the exact expression for the functional relation given by the graph.

For example, we recall that the graph on page 11 of the stretch produced by hanging different weights on a spring was a straight line which passed through the point (0,0). So we know that the functional relation between s and w is of the form $s = kw$. To determine k, we notice that $s = 2$ inches when $w = 4$ pounds, so that $2 = k4$ or $2/4 = 1/2$. The equation becomes $s = w/2$, which gives the relation between s and w. Note that any points whose coordinates are determined from the equation $s = w/2$ will lie on the straight-line graph on page 11.

5. The graph of the equation $y = kx + b$

If the functional relation between two variables y and x is given by the statement that y minus a constant b is proportional to x, we write

$$\frac{y - b}{x} = k \quad \text{or} \quad y - b = kx \quad \text{or} \quad y = kx + b$$

where k is the constant of proportionality. In this case, the quantity $y - b$ *is proportional to* x. If $b = 0$, then y is proportional to x, and we have $y = kx$, which is the case just discussed in Sec. 4.

What change in the curves for $y = kx$ is made by adding the constant b to the right-hand side of the equation? Do you expect the graph of the equation $y = kx + b$ to be a straight line? Of course, we observe that the graph of this equation will depend upon the value of the two constants k and b.

In order to answer these questions, let us plot the graphs for $y = 2x + 1$, $y = 2x + 2$, and $y = 2x - 2$. We make a table similar to Table 19 for each equation and plot the pairs of values (Fig. 13). We see that all the curves are straight lines but that only one of them passes through the point (0,0), namely, the one in which $b = 0$. Furthermore, the lines are all parallel; that is, they have the same slope.

If we plot graphs for the equation $y = -3x$, $y = -3x - 3$, and $y = -3x + 2$, we find that only one passes through the point (0,0) and that all the lines are parallel (Fig. 14).

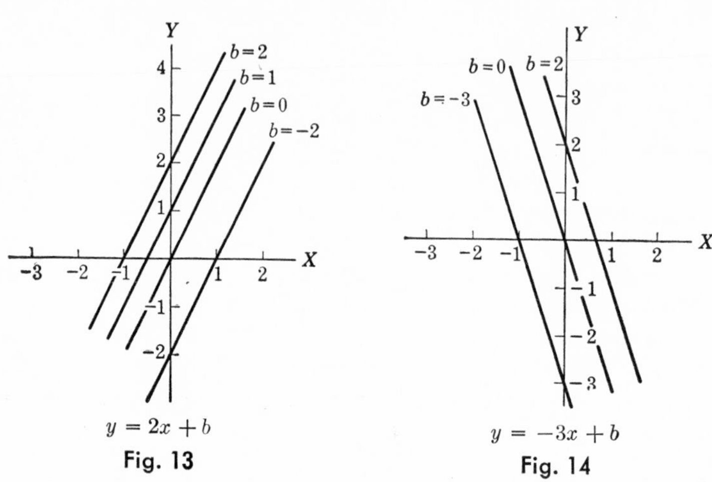

$y = 2x + b$
Fig. 13

$y = -3x + b$
Fig. 14

EXERCISES

Plot the curves for the following equations.

1. $y = 4x$
2. $y = -3x$
3. $y = \frac{x}{2} - 3$
4. $y = x + 1$
5. $y = 6x$
6. $y = 6x + 2$
7. $y = 6x - 2$
8. $y = 2x$
9. $y = -2x - 7$
10. $y = -2x + 1$

??????????? PROBLEM JUST FOR FUN ???????????

Find a number that will be doubled if 24 is added to ⅔ of the number.

???????????????? JUST FOR FUN ????????????????

6. The graphs of the equations $y = b$ and $x = c$

In the relation $y = kx + b$, let $k = 0$, and the equation becomes $y = b$. This is the equation of a line every point of which has a y value equal to b, that is, $y = b$ is a line parallel to the x axis and b units from it. Likewise, the equation $x = c$ is a line parallel to the y axis and c units from it (Fig. 15).

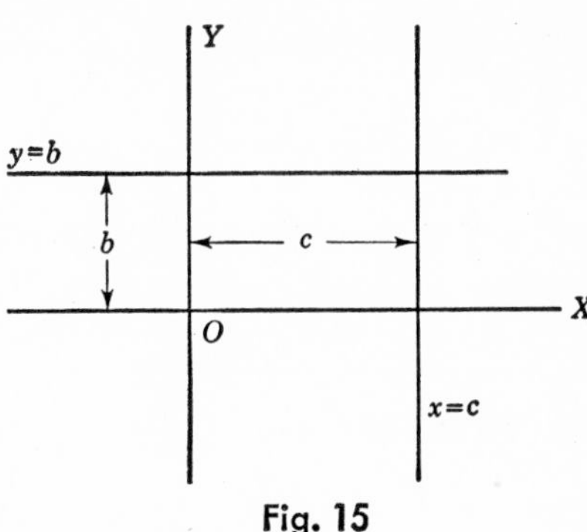

Fig. 15

EXERCISE

Plot the lines $y = 3$, $y = -2$, $y = 7$, $x = 5$, $x = -3$, $x = 0$, $y = 0$.

7. The equation for a functional relation exhibited by a table

Just as before, we can conclude that when the graph is a straight line, the functional relation between the two variables y and x is $y = kx + b$, where k and b are arbitrary constants which can be determined.

Example. Table 20 shows several temperatures, °C, on the centigrade scale with their equivalent temperatures, °F, on the Fahrenheit scale.

TABLE 20

°C	0	10	60	100	160	200
°F	32	50	140	212	320	392

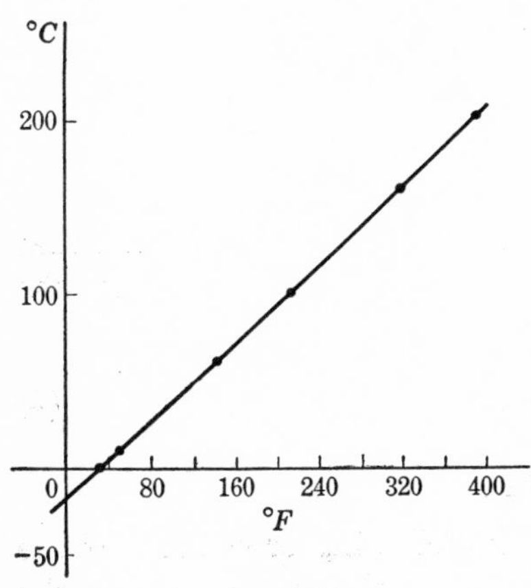

Fig. 16

Solution. In order to visualize the relation between the two temperature scales, we plot the data in Table 20 (Fig. 16). Since the graph is a straight line, we conclude that the functional relation between C and F is given by $F = kC + b$. In order to determine the two constants k and b, pick two corresponding pairs of values, for example, $C = 10°$ when $F = 50°$ and $C = 100°$ when $F = 212°$, and substitute them into the equation.

$$F = kC + b \tag{1}$$

obtaining the two equations

$$50 = 10k + b \tag{2}$$

$$212 = 100k + b \tag{3}$$

We need to determine a pair of values for k and b which when substituted into equations (2) and (3) will make the right-hand sides of the equations equal to the left-hand sides.

Clearly, $k = 5$ and $b = 0$ is a solution of equation (2). However, this is not a solution of equation (3), for $100 \times 5 + 0 = 500$ instead of 212. Likewise, $k = 0$ and $b = 212$ is a solution of equation (3). But this does not satisfy equation (2), for $10 \times 0 + 212 = 212$ and not 50. We can find many values of k and b which satisfy one of the two equations. However, our problem is to find the values of k and b which will make both equations true. In order to find this common solution, we have to solve the two equations simultaneously.

We subtract equation (2) from equation (3)

$$\begin{array}{r} 212 = 100k + b \\ 50 = 10k + b \\ \hline 162 = 90k \end{array}$$

and get

$$k = {}^{162}\!/_{90} = {}^{9}\!/_{5}$$

We multiply equation (2) by 10 to get

$$500 = 100k + 10b$$

from which we subtract equation (3)

$$\begin{array}{r} 500 = 100k + 10b \\ 212 = 100k + b \\ \hline 288 = 9b \end{array}$$

and get

$$b = {}^{288}\!/_{9} = 32$$

Substituting these values for k and b into equation (1), we find that the exact functional relation between the temperatures read on the centigrade and Fahrenheit thermometers is

$$F = {}^{9}\!/_{5}C + 32 \tag{4}$$

EXERCISES

Plot the data given in the tables for the following problems. If the graph is a straight line, find the exact functional relation between the variables. Do your equations have meaning for all values of the dependent variable? Discuss.

1. Table 21 shows the stretch S in inches of a spring as different weights W in pounds are hung from it.

TABLE 21

W	0	1	2	3	4
S	0	0.5	1.0	1.5	2.0

2. Table 22 shows the amount of potassium iodide in grams W which will dissolve in 100 grams of water at various temperatures T.

TABLE 22

T	10	20	30	40	50
W	136	144	152	160	168

3. Table 23 gives the volume V in cubic centimeters of a quantity of gas at T degrees centigrade. Find V when $T = 50°$.

TABLE 23

T	−33	12	27	42
V	160	190	200	210

4. Table 24 gives the pressure P in pounds per square foot due to water at various depths h in feet below the surface of the ocean.

TABLE 24

h	1.56	2.34	3.90	10.95	15.62
P	100	150	250	700	1000

5. The cost C in dollars of publishing a small pamphlet will vary with the number N to be printed, as shown in Table 25.

TABLE 25

N	1000	2000	3000	4000
C	150	170	190	210

6. The weight W in pounds of a barrel containing water is a function of the number of gallons g of water. Table 26 gives the relation between g and W.

TABLE 26

g	1	2	3	3.5	4
W	18	26	34	38	42

??????????? PROBLEM JUST FOR FUN ???????????

Alice skipped down to the spring, gaily swinging two pails. Exactly four quarts of water to bring. "Alas! Alack!" she wails, "One pail holds three quarts and the other five quarts. How, oh how, to measure four quarts?"

???????????????? JUST FOR FUN ????????????????

8. The equation of a straight line through two points

We have seen that we can determine the exact functional relation between two variables if the graph of the variation is a straight line. We did this by assuming that the relation was given by an equation of the form $y = kx + b$, where k and b were constants to be determined. We picked two pairs of corresponding values for the variables x and y and substituted them into the equation $y = kx + b$. We then solved these two equations in order to get the values of k and b. We were able to determine the values of k and b by knowing two points on the graph. We need just two points to determine a line, for if we have two points, we can draw a line through them.

If we draw a line through two points (5,4) and (1,−6), we know that the equation of the line will be given by $y = kx + b$. Let us determine the constants k and b. We substitute the two points into the equation and get

$$\begin{aligned} 4 &= 5k + b \\ -6 &= k + b \end{aligned}$$

If we subtract the second equation from the first we get

$$10 = 4k$$

and

$$k = {}^{10}\!/_{4} = 2.5$$

We substitute 2.5 for k in the second equation to get

$$-6 = 2.5 + b$$

Solving for b, we get $b = -8.5$. The equation of the line through the two points (5,4) and (1,−6) is

$$y = 2.5x - 8.5$$

We have concluded that the equation $y = kx + b$ yields a straight-line graph when plotted. Any equation of this type which involves only the first power of the variables is called a linear equation.

EXERCISES

Find the equation for the lines through the following pairs of points. Use the equation $y = kx + b$, and determine the value for k and b in each case.

1. $(0,0)$, $(-1,3)$

2. $(2,-1)$, $(-3,4)$

3. $(-3,-1)$, $(4,5)$

4. $(-6,2)$, $(8,7)$

5. $(5,0)$, $(5,9)$

6. $(-2,4)$, $(8,4)$

7. (x_1,y_1), (x_2,y_2)

??????????? PROBLEM JUST FOR FUN ???????????

Farmer Brown decides to build a fence around a field which is 10 rods square. How many posts will be needed to enclose the land if the posts are set exactly 1 rod apart?

?????????????????? JUST FOR FUN ??????????????????

CHAPTER

5

Translation into Equations

(An Equation Is a Sentence Is a Sentence Is a Sentence . . .)

> We can always depend upon it that algebra which cannot be translated into good English and sound common sense is bad algebra.
>
> W. K. Clifford

Only in the classroom will we encounter equations tailor-made for us to solve. If our knowledge of mathematics is confined to the solution of such equations, it will be worthless. In life we meet problems stated in words and not in x's and y's. We must translate these words into symbols, which are the mathematical language, before our mathematics becomes useful. In this translation of words into equations and subsequent solution, we see the truly practical nature of algebra.

To solve problems in algebra, we represent by a letter the unknown number which we are trying to find. The statement of the problem leads to the formulation of an equation involving this letter. We try to solve this equation for the unknown quantity. The power of this method lies in the fact that *we may treat this letter just as though we knew its value.*

1. A game

There is a common tendency for students to regard algebra as a set of rules of operation which they use to build certain combinations of letters and numbers. By taking this narrow view of the subject, they lose sight of the real meaning of algebra. The development of algebraic expressions has a practical use when it is applied to solving problems.

Consider the following game. I tell you to think of a positive number, and you think of the number 6; but, being algebraically inclined, I think of *any* number x. Then I tell you to add 3, and I add 3 to x:

$$6 + 3 = 9 \qquad x + 3$$

Now square the result:

$$9^2 = 81 \qquad (x + 3)^2 = x^2 + 6x + 9$$

Substract 6 times the original number:

$$81 - (6)(6) = 81 - 36 = 45 \qquad x^2 + 6x + 9 - 6x = x^2 + 9$$

Subtract 9:

$$45 - 9 = 36 \qquad x^2 + 9 - 9 = x^2$$

Now, I ask you to give me your answer, 36. Comparing this with my general result x^2, I conclude that $x^2 = 36$, or $x = 6$; hence your number must have been 6.

I have forced you in this simple game to perform certain arithmetical steps, while I have been performing algebraic operations. The only difference between your calculations and mine is that you operate with a specific number 6, while I operate with *any* number x. I have gone through the same operations of addition, subtraction, multiplication, etc., as you have. In a certain sense, I have generalized your calculation by using a general (any) number x instead of the specific number 6. In this respect, we might call algebra *generalized arithmetic.* But what have I gained? To some, I grant that I have made things harder; but in reality, I am saving myself a lot of hard work. Suppose I tell you to think of another number, and ask you to perform the same calculations as before. At the end you give me the number 81. Then, without performing any calculations at all, I merely set $x^2 = 81$ and conclude that your number was 9. My algebraic calculation and final result x^2 holds for whatever positive number you choose, for I let x be any number that you could choose.

Example. How to tell a person's age and month of birth. (Have the person whose age is to be discovered do the figuring.)

Solution. For example, suppose a coed is 19 and was born in December. Let her put down the number of the month in which she was born and proceed as follows:

Number of month of birth..........	12
Multiply by 2.......................	24
Add 5............................	29
Multiply by 50.....................	1,450
Then add her age, 19...............	1,469
Subtract 365, leaving...............	1,104
Now add 115.......................	1,219

She then announces the result 1,219, whereupon she may be informed that her age is 19, and December, or the twelfth month, is the month of her birth. The two figures on the right in the result will always indicate the age, and the remaining figure or figures the month in which her birthday comes.

2. The method of procedure

Experience shows that the translation of the problem into the language of algebra is usually the most difficult part of the work. For that reason, we suggest a series of steps which will help the student.

1. *Read the problem carefully.* Unless the statement of a problem is clearly understood, it is useless to try to solve the problem. Careful thought is an essential part of this reading.
2. *Write an accurate statement of what the unknown variable is to represent.*
3. *Express the given data in terms of the unknown variable.*
4. *Write the relations of the problem in terms of the unknown,* thus forming an algebraic equation.
5. *Solve the resulting equation.*
6. *Formulate the answer in the terms first used.*
7. *Check your results in the original statement of the problem.* This will catch errors. Also, sometimes the algebra will give numbers which are physically impossible as answers, for example, a negative length.

Success in this work *requires clear* and *orderly reasoning.* An *orderly arrangement* of the written work not only aids in the explanation of the reasoning but is valuable help in securing clear and accurate thought.

3. Problems involving one unknown

We are now ready to translate some simple problems into the language of algebra and solve the resulting equations.

Example 1. A student club has a cover charge of 35 cents per person. This charge is to help defray the expense of operation and entertainment. If one wishes to drink Cokes, he may order them at 10 cents per Coke. If the bill for a party of two came to $1.10, how many Cokes did this couple drink?

Solution.

$$\text{Let } x = \text{the number of Cokes consumed}$$

Then

$$10x = \text{cost of these Cokes in cents}$$

Also

$$35 + 35 = 70 \text{ cents} = \text{the cover charge for this couple}$$

Since the total cost = \$1.10 = cover charge + cost of Cokes, we have

$$110 = 70 + 10x$$

which is the algebraic equation which expresses the relations stated in the problem. To solve this equation for x, subtract 70 from each member and then divide by 10:

$$110 - 70 = 10x$$
$$40 = 10x$$

and

$$x = 4$$

Thus we find that the couple ordered 4 Cokes.

Let us check this answer: 4 Cokes at 10 cents per Coke cost 40 cents; the cover charge for two people is 70 cents, and the bill is equal to $40 + 70 = 110$ cents.

EXERCISES

Work the following problems using the method outlined above. *Always* check your answer.

1. How many Cokes at 10 cents each were ordered by a party of three if the bill was \$1.75, when the cover charge is 35 cents per person?

2. A party service delivers Cokes. The delivery fee is 25 cents. Each Coke costs 5 cents, and the bottle deposit is 2 cents. Find an algebraic expression for the cost of having n bottles of Coke delivered.

3. If there were 24 Cokes delivered in Prob. 2, find the total charge.

4. What would be the bill in Prob. 3 if there were 10 empty bottles to be exchanged?

5. A well-known pitcher signs up with a ball club. His contract calls for \$25,000 plus a \$500 bonus for each game he wins. Write an algebraic expression for this player's salary if he wins n games in one season.

6. What will be the pitcher's salary in Prob. 5 if he wins eight games during the season?

7. A university contributes an amount equal to 10% of an employee's salary into his pension retirement fund, and the employee contributes 5% of his salary. In addition, the university takes out \$4.55 for hospital insurance and \$4.80 for life insurance each month. What is the employee's monthly salary, if \$25.60 is the total amount withheld each month?

8. How much money is placed in the retirement fund each month for the employee in Prob. 7?

9. It costs a farmer \$8 for each baby pig, and it costs 10 cents a pound to fatten the pigs. If a farmer gets 18 cents per pound for his hogs, how much must each hog weigh if the profit per hog is to be \$10?

10. A grocer needs 15% of his sales to cover profit and overhead. There is a fixed overhead of $700 a month for rent, heat, electricity, etc., and a variable overhead of 2 cents of every sales dollar for checking, cashiers, stocking shelves, etc.

a. Find the sales volume needed to break even.

b. Find the sales volume needed to make a monthly profit of $600.

??????????? PROBLEM JUST FOR FUN ???????????

On his last birthday, Grandfather claimed that he had lived one-fourth of his life as a boy, one-sixth as a youth, and one-third as a man and had spent 13 years in his dotage. How old was Grandfather?

???????????????? JUST FOR FUN ????????????????

Example 2. A salesman makes a commission of $75 on one type of car and $100 on another type. One year this salesman sold 39 cars and received commissions totaling $3,300. How many sales of each type did he make?

Solution.

$$\begin{aligned} \text{Let } x &= \text{number of cars sold at \$100 commission} \\ 39 - x &= \text{number of cars sold at \$75 commission} \\ 100x &= \text{number of dollars commission at \$100 per car} \\ 75(39 - x) &= \text{number of dollars commission at \$75 per car} \end{aligned}$$

The total number of dollars commission is

$$100x + 75(39 - x) = 3{,}300$$

or

$$\begin{aligned} 100x + 2925 - 75x &= 3{,}300 \\ 25x &= 3{,}300 - 2{,}925 = 375 \end{aligned}$$

Then

$$x = {}^{375}\!/_{25} = 15$$

and

$$39 - x = 24$$

This salesman sold 15 cars for which he got $100 per car commission, 15 × 100 = $1,500, and 24 cars for which he got $75 per car commission, 24 × 75 = $1,800; $1,500 + $1,800 = $3,300, which was his total commission.

EXERCISES

Work the following problems. Be sure to check your answers.

1. In a 1-year period an automobile salesman sold 39 cars. He sold twice as many cars on which he got a commission of $75 per car as cars on which he got a commission of $100. Find the total commission made by this salesman.

2. A salesman sold a total of 60 cars of two types during a 1-year period. He received a commission of \$80 per car for three-fourths of the cars sold. How much commission did he receive on each of the other cars if his total commission amounted to \$4,500?

3. At a sale a housewife bought 60 cans of food. She paid 20 cents per can for some and 12 cents per can for the remainder. How many cans at each price did the housewife buy if she paid \$7.84?

4. Find three consecutive integers whose sum is 54.

Hint: N = one number, $N + 1$ = second number, and $N + 2$ = third number.

5. Find three consecutive even integers whose sum is 54.

Hint: $2N$ = one number, $2N + 2$ = second number, and $2N + 4$ = third number, where N is an integer.

6. A farmer receives \$16.90 for his eggs. He gets 46 cents per dozen for some and 32 cents per dozen for the remainder. How many dozen of each grade did he sell if he sells 48 dozen eggs?

7. An art dealer bought 10 paintings at an auction. Some were classical and some modern. The total cost was \$1,387.90. The average cost of the classical paintings was \$212.50, and the average cost of the modern paintings was \$107.20. How many of each type did the dealer buy?

8. The weight in pounds that can be lifted by a balloon filled with helium is equal to 0.069 times the volume of the gas in cubic feet. If the bag, gear, ropes, and basket weigh 90 pounds, write an expression for the payload that can be lifted. Payload is the weight in excess of the weight of the gear, basket, and bag.

9. What volume of helium gas in Prob. 8 is needed to lift a payload of 250 pounds?

10. What payload can be lifted by the balloon in Prob. 8 if the volume of the gas is 10,000 cubic feet?

??????????? PROBLEM JUST FOR FUN ???????????

```
         H U N G
U P ) D O P E Y
      D U
        U P
        U P
          E Y
          E Y
```

This is a problem in long division. Each letter represents a number. There are plenty of clues, too! For instance, U must be 1, since U times U P = U P. To help the cause, we will tell you that D = 5.

???????????????? JUST FOR FUN ????????????????

4. Problems involving two unknowns

Example 3. A man has \$5.25 in nickels and dimes. The number of dimes is three times the number of nickels. How many nickels and dimes does he have?

Solution.

$$\text{Let } N = \text{number of nickels}$$

Then

$$3N = \text{number of dimes}$$
$$0.05N + 0.10\,(3N) = 5.25$$

or

$$5N + 30N = 525$$
$$N = 15$$

and

$$3N = 45$$

That is, there are 15 nickels and 45 dimes.

Check.

$$15(5) + 45(10) = 75 + 450 = 525 = \$5.25$$

Many problems that we have solved by using only one variable can be solved by using two variables and writing two equations. For instance, we may solve Example 3 in the following way:

Second Solution.

$$\text{Let } N = \text{number of nickels}$$
$$D = \text{number of dimes}$$
$$0.05N = \text{value of the nickels}$$
$$0.10D = \text{value of the dimes}$$

Then

$$D = 3N$$

and

$$0.05N + 0.10D = 5.25$$

or

$$5N + 10D = 525$$

which reduces to

$$N + 2D = 105$$

The two equations to be solved are

$$D = 3N \qquad \text{and} \qquad N + 2D = 105$$

Substituting $D = 3N$ into the second equation gives

$$N + 2(3N) = 105$$
$$7N = 105$$
$$N = 15$$

and

$$D = 3N = 45$$

The number of nickels in the collection is 15, and the number of dimes is 45.

EXERCISES

Solve the following problems by using one unknown and one equation, or by using two unknowns and writing two equations. *Always check your answers.*

1. The sum of $1.20 is to be divided between two boys. The older boy is to get twice as much as the younger boy. How much does each boy get?

2. A metal pipe 10 feet long is to be divided into two pieces. Find the length of each piece if one is two-thirds as long as the other.

3. A rectangular field is 35 feet longer than it is wide. If the length of the fence around this field is 310 feet, find the dimensions of the field.

4. An estate of $5,628 is to be divided between a mother, two sons, and one daughter. The mother is to receive as much as all the children, and the daughter is to receive one-half as much as each son. How much does each person get?

5. A boy receives $2.19 from the sale of 90 newspapers and magazines. If the newspapers sold for 2 cents and the magazines sold for 5 cents, how many of each did this boy sell?

6. A woman buys 15 pounds of walnuts. Some of the walnuts are 3 pounds for a quarter and the rest are 2 pounds for a quarter. How many pounds of each variety did she buy if she paid $1.50 for the 15 pounds of walnuts?

7. A grocery clerk has some coffee worth 33 cents per pound and some worth 25 cents per pound. How many pounds of each should be used to make a 100-pound mixture worth 29 cents per pound?

8. A foreman assigned a boy the job of unpacking 100 glass articles. He would pay the boy 2 cents for each article he unpacked safely but would charge the boy 7 cents for each article that was broken. If the boy received $1.55, how many articles did he break?

9. A student has quiz grades of 68 and 73 What grade must he achieve on a third quiz to have an average of 79?

10. A student has an average grade of 81 on three quizzes. What grade must he get on a fourth quiz to bring his average up to 82? To lower his average to 75?

11. A boy goes on a spending spree and spends half his money for a movie and one-third of what remains for candy. On the way home he buys two comic books for 15 cents. How much money did he have to start with if he has a nickel left?

12. A child's bank has $11.25 in nickels, dimes, and quarters. There are two more dimes than nickels, and the number of quarters is one-half the number of nickels and dimes together. How many are there of each type of coin?

13. If the sum of two numbers is 32, and four times the smaller exceeds three times the larger by 9, find the numbers.

14. If the sum of two numbers is 42 and their difference is 4, find the numbers.

15. A grocer charged Mrs. Smith $1.50 for 10 pounds of flour and 6 pounds of sugar and charged Mrs. Brown 65 cents for 2 pounds of sugar and 5 pounds of flour. Determine the cost per pound of sugar and flour.

16. A theater charged 40 cents admission for adults and 20 cents for children. How many adults and children were in the audience of 806 if the box-office receipts were $262?

??????????? PROBLEM JUST FOR FUN ???????????

What happened to the 10 cents?

Two brothers had 60 apples apiece to sell. One boy sold his apples at two for a nickel and received $1.50 for his apples. The other boy sold his apples at three for a nickel and received $1 for his apples. The following day the two boys decided to combine their businesses. They put the 120 apples together and sold them at the rate of five apples for a dime (two for a nickel plus three for a nickel). The boys took in $2.40 instead of the anticipated $2.50. Can you account for this apparent discrepancy?

???????????????? JUST FOR FUN ????????????????

Example 4. How many cubic centimeters of a solution that is 90% alcohol by volume must be added to 1,000 cubic centimeters of a solution that is 20% alcohol by volume to make a solution that is 45% alcohol?

Solution.

Let x = number of cubic centimeters of solution to be added

$$x + 1{,}000 = \text{final volume}$$

Number of cubic centimeters of alcohol in original solution

$$= {}^{20}\!/_{100}(1{,}000) = 200 \text{ cubic centimeters}$$

Number of cubic centimeters of alcohol added $= ({}^{90}\!/_{100})x$

Number of cubic centimeters of alcohol in final solution

$$= {}^{45}\!/_{100}(x + 1{,}000)$$

Since the original volume of alcohol plus the volume added must equal the volume of alcohol in the final solution, we get

$$\begin{aligned} 200 + ({}^{90}\!/_{100})x &= {}^{45}\!/_{100}(x + 1{,}000) \\ 20{,}000 + 90x &= 45x + 45{,}000 \\ 45x &= 25{,}000 \\ x &= \frac{5{,}000}{9} = 555.5 \text{ cubic centimeters} \end{aligned}$$

Check this result.

EXERCISES

1. How many cubic centimeters of water must be added to 1,000 cubic centimeters of a 75% sugar solution to make a 60% solution?

2. How many gallons of two liquids, one 90% alcohol and the other 30% alcohol, must be used to make a 30-gallon mixture with 50% alcohol?

3. A creamery desires to obtain 200 pounds of milk that tests 4% butterfat by mixing milk that tests 4.2% butterfat with milk that tests 3.8% butterfat. How much milk of each test is needed?

4. If ice cream is to contain 12% butterfat, how much cream containing 40% butterfat must be added to 100 pounds of a mixture containing 10% butterfat in order that the resulting mixture contain the required 12% butterfat?

5. A man can sell a piece of property for $5,000 and realize a profit of 10% over the purchase price. How much did he pay for the property?

6. A 98% solution of sulfuric acid is to be diluted with distilled water to make a 90% solution. How many gallons of the original solution and how many gallons of water are necessary to make 10 gallons of the 90% solution?

7. The enrollment in a Scout troop was 32. The troop increased its enrollment by 25%, and later 25% of the boys in the troop moved to another community. How many boys remained in the troop?

8. The sum of two numbers is 65, and their difference is 19. Find the two numbers.

9. Three years from now a mother will be three times as old as her son will be. Two years ago she was four times as old as her son was. Find the age of the mother and the boy

10. A ranch is rectangular in shape, and the long side is twice as long as the short side. The area in square miles is numerically equal to the perimeter in miles. Find the dimensions of the ranch.

??????????? PROBLEM JUST FOR FUN ???????????

Two boys shoot marbles. If a boy loses, he gives the other boy one marble. When the boys finish playing, one has won three times, and the other has seven more marbles then when he started. How many games did they play?

???????????????? JUST FOR FUN ????????????????

Example 5. A man who can row 3 miles per hour in still water finds that he can row 10 miles upstream in the same time as he can row 20 miles downstream. Find the velocity of the stream.

Solution.

Distance = average velocity times time

Let V = velocity of the stream in miles per hour

Then

$$V + 3 = \text{velocity of the man when rowing downstream}$$

and

$$3 - V = \text{velocity of the man when rowing upstream}$$

$$\text{Time to row 20 miles downstream} = \frac{20}{V + 3}$$

$$\text{Time to row 10 miles upstream} = \frac{10}{3 - V}$$

These two times are equal; therefore,

$$\frac{20}{V + 3} = \frac{10}{3 - V}$$

or

$$20(3 - V) = 10(V + 3)$$

and

$$\begin{aligned} 6 - 2V &= V + 3 \\ 3V &= 3 \\ V &= 1 \text{ mile per hour} \end{aligned}$$

Check.

$$\begin{aligned} \text{Net upstream velocity} &= 3 - 1 = 2 \text{ miles per hour} \\ \text{Net downstream velocity} &= 3 + 1 = 4 \text{ miles per hour} \\ \text{Time to row 20 miles downstream} &= {}^{20}/_{4} = 5 \text{ hours} \\ \text{Time to row 10 miles upstream} &= {}^{10}/_{2} = 5 \text{ hours} \end{aligned}$$

EXERCISES

1. Two trains start from the same place and run in opposite directions at the rates of 35 miles per hour and 50 miles per hour. When will the distance between the two trains be 170 miles?

2. Work Prob. 1 if the two trains are traveling in the same direction.

3. A man starts walking at the rate of 3 miles per hour. Three hours later another man starts from the same place and rides a bicycle at the rate of 10 miles per hour. How far and how long will the latter have to travel to overtake the first man?

4. At noon a freight train traveling at 25 miles per hour is 90 miles ahead of an express train traveling at 40 miles per hour. When and where will the express train overtake the freight?

5. When will the express train in Prob. 4 be 40 miles behind the freight?

6. A sound made at the end of a steel railroad rail travels in the air at 1,100 feet per second and in the steel at 16,500 feet per second. The two sounds, i.e., the sound traveling through the air and that traveling through the metal, are heard 6 seconds apart by an observer at the other end of the rail. How long is the rail?

7. Two boys start pedaling bicycles toward each other. They are 20 miles apart at the start and meet 2 hours later. If one boy can pedal 1 mile per hour faster than the other, find their speeds.

8. A motorcycle starts west on U.S. Highway 30 at 25 miles per hour. Two hours later an automobile starts from a point 50 miles east of the motorcycle's starting point and drives at an average speed of 40 miles per hour until it overtakes the motorcycle. How long does it take for the car to overtake the motorcycle?

9. A motorboat that has a speed of 20 miles per hour in still water requires 3 hours to make a trip upstream and 2 hours to return to the original starting position. What was the velocity of the stream?

10. A motorboat travels 8 miles downstream in 20 minutes and makes the return trip in 30 minutes. What is the speed of this boat in still water and the rate of the current?

??????????? PROBLEM JUST FOR FUN ???????????

A "Weighty" Problem

Using a balance, Eager Beaver discovers that 3 tacks plus 1 file will exactly balance 12 nails. Also, 1 file will exactly balance 1 tack plus 8 nails. How many tacks will 1 file balance?

???????????????? JUST FOR FUN ????????????????

Example 6. A tank can be filled by one pump in 20 hours and by a second pump in 50 hours. How long will it take to fill the tank using both pumps?

Solution.

Let x = number of hours required to fill the tank if both pumps are used
$1/20$ = part of tank filled by first pump in 1 hour
$1/50$ = part of tank filled by second pump in 1 hour

so that

$x \cdot 1/20$ = part of tank filled by first pump in x hours

and

$x \cdot 1/50$ = part of tank filled by second pump in x hours

But in x hours the tank is exactly filled, hence

$$\frac{x}{20} + \frac{x}{50} = 1$$

where we write 1 to indicate 1 tankful. Multiplying both members of this equation by 100, we get

$$5x + 2x = 100$$

Then

$$7x = 100 \qquad \text{and} \qquad x = 100/7 = 14\tfrac{2}{7}$$

Therefore, the two pumps working together will fill the tank in $14\frac{2}{7}$ hours.

Check.

$$\frac{100}{7} \cdot \frac{1}{20} + \frac{100}{7} \cdot \frac{1}{50} = \frac{5}{7} + \frac{2}{7} = \frac{7}{7} = 1$$

EXERCISES

1. A tank can be filled by one pipe in 5 hours and emptied by another pipe in 8 hours. When the tank is half full, both pipes are opened. How long will it take to fill the tank?

2. One pipe can empty a tank in 2 hours and another pipe can empty it in 4 hours. A third pipe can fill the tank in 3 hours. If the tank is full and all three pipes are opened, how long will it take to empty the tank?

3. A printing press can print the daily quota of papers in 4 hours. After operating $2\frac{1}{2}$ hours, this press breaks down and is replaced by another press that prints the daily quota in 7 hours. How long will it take the second press to finish printing the daily quota?

4. A pipe A can fill a tank in one-half the time that it takes a second pipe B to fill the tank. Pipe B can fill the tank in two-thirds the time it takes a third pipe C. If it takes 18 hours to fill the tank when all three pipes are turned on, how long will it take each pipe working alone to fill the tank?

5. Two pumps pumping together can fill a reservoir in 10 days. At the end of 7 days one pump breaks down and the other pump finishes the job in 5 days. How long would it take each pump working alone to fill the reservoir?

6. One farmer operating a tractor can plow a field of 200 acres in 10 days. After he has been plowing for 3 days, a neighbor using another tractor helps the farmer to finish plowing the 200 acres in 4 days. How long would it have taken the neighbor to plow the field if he had worked alone?

7. One machine can cap 1,800 bottles in one hour, and another machine can cap 1,500 bottles in an hour. If there are 20,000 bottles to be capped and the slower machine is started 2 hours after the faster machine, how long will it take to cap the 20,000 bottles?

8. After 40 quarts of beer was drawn from one of two equal barrels and 120 quarts of beer was drawn from the other, the first barrel contained twice as much as the other. If each barrel was full at the start, how many quarts did they hold?

9. Sally spent two-thirds of her money for a dress and one-fifth of her money for a hat. How much did she spend for each article if she had $3 left?

10. When John opened his savings bank, he found that he had 28 coins whose value was $3.40. If there were only dimes and quarters in this bank, how many of each were there?

11. A radiator which has a 16-quart capacity is filled with a 10% alcohol solution. If it requires a 30% alcohol solution to protect the radiator, how much 95% alcohol must be added to the original 10% solution to make a 30% alcohol solution?

Hint: Some of the 10% solution will have to be drained before more can be added.

??????????? PROBLEM JUST FOR FUN ???????????

Vital Statistics

In one year during the gold-rush days, 30% of the female population of Nome, Alaska, got married. But during the same year only 1.7% of the male population got married. Assuming that bigamy was outlawed, calculate the ratio of men to women in Nome.

????????????????? JUST FOR FUN ?????????????????

CHAPTER

Quadratic Equations and Relations

(*No Third Degree Here*)

> It is often said that an equation contains only what has been put into it. . . . But there is something more: analysis, by the simple play of its symbols, may suggest generalizations far beyond the original limits.
>
> E. PICARD

1. The graph of the equation $y = kx^2$

The statement that one quantity y varies as the square of another quantity x is encountered in many problems of practical nature. The standard equation for this variation is given by $y = kx^2$. In order to visualize this variation, we will plot the graph of this equation for $k = 1$, 4, $\frac{1}{4}$, -1, -4, and $-\frac{1}{4}$. As before, we form a table of values for each equation and plot the corresponding pairs of values.

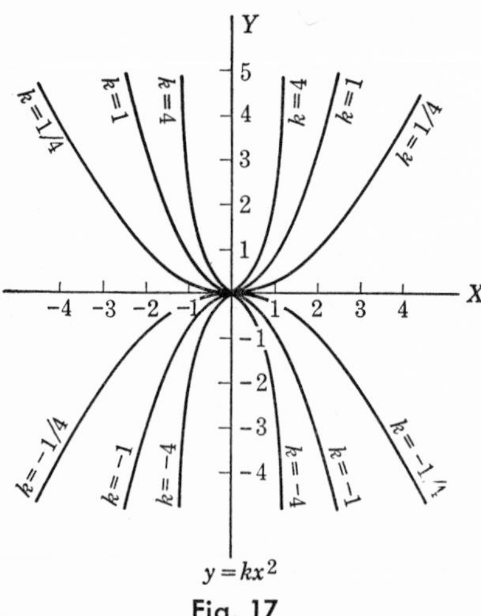

$y = kx^2$

Fig. 17

When we examine the curves in Fig. 17, we see that they all pass through the point (0,0). If k is positive, the curves open upward and do not extend below the x axis. If k is negative, the curves open downward and do not extend above the x axis. The origin is called the vertex of these curves. The steepness of the curves depends upon the value of k.

We also notice that the left-hand side of each curve is the mirror image of the right-hand side. We call this property symmetry and say that each curve is symmetrical with respect to the y axis. This axis of symmetry is called the *axis of the curve.*

If x is proportional to y^2, $x = ky^2$. We plot this equation for $k = 1$, 4, $\frac{1}{4}$, -1, and -4 (see Fig. 18).

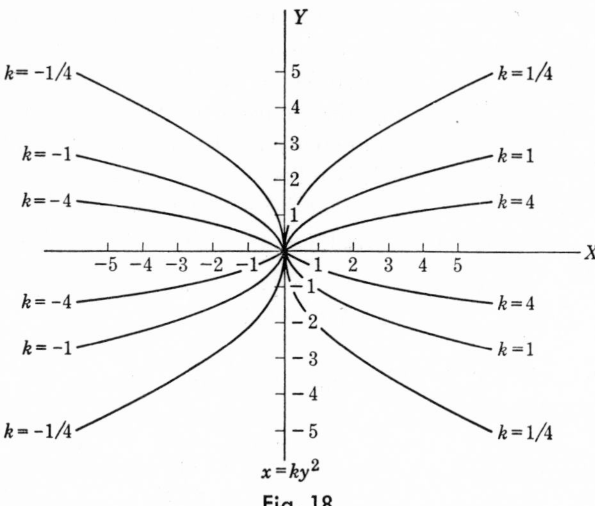

Fig. 18

We see that these curves are symmetrical with respect to the x axis, and in this case, the x axis is the axis of symmetry for these curves. The curve opens to the left if k is negative and does not extend to the right of the y axis. The curve opens to the right if k is positive and does not extend to the left of the y axis. The origin is the vertex for these curves.

2. The parabola

The curves whose equations are $y = kx^2$ or $x = ky^2$ are called *parabolas.* The axis of symmetry is called the *axis of the parabola,* and the origin is the vertex of the parabola.

The parabola is a much-used curve and is frequently encountered in the world about us. The orbits of a few of the comets and the path of a projectile in a vacuum are parabolas. The arches of a bridge and the high ceilings in churches are often in parabolic form. The cable of a suspension bridge which is loaded uniformly per horizontal foot will hang in the shape of a parabola. The surface of a rotating liquid and the reflecting surfaces used in headlights, searchlights, and telescopes are parabolic in form. By this we mean that any cross section through the axis of symmetry is a parabola.

A parabolic mirror has the property that parallel rays of light coming from a distant object are reflected from the mirror in such a way that all pass through a point. This point is called the *focus*. Likewise, if a source of light is placed at the focus of the mirror, the light rays will reflect from the mirror as parallel rays. Such parabolic reflectors are used when it is desired to deliver an intense beam of light, for example, the automobile headlight. A parabolic reflector may also be used to direct sound waves. The sound created at the focus of a parabolic band shell is reflected back to the audience in the same manner as light rays would be reflected (Fig. 19). This eliminates "dead spots" in hearing conditions.

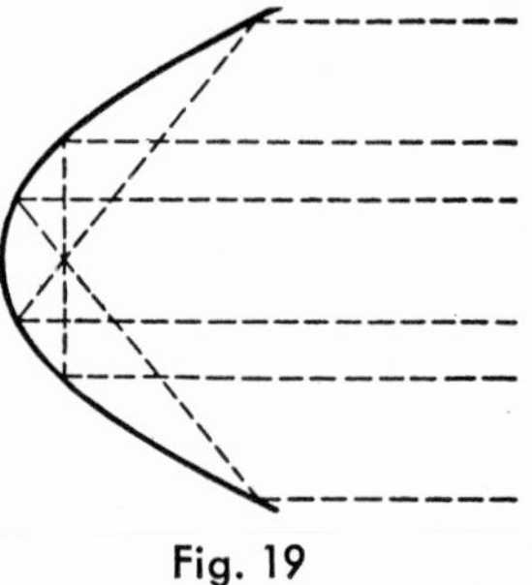

Fig. 19

EXERCISES

Plot the curves for the following equations

1. $y = 2x^2$
2. $y = -2x^2$
3. $x = 3y^2$
4. $x = -3y^2$
5. $x = -2y^2$
6. $y = -3x^2$
7. $y^2 + 3x = 0$
8. $2y = 5x^2$

??????????? PROBLEM JUST FOR FUN ???????????

The Duchess owns a necklace which has 21 diamonds. The middle diamond is the largest and most expensive. The diamonds are arranged so that starting from one end of the necklace, each successive diamond is worth $100 more than the preceding one. This is true right up to and including the middle diamond. Starting from the other end, each diamond up to and including the large one is worth $150 more than the preceding one. If the necklace is worth $32,450, what is the value of the large diamond?

???????????????? JUST FOR FUN ????????????????

3. The equation for a functional relation exhibited by a table

We recall that the curve in Fig. 10 (page 19) for the functional relation given by Table 15 (page 19) has a shape similar to the upper portion of the curves for $x = ky^2$ in Fig. 18. We wonder if the equation giving the functional relation between the distance D and the height h is $h = kD^2$. In order to determine the value of k, we select a pair of values from the table, for example, $D = 12.3$ miles when $h = 100$ feet, substitute these values into the equation, and solve for k.

$$100 = k(12.3)^2$$

or

$$k = \frac{100}{(12.3)^2}$$

Then

$$h = \frac{100}{(12.3)^2} D^2$$

or

$$100D^2 = (12.3)^2 h$$

If this equation represents the relation given by Table 15, we can check it by substituting another value for h and solving for D. When $h = 400$ feet,

$$100D^2 = (12.3)^2(400)$$

and

$$D^2 = 4(12.3)^2$$
$$D = \pm 2(12.3) = \pm 24.6$$

The negative value for D has no meaning in this problem. We may check other values also and conclude that we have the true equation of the functional relation.

EXERCISES

Plot the tabulated data for the following problems. If the curve appears to have the shape of a parabola, find and check the equation for the functional relation between the variables. Do the equations have meaning for all values of the dependent variable? Discuss.

1. Neglecting friction, the distance s in feet that a body falls from rest is a function of the time of fall t in seconds. This relation is given in Table 27.

TABLE 27

t	0	0.5	1	2	3	4
s	0	4.025	16.1	64.4	144.9	257.6

2. For a fixed opening the length of exposure t in seconds necessary to photograph a given subject by photoflood lamp is a function of the distance s in feet of the subject from the source of light. The relation between t and s is given in Table 28.

TABLE 28

s	0	4	6	8	9
t	0	0.89	2	3.55	4.5

3. If the source of illumination is constant, the exposure time t in seconds is a function of the lens "f opening." Table 29 expresses the relation between f and t. What exposure time is needed for an opening of f 11? f 5.6?

TABLE 29

f	2	4	8	12
t	0.000625	0.0025	0.0100	0.0225

4. The heat H in calories generated in a resistance element per second depends upon the amount of electric current I in amperes sent through the wire. Table 30 gives the relation between H and I.

TABLE 30

I	0	1	2	3	4
H	0	2.4	9.6	21.6	38.4

5. The surface area S of a solid depends upon a dimension d. Table 31 gives the relation between S and d.

TABLE 31

d	0	0.25	0.33	0.75	1.0
S	0	0.785	1.38	7.07	12.57

6. Neglecting friction, the distance s in feet that a ball rolls down an inclined plane is a function of the time t in seconds. Table 32 shows the relation between s and t for a certain inclined plane.

TABLE 32

t	0	1	2	2.5	3
s	0	8	32	50	72

??????????? PROBLEM JUST FOR FUN ???????????

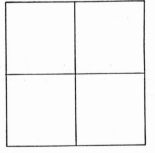

Here we have a window which is square, with inside dimensions of 1 foot. The window is divided by narrow bars (width negligible) into four lights measuring ½ foot on every side. Make another window each of whose four sides shall be 1 foot, but divided by narrow bars into eight lights whose sides shall all be ½ foot.

???????????????? JUST FOR FUN ????????????????

4. Equations of the second degree in one unknown

If the highest power of the variable in an expression is 2, the expression is said to be quadratic, or of the second degree, in this variable. The expression $ax^2 + bx + c$ is quadratic in x; the expression $dx^2 + exy + fy^2$ is quadratic in both x and y. Any equation of the second degree in one unknown x may be written as

$$ax^2 + bx + c = 0$$

where a, b, and c are constants. This equation states that for some value or values of x (to be determined), the left-hand side $ax^2 + bx + c$ is equal to the right-hand side, namely, 0. To find these solutions, we might set the right-hand side equal to y and plot the equation $y = ax^2 + bx + c$. The solutions would be the points where $y = 0$, that is, the points at which the curve crosses the x axis.

To illustrate this method, let us consider the following problem:

Example. A gardener has a rectangular plot of ground 30 feet by 20 feet, on which he plans to build a flower bed surrounded by a grass strip. If he wants 400 square feet of grass, how wide should the strip be?

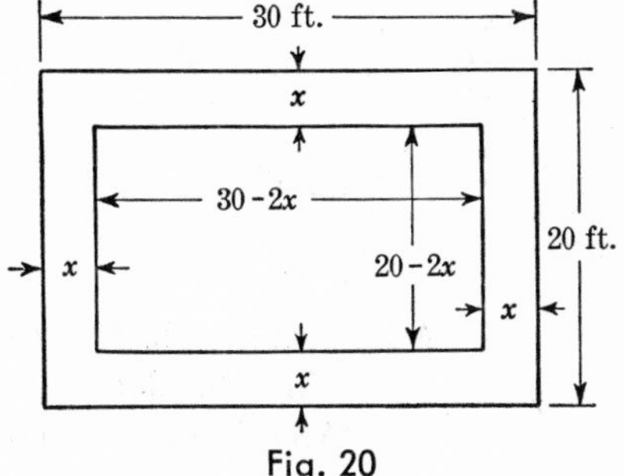

Fig. 20

Solution (Fig. 20).

$$\begin{aligned} \text{Let } x &= \text{width of strip in feet} \\ 20 - 2x &= \text{width of flower bed} \\ 30 - 2x &= \text{length of flower bed} \\ (20)(30) &= 600 \text{ square feet} = \text{area of plot} \\ (20 - 2x)(30 - 2x) &= \text{area of the flower bed} \\ 600 - (20 - 2x)(30 - 2x) &= \text{number of square feet in grass} \end{aligned}$$

Hence

$$600 - (30 - 2x)(20 - 2x) = 400$$

This equation reduces to

$$4x^2 - 100x + 400 = 0$$

or

$$x^2 - 25x + 100 = 0$$

In order to find a solution of this equation graphically, set the left-hand member equal to y. The solution will be the value or values of x for which y is zero. In order to plot the equation $x^2 - 25x + 100 = y$, we form a table of values (Table 33)

TABLE 33

x	0	5	10	15	20	25
y	100	0	−50	−50	0	100

and plot the curve for $y = x^2 - 25x + 100$.

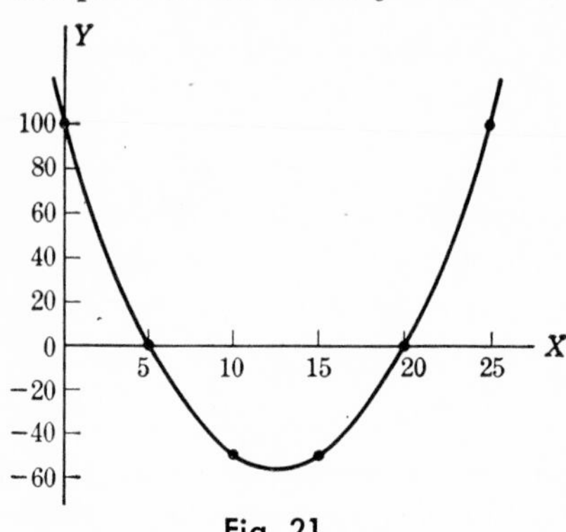

Fig. 21

From Fig. 21 we conclude that $y = 0$ when $x = 5$ and 20. Both $x = 5$ and $x = 20$ satisfy the equation $x^2 - 25x + 100 = 0$.

We find that we have two values of x which formally satisfy the equation $x^2 - 25x + 100 = 0$. We wish to decide whether both these solutions satisfy the given problem. If we take $x = 5$ and put it back into the original statement of the problem, we find that

$$\text{Area of flower bed} = 10(20) = 200 \text{ square feet}$$
$$\text{Area of plot} = 20(30) = 600 \text{ square feet}$$
$$\text{Area in grass} = 600 - 200 = 400 \text{ square feet}$$

which is exactly the value demanded by the problem.

If we take $x = 20$ feet and try to put it back into the statement of the problem, we find at once that we cannot satisfy the conditions of the problem.

$$\text{Width of flower bed} = 20 - 2x = 20 - 2(20) = -20$$
$$\text{Length of flower bed} = 30 - 2x = 30 - 2(20) = -10$$

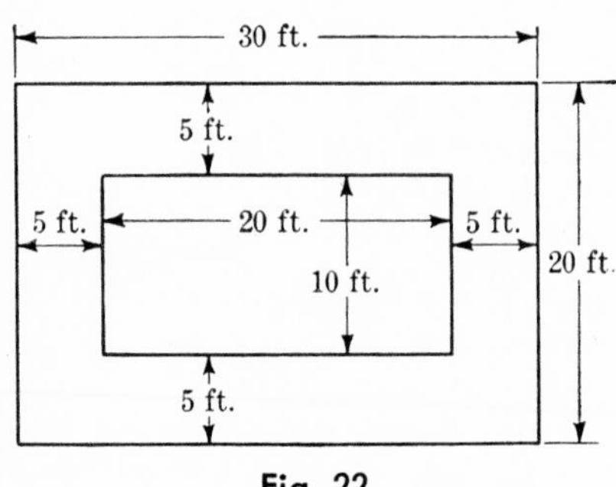

Fig. 22

We get two negative values, which when multiplied together give a positive value, which is a correct mathematical solution of the equation, although the negative values have no meanings as dimensions of a flower bed and a grass strip. It is always necessary to check our answers to see if they make sense.

We were able to find a solution to our problem using graphical methods. But it was a long and tedious process, because we had to construct the table of values and plot this table.

5. The quadratic formula

To avoid the tedious graphical method, we generally use the quadratic formula. The quadratic equation of the form

$$ax^2 + bx + c = 0$$

has as its solutions

$$x = \frac{-b \pm \sqrt{b^2 - 4ac}}{2a}$$

This is called the *quadratic formula.* This formula may be derived by a method called *completing the square.* The two solutions of the quadratic equation are

$$x = \frac{-b + \sqrt{b^2 - 4ac}}{2a} \quad \text{and} \quad x = \frac{-b - \sqrt{b^2 - 4ac}}{2a}$$

These two solutions are formal solutions of the quadratic equation and, when substituted into the left-hand side of the equation, will reduce that side to zero. If we have a practical problem to solve (for example, the flower-bed problem solved by the graphical method), one of the solutions may be mathematically correct but physically impossible, so we must always check this.

The equation derived in the flower bed problem was

$$x^2 - 25x + 100 = 0$$

In this equation, $a = 1$, $b = -25$, and $c = 100$. Substituting into the quadratic formula, we obtain

$$x = \frac{-(-25) \pm \sqrt{(-25)^2 - 4(1)(100)}}{2(1)} = \frac{25 \pm \sqrt{625 - 400}}{2}$$

$$= \frac{25 \pm \sqrt{225}}{2} = \frac{25 \pm 15}{2}$$

Hence $x = 20$ and 5, but only $x = 5$ has physical meaning.

EXERCISES

1. Find two consecutive integers whose product is 462.
Hint: N = one number, $N + 1$ = the other number.

2. Find two consecutive even numbers whose product is 1224.
Hint: $2N$ = one number and $2N + 2$ = the other number, where N is an integer.

3. The length of a rectangle is 14 feet greater than the width. Find the length and width of the rectangle if the area is 240 square feet.

4. The length of a rectangle is 4 feet greater than the width. Find the dimensions of the rectangle if the area is 96 square feet.

5. The perimeter of a rectangle is 30 feet. Find the length and width of this rectangle if the area is 56 square feet.

6. The hypotenuse of a right triangle is 17. Find the legs of the triangle if one leg is one unit less than twice the other leg.

7. If the number of feet in the perimeter of a square is equal to the number of square feet in the area, find the length of the side of the square.

8. The area of a square after adding 2 feet to each side is 576 square feet. What were the original dimensions of the square?

9. Find a positive number which when increased by 20 is equal to 69 times the reciprocal of the number.

10. A picture which is 9 inches wide and 12 inches long is surrounded by a frame which has 162 square inches. What is the width of the frame?

11. A merchant bought a shipment of vases for $100. He sold all but three of them which were broken by careless clerks. If he makes a profit of $4 on each vase sold and a total profit of $98, how many vases were in the shipment?

12. Two ships start from the same point at noon. One sails north at a speed of 6 knots, and the other sails east at a speed of 8 knots. When will the ships be 100 miles apart? (A knot is nautical language for 1 sea mile per hour.)

13. A box contains 600 cubic inches. The length is 12 inches, and the width is 5 inches greater than the height. Find the dimensions of the box.

14. A rectangular piece of metal is 3 inches longer than it is wide. From each corner a 1-inch square is cut out and the sides turned up to form an open box which contains 130 cubic inches. Find the dimensions of the piece of tin.

15. One pipe alone can fill a tank in 4 hours less than it takes a second pipe by itself to fill the tank. If both pipes working together can fill the tank in 2 hours, how long does it take each pipe to fill the tank?

??????????? PROBLEM JUST FOR FUN ???????????

Six little kittens sittin' on a fence;
One weighs more because he is more dense.
Can you separate him from the other five,
Which all have the same weight, dead or alive?
Put them on a balance, but only twice,
To find the one so fat and nice.

???????????????? JUST FOR FUN ????????????????

6. Another equation for the parabola

We already know that $y = kx^2$, or $x = ky^2$, is the equation for the parabola with vertex at the origin. The equation

$$y = kx^2 + bx + c \qquad \text{or} \qquad x = ky^2 + dy + e \qquad (k \neq 0)$$

when plotted, gives a curve which is a parabola. If the constants b and c or d and e are equal to zero, the vertex of the parabola is at the origin. The position of the vertex of the parabola depends upon the value of the constants b and c or d and e.

Let us plot the curve defined by the equation $y = x^2 + x - 6$. In drawing the graph of the equation, it is helpful to find the points at which the curve cuts the two axes. Set $y = 0$ and get the equation $x^2 + x - 6 = 0$, which has $x = 2$ and $x = -3$ as solutions. Hence our curve crosses the x axis at $x = 2$ and -3. Also, when $x = 0$, $y = -6$, and the curve crosses the y axis at the point $y = -6$. Since we know that the equation represents a parabola, we have some knowledge of the shape of the curve. We mark these axis crossings on the graph paper and find the coordinates of a few other points, for example, $(1,-4)$ and $(-2,-4)$, to help us draw the curve. The vertex of the parabola $y = x^2 + x - 6$ is at the point $(-0.5,-6.25)$ (Fig. 23).

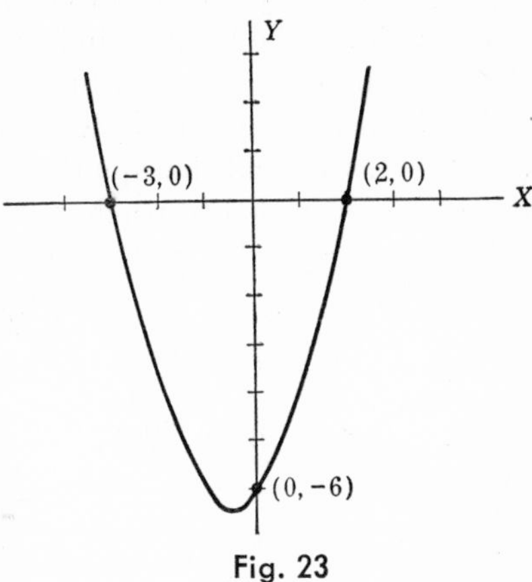

Fig. 23

EXERCISES

Plot the curves for the following equations.

1. $y = 2x^2 + 3$
2. $y = -4 - x^2$
3. $x = y^2 - 4$
4. $9x = y^2$
5. $y = 4x - x^2$
6. $x = 9y - y^2$
7. $y = (x - 5)(x + 1)$
8. $y = 2(x - 3)(x - 1)$

??????????? PROBLEM JUST FOR FUN ???????????

A tree is 4 feet in circumference. A squirrel, in climbing this tree, goes once around the tree for each vertical 6 feet of climb. If the squirrel climbs to a height of 18 feet, how far does he climb?

???????????????? JUST FOR FUN ????????????????

7. Finding the exact representation for a relation given by a table

We have previously found the exact formula for functional relations exhibited by a table of values when the graph was a straight line or a parabola with the vertex at the origin. If the graph has the shape of a parabola with the vertex at a point different from the origin, we can still find the equation. It will be of the form

$$y = kx^2 + ax + b \qquad \text{or} \qquad x = ky^2 + cy + d$$

We need to find the value of the three constants. If the axis of the parabola is parallel to the y axis, we use the first form; and the second when the axis is parallel to the x axis.

Example. The height h in feet of a cable of a suspension bridge above the deck of the bridge is a function of the horizontal distance D in feet from the center of the bridge. Table 34 gives the relation between h and D. Let us find the equation of the curve of the cable and the length of a support needed to reach vertically from the cable to the floor of the bridge at a point 30 feet from the center.

TABLE 34

D	0	±10	±20	±40	±50	±100
h	10	10.4	11.3	16.4	20	50

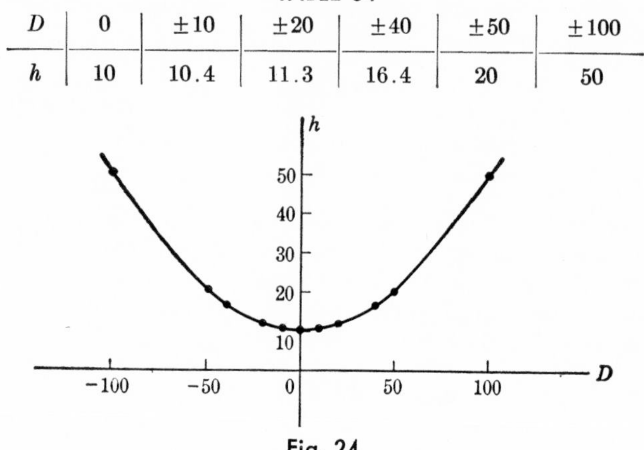

Fig. 24

Solution.

Since the axis of the parabola is parallel to the y axis, we assume that the relation between h and D is given by the equation

$$h = kD^2 + aD + b$$

In order to determine the three constants k, a, and b, we select three points on the curve, for example, (0,10), (50,20), and (100,50), and substitute these values into the equation. We get

$$\begin{aligned} 10 &= b \\ 20 &= k(50)^2 + a(50) + b \\ 50 &= k(100)^2 + a(100) + b \end{aligned}$$

Solving these equations, we find that $b = 10$, $a = 0$, and $k = 1/250$. The equation for the parabola is

$$h = \frac{D^2}{250} + 10$$

When $D = 30$ feet, $h = \frac{(30)^2}{250} + 10 = 13.6$ feet.

This is the length of a support needed to reach from the cable to the deck of the bridge at a distance of 30 feet from the center of the bridge.

EXERCISES

1. Neglecting air resistance, a stone thrown into the air rises for a time and then falls back to the ground. Table 35 gives the height h in feet of the stone above the ground at various times t in seconds. Determine the equation for this relation. What is the maximum height reached by the stone? At what time is the stone 20 feet above the ground? Can t take on negative values? Can t have values greater than 4? Explain.

TABLE 35

t	0	1	2	3	4
h	0	48	64	48	0

2. The height h in feet of a baseball when thrown upward at an angle of 45° with the horizontal is a function of the horizontal distance D. The relation between D and h is given in Table 36. Find the equation of the path. How high will the ball rise? What is the horizontal distance it will travel? At what horizontal distance will the ball be 18 feet above the ground?

TABLE 36

D	0	10	20	50	75	100
h	0	9	16	25	18.75	0

??????????? PROBLEM JUST FOR FUN ???????????

A child weighs four-fifths of its weight and 10 pounds. What is its weight?

???????????????? JUST FOR FUN ????????????????

8. The graph of the equation $xy = k$

Let us now determine the curve that represents the relation given by the statement that y is inversely proportional to x. That is, $y = k/x$, or $xy = k$. This type of variation is one of the common types and is frequently encountered in the sciences.

We will graph $xy = k$ for $k = 1, 2, -1$, and -2. Notice that if we set x or y equal to zero we are unable to solve for the other variable. This means that the curve does not cross the x axis or y axis. Likewise, since $y = k/x$, y will increase as x decreases. Also, y will decrease as x becomes larger.

We find that the curve for $xy = k$ has two branches for each value of k. If k is positive, the two branches lie in the first and third quadrants (Fig. 25). If k is negative, the two branches lie in the second and fourth quadrants (Fig. 25a). The curves do not cross the x or y axes.

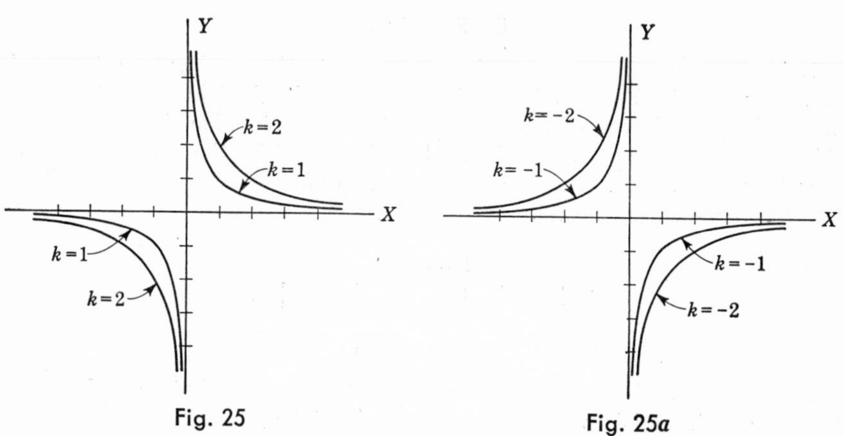

Fig. 25 Fig. 25a

Curves represented by the equation $xy = k$ have this characteristic shape, and they are called *rectangular hyperbolas.*

In many physical problems in which the variation is expressed by the equation $xy = k$, only one branch of the hyperbola has any physical significance. That is, the independent variable does not take on both positive and negative numbers. For example, if the temperature is kept constant, the volume of an enclosed gas is inversely proportional to the pressure, and we have $PV = k$. Since negative values of pressure and volume are never possible, only that portion of the hyperbola lying in the first quadrant has meaning.

EXERCISES

Plot the curves for the following equations.

1. $PV = 6$

2. $xy = -5$

3. $yx = 4$

4. $yx^2 = 4$

??????????? PROBLEM JUST FOR FUN ???????????

From the main tracks, *M*, two shunting tracks, *A* and *B*, branch off. Both tracks, *A* and *B*, lead to a short track *s*, which is just long enough to accommodate

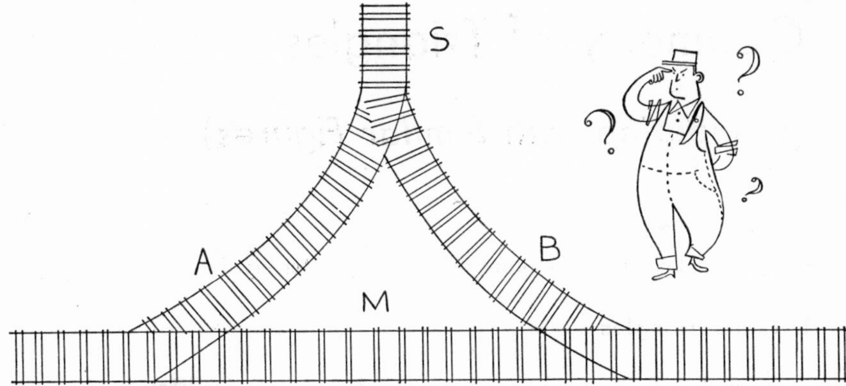

one car. There is a coal car *C* standing on track *A*, and a tank car *T* standing on track *B*. The engineer of a switch engine has orders to move the coal car onto track *B* and the tank car onto track *A*. How does the engineer accomplish this change?

??????????????? JUST FOR FUN ???????????????

CHAPTER

7

Geometry of Triangles

(Computing with Similar Figures)

Let no one ignorant of Geometry enter my door. PLATO

1. Plane triangles

In geometry we learned that a triangle is characterized by six elements—three sides and three angles. The triangle is completely determined and can be constructed provided we know the size of

1. Two angles and one side, or
2. Two sides and the angle between, or
3. Three sides

If the triangle is a right triangle, one of the angles, namely, the right angle, is known. In order to construct a right triangle we need to know only the size of

1. One side and one acute angle or
2. Any two sides

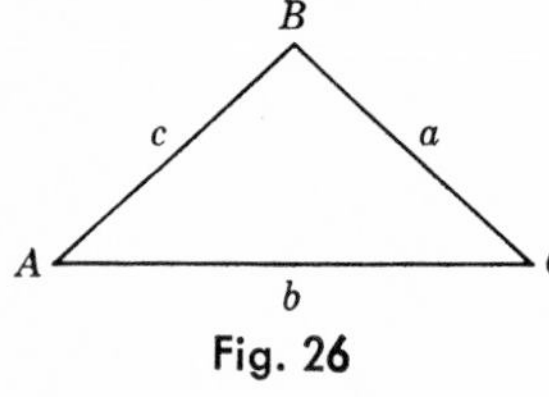

Fig. 26

We will follow the notation used in plane geometry. The vertices of the triangle will be denoted by the capital letters, A, B, and C, and the sides opposite the vertices will be denoted by the lower-case letters a, b, and c. In the triangle shown in Fig. 26, c is the side opposite the vertex C; a is the side opposite the vertex A, etc.

2. Right angles

The peoples of the ancient world defined the right angle as the angle that a plumb line makes with the water level or the horizon. These people had a very simple rule for making an angle of 90°. They knew that a triangle with sides 3, 4, and 5 units in length is a right triangle, and they staked out such a triangle whenever they needed to construct a right angle.

3. Construction of triangles. Scale drawings. Similar triangles

In plane geometry we learned that given three parts of a triangle (one of which must be a side), we can construct the triangle, using a ruler and a compass. The next step is to find the size of the remaining sides and angles. With a ruler, we can measure the length of the sides of the triangle. Using the protractor, we can construct an angle of any size. The accuracy with which we can measure the length of the sides and the angles of the triangle depends upon the accuracy with which we can read the ruler and the protractor we are using. Surveyors have devices by which they can measure a distance or an angle with great accuracy. In general, we are not concerned with such great accuracy here.

If the given dimensions of length are too great for the triangle to fit onto the paper, we choose a smaller length to represent the original length. That is, we choose a suitable scale and draw the triangle to scale. The lengths are multiplied by convenient fractions *but the angles are not changed.* From such scale drawings we can determine the size of the unknown parts of the triangle by measuring these parts with the ruler and protractor.

When we make a scale drawing, we are assuming that the figure is similar to the original or desired figure, and we apply all the properties about similar geometric figures that we learned in plane geometry. Two triangles are similar if their angles are equal.

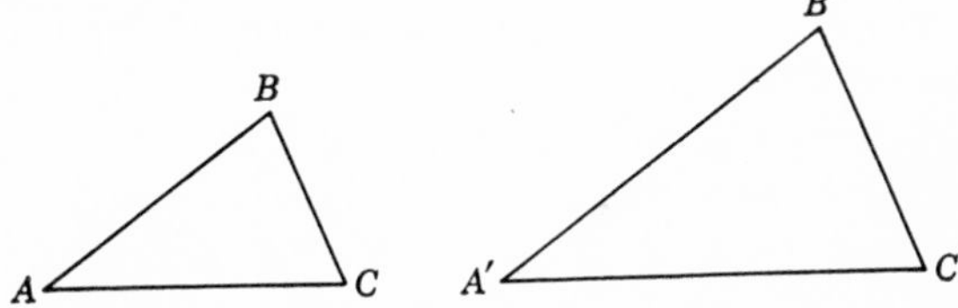

Fig. 27

If the triangles ABC and $A'B'C'$ (Fig. 27) are similar, the ratio of the corresponding sides is a constant. That is,

$$\frac{AB}{A'B'} = \frac{AC}{A'C'} = \frac{BC}{B'C'}$$

Two triangles are congruent if their angles and sides are equal (Fig. 28). In this case, the ratio of the corresponding sides is equal to 1.

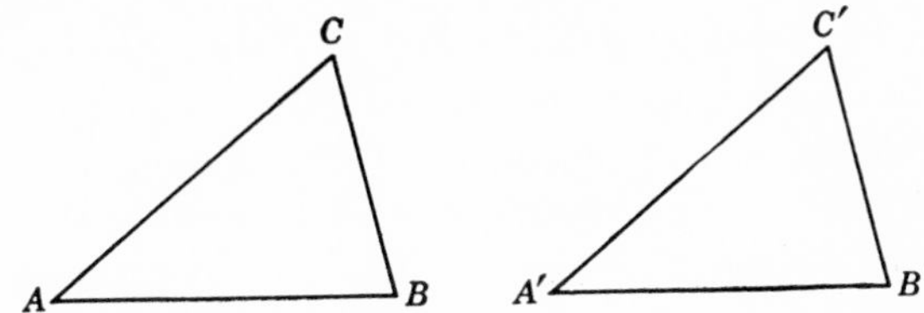

Fig. 28

We can use scale drawings to solve practical problems involving triangles. From scale drawings we can often obtain dimensions or measurements of distances which might be difficult or impossible to measure directly. Scale drawings are also very useful:

1. In estimating results
2. As an aid in visualizing the conditions of the problem
3. As a check on the results obtained by computation

Example. In order to find the distance between two buildings, A and B, which are separated by a high hill, a point C was chosen from which both A and B could be seen. The angle between CA and CB and the two distances CA and CB were measured and found to be $70°30'$, 2,000 feet, and 3,500 feet. Find the distance AB.

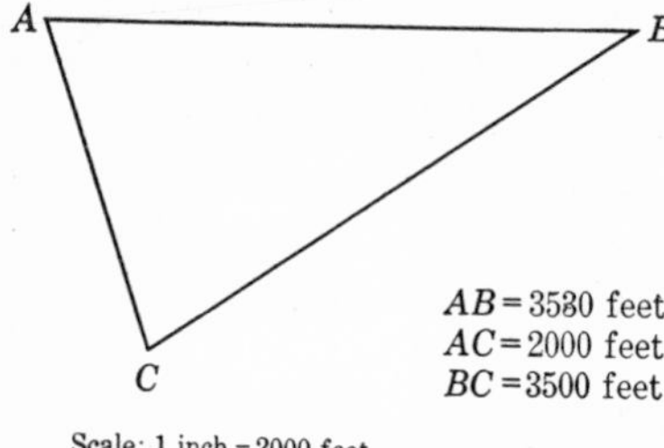

Fig. 29

Solution. In order to solve this problem we select a suitable scale and construct the triangle ABC, which is similar to the triangle formed by the base of the two buildings and the point C (Fig. 29). Thus to find the distance between the two buildings A and B, we need to measure the side AB of the triangle. It is to be noted here that the accuracy of the work depends upon the size of the drawing and the care with which the triangle is constructed.

4. Some definitions

Before proceeding to solve verbal problems, we need to define three special angles.

Angles of elevation and depression (Fig. 30). When an observer views an object O, the line OE joining O to E (the eye of the observer) is called the *line of sight*. The angle between the line OE and a horizontal line EH is called the *angle of elevation*, or *angle of depression*, of O, according as the object O is higher or lower than the eye E.

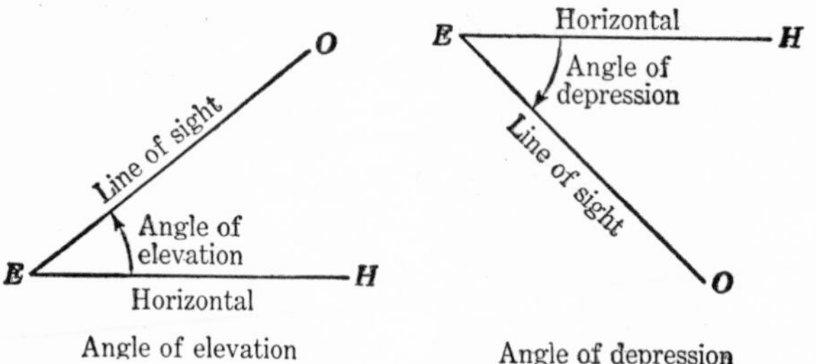

Fig. 30

Angle of Inclination. The angle between a line and the horizontal is called the *angle of inclination.* Both angle of elevation and angle of depression are special cases of the angle of inclination.

EXERCISES

Use the graphical method to solve the following problems.

1. The angle of elevation of the sun is 40°, and the length of a man's shadow is 7 feet. Find the height of the man.

2. The inclination of a hill is 20°. If a boy walks 1 mile up the hill, how many feet has he risen? How many feet has he advanced in the horizontal direction?

3. A chord of a circle is 20 feet. The angle between the two lines joining the end points of the chord to the center of the circle is 60°. Find the radius of the circle.

4. In order to measure the width of a river (Fig. 31), the distance between two points A and B, close to and parallel to the river bank, was measured and found to be 400 ft. A tree T on the opposite bank was used as a point. The angle between AT and AB was measured by a transit and found to be 40°. The angle between BT and AB was found to be 90°. Find the width of the river.

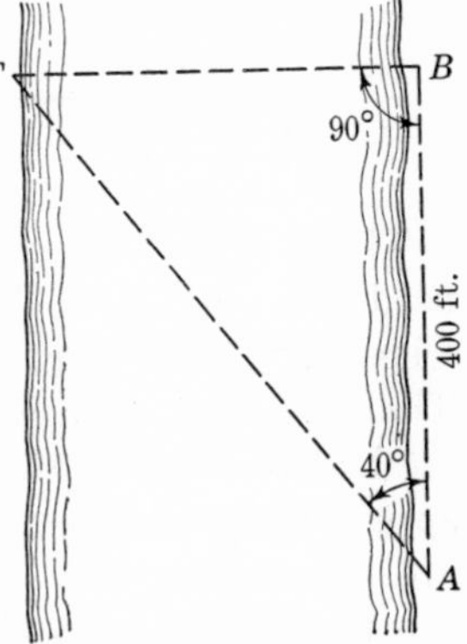

Fig. 31

5. A tree standing on the bank of a stream is known to be 60 feet high. From the opposite bank the angle of elevation of the top of the tree, measured from a point 4 feet above the foot of the tree, is found to be 20°. Find the width of the stream.

6. Mount Hood is 51 miles from Portland, Ore., in a direction 14° south of east. How far south and how far east is the mountain from the city?

??????????? PROBLEM JUST FOR FUN ???????????

Construct geometrically the square root of a positive integer n.

???????????????? JUST FOR FUN ????????????????

5. Shadow reckoning and some history

We can often use similar triangles to solve practical problems. For example, we can determine the height of a tree or a building by measuring its shadow. To find the height of a tree we compare the triangle formed by the top and foot of the tree and the tip of its shadow with the triangle formed by the top, bottom, and tip of the shadow of a vertical pole (Fig. 32). The two triangles ABC and $A'B'C'$ are similar, and we can write

$$\frac{AB}{A'B'} = \frac{BC}{B'C'}$$

Since we are able to measure the three distances BC, $A'B'$ and $B'C'$, we can easily calculate the inaccessible height AB of the tree.

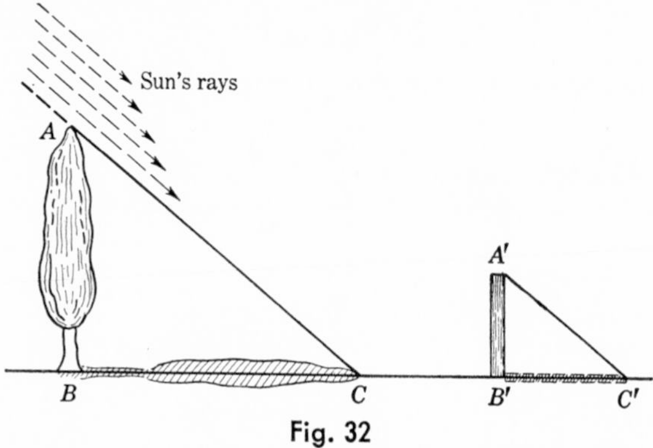

Fig. 32

Thales (640–546 B.C.), who was one of the founders of Greek geometry, used this method to determine the height of the Egyptian pyramid of Cheops. To be sure, the Egyptians had measured the pyramid before Thales showed them his method. The Egyptians also used the shadow method to measure the height of their pyramids, but they used a very special right triangle, namely, the right triangle in which the two legs are equal (Fig. 33). They constructed the perpendicular bisector of the base of the pyramid, and on this bisector they erected a pole and constructed in the sand a circle with radius equal to the height of the pole and centered at the center of the pole. When the shadow of the pole just touched the circle on the perpendicular bisector, they knew that the length of the shadow of the pyramid plus half the base of the pyramid was equal to the height of the pyramid. The Egyptians knew

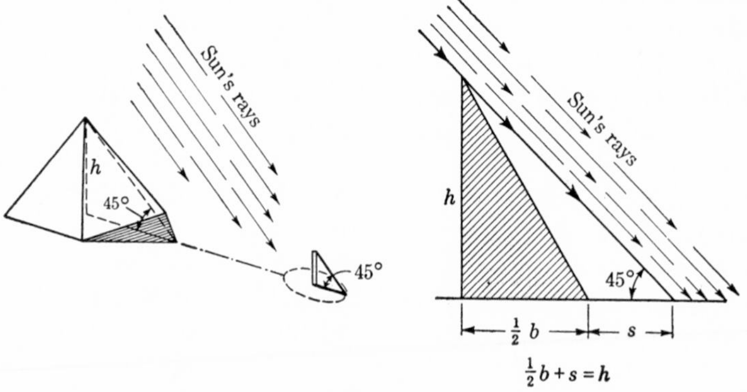

Fig. 33

that there were only two days each year on which they could use this method to measure the heights of the pyramids. Thales' method did not depend upon the position of the sun, and he could determine the height on any day that the sun shone.

EXERCISES

Solve the following problems, making use of the properties of similar triangles.

1. A man 6 feet tall is standing at the foot of a tree. If the shadow of the tree and of the man are 40 feet and 4 feet in length, respectively, find the height of the tree.

2. A 1-foot pole casts a shadow of 2 feet when the shadow of a cliff is 30 feet. What is the height of the cliff?

3. A boy 5 feet tall stands in an attic in which the roof slopes down to the floor. When the boy stands 4 feet from the edge of the floor, his head touches the roof. Find the angle that the ceiling makes with the floor, and the height of the roof at the mid-point, if the attic is 20 feet wide.

4. A 15-foot ladder leans against a wall with its foot 5 feet from the wall. A man stands on a rung which is 8 feet from the bottom of the ladder. How far is the man from the wall and from the ground?

5. A silver dollar has a diameter of $1\frac{1}{2}$ inches and when placed 4.6 yards from the eye will just block out the disc of the moon. If the diameter of the moon is 2,160 miles, find the distance of the moon from the earth.

??????????? PROBLEM JUST FOR FUN ???????????

Find the right triangle of largest area which can be constructed upon a given line as hypotenuse.

???????????????? JUST FOR FUN ????????????????

6. More historical notes

The word "geometry" comes from two Greek words: *ge*, which means "the earth," and *metron*, which means "to measure." Thus geometry is connected with earth measurement. The ancient peoples found it necessary to measure the space they lived in, and geometry had its early roots in the determination of the size and shape, distances and angles, areas and volumes of this space. Much of the early geometric knowledge was discovered by Egyptians, who were practical workmen who built the great pyramids, surveyed the land along the Nile River, and achieved prominence as astronomers. The Egyptians combined their knowledge of astronomy and architecture to orient their temples and pyramids so that rays of certain stars could penetrate deep into the buildings by shining through specially planned hallways and arches.

Eratosthenes (born about 284 B.C.) combined the knowledge of geometry, geography, and astronomy to determine the size of the earth. The method he used to measure the circumference of the earth is as follows:

When Eratosthenes was at Syene, which was 500 miles south of Alexandria, he noticed that at noon the sun shone straight down into a deep well, and its reflection from the water at the bottom struck his eye as he looked, which proved that the sun was directly overhead. On the same day at Alexandria it was observed from the shadow of a tall pillar that the sun was $7\frac{1}{2}°$ south from the vertical at noon. Since the Egyptians regarded the rays from the sun as being parallel, we can draw the diagram shown in Fig. 34. Erathosthenes reasoned that

$$\frac{360°}{7.5°} = \frac{\text{circumference of the earth in miles}}{500 \text{ miles}}$$

Solving this equation, we find that the value of the circumference of the earth is approximately 25,000 miles.

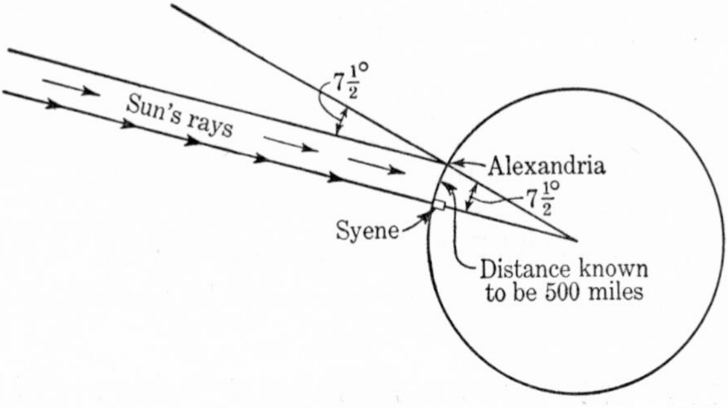

Fig. 34

The Greek scholars observed the use that the Egyptians made of geometry and gathered and systematized the Egyptian geometrical formulas, which were often only practical approximations. The most important among these scholars were Thales (640–546 B.C.), Pythagoras (580?–500 B.C.), Plato (429–348 B.C.), and Euclid (born about 365 B.C.). They idealized the practical geometrical ideas of the Egyptians, and the concepts of points, lines, areas, and volumes became abstractions in the minds of the Greeks. Since the Greeks by nature were fond of logic, they applied this logic to the formulas of the Egyptians to see why these statements should be true. This is the way that the mensuration facts of the Egyptians were organized into the systematic, deductive study which we call geometry. The geometry written by Euclid reads much the same as our textbooks on geometry today.

The outstanding contribution made by the Greek scholars to the field of mathematics was the establishing of mathematics as a deductive system.

The Egyptians used special right triangles, usually one in which the acute angles were 45° or one in which the sides had ratios of 3:4:5, to solve their practical problems. They frequently solved their problems graphically by making scale drawings in the sand. The Greeks were less inclined toward measurement and tried to deduce the answer by logical deduction.

CHAPTER

Definition of the Trigonometric Functions

(*Sine, Cosine, and Tangent*)

But neither thirty years, nor thirty centuries, affect the clearness, or the charm of Geometrical truths. Such a theorem as "the square of the hypotenuse of a right-angled triangle is equal to the sum of the squares of the sides," is as dazzlingly beautiful now as it was in the day when Pythagoras first discovered it, and celebrated its advent, it is said, by sacrificing a hecatomb of oxen—a method of doing honor to Science that has always seemed to me slightly exaggerated and uncalled for. One can imagine oneself, even in these degenerate days, marking the epoch of some brilliant scientific discovery by inviting a convivial friend or two, to join one in a beef steak and a bottle of wine. But a hecatomb of oxen! It would produce a quite inconvenient supply of beef.

C. L. DODGSON (*Lewis Carroll*)

1. Ratio of the sides of similar triangles

We have seen that it is possible to solve problems involving triangles by the graphical method. But this method of solving problems is much too crude for a modern science. The mathematician prefers to do less measuring and more figuring, and tries to find ways by which he can solve these same problems analytically.

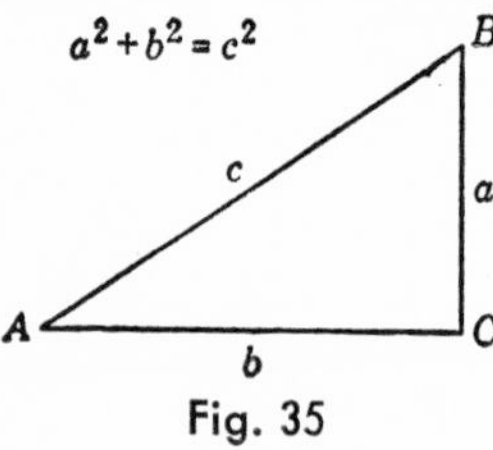

Fig. 35

We already know some facts that will enable us to solve for the unknown parts of a triangle. If two of the angles are given, we can find the value of the third angle, because the sum of the three angles of a triangle is 180°. If the triangle is a right triangle, one acute angle is sufficient to enable us to find the other acute angle, because the sum of the two acute angles in a right triangle is 90°. If two sides of a right triangle are given, the other side may be found by using the Pythagorean theorem.

Earlier we were able to determine the height of a tree by measuring the length of its shadow and finding the ratio of two sides of a right triangle $A'B'C'$ which had the same acute angle $B'C'A'$ as the angle BCA in the given triangle. We should become very weary, if every time we wished to determine an inaccessible side of a right triangle, we had to construct a similar right triangle whose sides we could measure in order to determine their ratio.

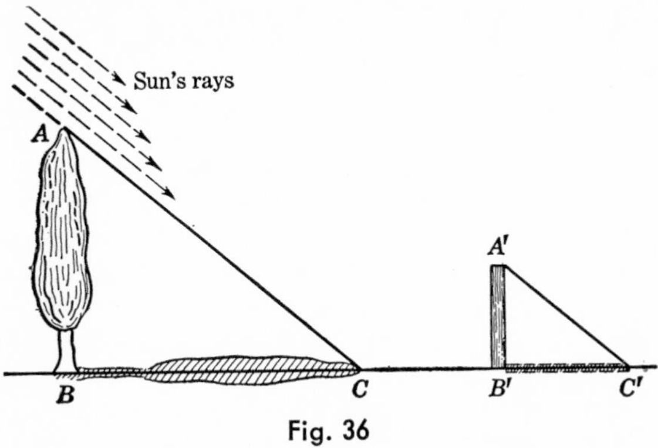

Fig. 36

It is natural for us to wonder if there is some special magic in these ratios of the sides of these triangles having an acute angle equal to angle BCA. Let us investigate these ratios of the sides of triangles.

Given an acute angle A (Fig. 37), from a point P on one side we drop a perpendicular PQ to the other side. In this way a right triangle AQP is formed, in which the line AP is the hypotenuse, PQ is the side opposite angle A, and AQ is the side adjacent to angle A. Then the first ratio used in the example above in this case is

$$\frac{PQ}{AQ} = \frac{\text{side opposite}}{\text{side adjacent}}$$

If we take another point P' on the same side of angle A and drop another perpendicular $P'Q'$ to the other side, we form another right triangle. For this triangle we may write

$$\frac{\text{Side opposite}}{\text{Side adjacent}} = \frac{P'Q'}{AQ'}$$

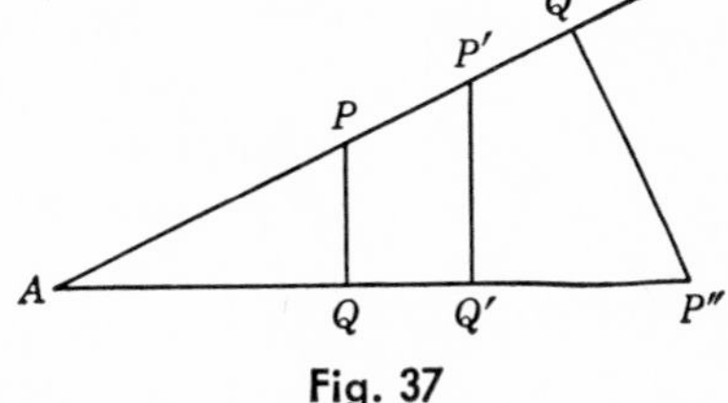

Fig. 37

If we take a point P'' on the other side of angle A and drop a perpendicular $P''Q''$ to the other side, we form a third right triangle. For this triangle we may write

$$\frac{\text{Side opposite}}{\text{Side adjacent}} = \frac{P''Q''}{AQ''}$$

Since angle A is common to the three right triangles, the three triangles are similar, and the corresponding sides are proportional. Then

$$\frac{PQ}{AQ} = \frac{P'Q'}{AQ'} = \frac{P''Q''}{AQ''} = \text{constant} = \frac{\text{side opposite angle } A}{\text{side adjacent angle } A}$$

That is, keeping angle A fixed, the ratio $\frac{\text{side opposite}}{\text{side adjacent}}$ is equal to a constant and does not depend upon the size of the sides.

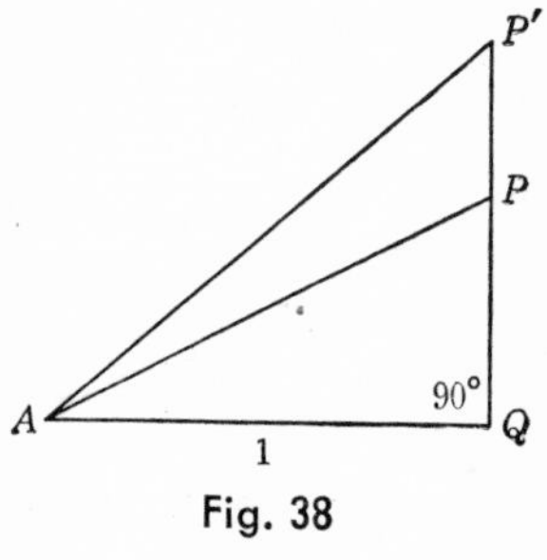

Fig. 38

2. Further properties of these ratios

Let us see what effect changing the size of angle A has upon the ratio of the side opposite an acute angle to the side adjacent in a right triangle. To do this, we construct a right angle (Fig. 38) and measure off a distance 1 on one of the legs. At the point A we construct two different acute angles PAQ and $P'AQ$. Since the side AQ is equal to 1,

$$\frac{\text{Side opposite angle } QAP}{\text{Side adjacent angle } QAP} = QP$$

and

$$\frac{\text{Side opposite angle } QAP'}{\text{Side adjacent angle } QAP'} = QP'$$

We conclude that this ratio does depend upon the size of the angle, and the larger angle gives the larger ratio.

We can conclude that in a right triangle the ratio of the side opposite an acute angle to the side adjacent is a function of the angle only and for a fixed angle does not depend upon whether the triangle is large or small. For a given angle this ratio is constant and needs to be determined only once. This ratio plays such an important role in the solution of right triangles that it has been given the name *tangent of the angle,* which we define

$$\text{Tangent of } A = \tan A = \frac{\text{side opposite angle } A}{\text{side adjacent angle } A}$$

Example. Let us illustrate the usefulness of this property of the angle. At a point 30 feet from a steep cliff (Fig. 39), the angle of elevation of the cliff was measured and found to be 20°. If for an angle of 20° the ratio of the side opposite to the side adjacent, which is the tan 20°, is known to be 0.3640, find the height of the cliff.

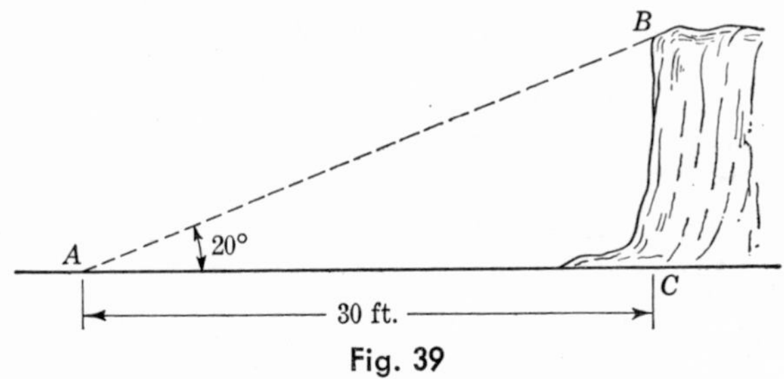

Fig. 39

Solution. Applying the definition, we write

$$\tan 20° = \frac{BC}{30}$$

$$0.3640 = \frac{BC}{30}$$

and we get

$$BC = 30(0.3640) = 10.92 \text{ ft}$$

Because we knew the value of the ratio, we did not need to construct a similar triangle to solve this problem.

3. The six trigonometric functions

Looking at Fig. 40, we see that there are six different ratios, namely, $\frac{a}{b}, \frac{a}{c}, \frac{b}{c}, \frac{b}{a}, \frac{c}{a}$, and $\frac{c}{b}$. Just as we did in the case of the tangent, we can show that all these ratios are functions of the angle A only and do not depend on the magnitude of the sides of the triangles. These ratios have all been given names. They are called tangent, sine (pronounced *sign*), cosine (pronounced *co-sign*), cotangent, cosecant, and secant, respectively. Since we have seen that these ratios do not depend on the size of the right triangle formed, we may compute them directly from the sides of any one triangle (Fig. 40). We may write

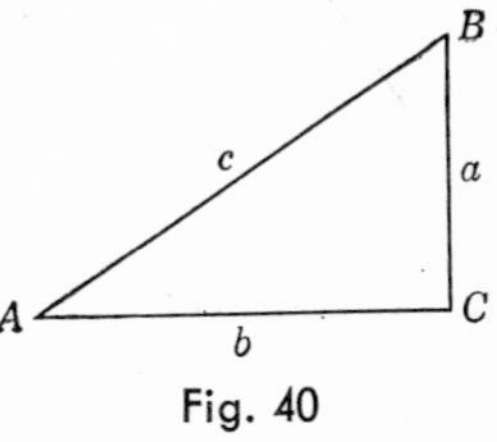

Fig. 40

$$\text{Tangent of } A = \tan A = \frac{\text{side opposite angle } A}{\text{side adjacent angle } A} = \frac{a}{b}$$

$$\text{Sine of } A = \sin A = \frac{\text{side opposite angle } A}{\text{hypotenuse}} = \frac{a}{c}$$

$$\text{Cosine of } A = \cos A = \frac{\text{side adjacent angle } A}{\text{hypotenuse}} = \frac{b}{c}$$

$$\text{Cotangent of } A = \cot A = \frac{\text{side adjacent angle } A}{\text{side opposite angle } A} = \frac{b}{a}$$

$$\text{Cosecant of } A = \csc A = \frac{\text{hypotenuse}}{\text{side opposite angle } A} = \frac{c}{a}$$

$$\text{Secant of } A = \sec A = \frac{\text{hypotenuse}}{\text{side adjacent angle } A} = \frac{c}{b}$$

We notice that cotangent, cosecant, and secant are reciprocals of tangent, sine, and cosine, respectively. For this reason they are used less often than the first three functions. In our work we will use only the tangent, sine, and cosine.

We must remember that these functions are defined for an acute angle by means of right triangles. The angles of a triangle which is not a right triangle also have sines, cosines, and tangents, but we cannot compute them directly from the sides of the triangle. We must drop perpendiculars and create right triangles before the preceding definitions apply.

EXERCISES

Write out the value of the sine, cosine, and tangent for the following:

1. Angle B in the triangle ABC given in Fig. 40.
2. Angles M and N in the triangle in Fig. 41.
3. Angles P and R in the triangle in Fig. 42.
4. Angles A and B in the triangle in Fig. 43.

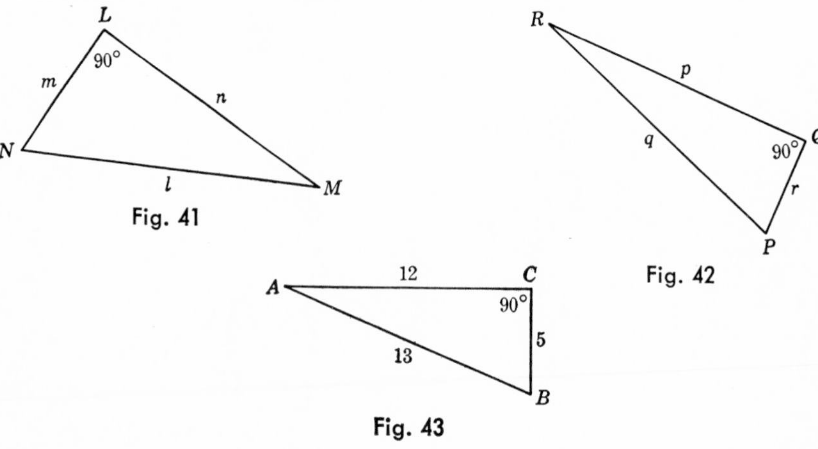

Fig. 41

Fig. 42

Fig. 43

??????????? PROBLEM JUST FOR FUN ???????????

In the figure below, the triangles are right triangles. What is the length of the hypotenuse A?

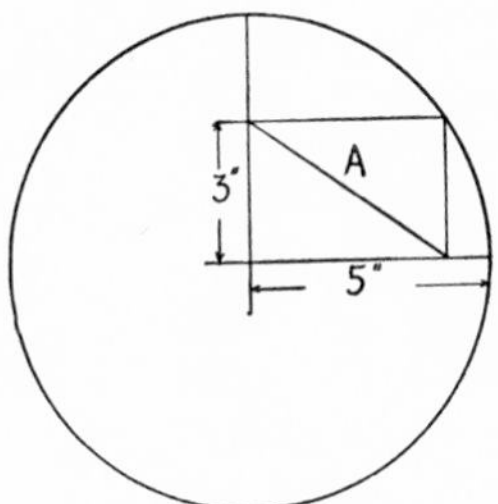

??????????????? JUST FOR FUN ???????????????

CHAPTER

9

Special Right Triangles

(30, 45, and 60 Degrees)

There is perhaps nothing which so occupies, as it were, the middle position of mathematics, as trigonometry. J. F. HERBART

1. The 45° triangle

Let us find the value of the ratios, sine, cosine, and tangent for two special right triangles. We construct a right triangle in which the two acute angles are equal to 45° (Fig. 44). We know that the two sides of this right triangle are equal. We may find the hypotenuse c by the Pythagorean theorem.

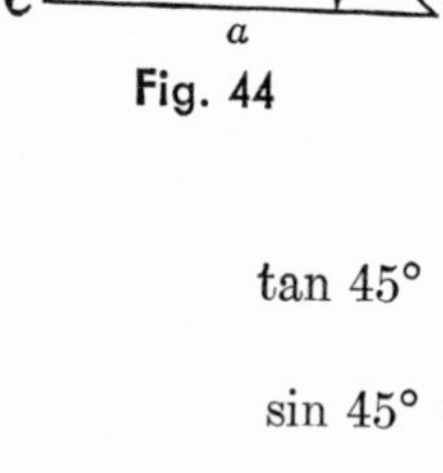

Fig. 44

$$c^2 = a^2 + a^2 = 2a^2$$
$$c = a\sqrt{2}$$

Now we write the values of the three functions

$$\tan 45° = \frac{\text{side opposite}}{\text{side adjacent}} = \frac{a}{a} = 1$$
$$\sin 45° = \frac{\text{side opposite}}{\text{hypotenuse}} = \frac{a}{a\sqrt{2}} = \frac{1}{\sqrt{2}} = 0.707$$
$$\cos 45° = \frac{\text{side adjacent}}{\text{hypotenuse}} = \frac{a}{a\sqrt{2}} = 0.707$$

2. The 30° and 60° triangle

Next we construct an equilateral triangle (all three sides equal) and bisect one side, forming right triangles with 30° and 60° angles (Fig. 45).

Again using the Pythagorean theorem, we compute the side b.

$$\begin{aligned} a^2 + b^2 &= (2a)^2 \\ &= 4a^2 \\ b^2 &= 3a^2 \\ b &= a\sqrt{3} \end{aligned}$$

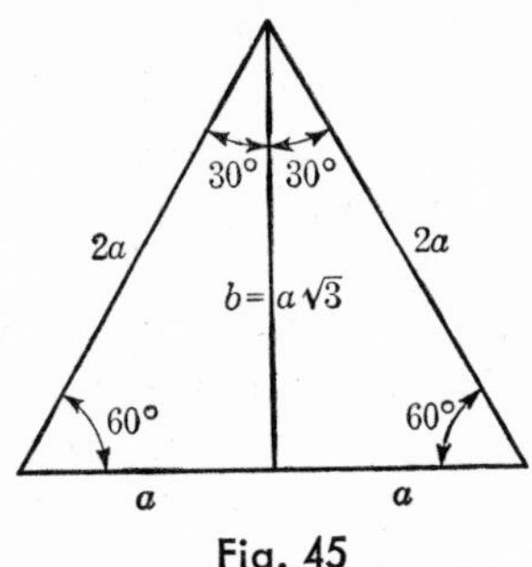

Fig. 45

From our definitions we read

$$\tan 60° = \frac{\text{side opposite}}{\text{side adjacent}} = \frac{a\sqrt{3}}{a} = \sqrt{3} = 1.732$$

$$\sin 60° = \frac{\text{side opposite}}{\text{hypotenuse}} = \frac{a\sqrt{3}}{2a} = \frac{\sqrt{3}}{2} = 0.866$$

$$\cos 60° = \frac{\text{side adjacent}}{\text{hypotenuse}} = \frac{a}{2a} = \frac{1}{2} = 0.500$$

$$\tan 30° = \frac{\text{side opposite}}{\text{side adjacent}} = \frac{a}{a\sqrt{3}} = \frac{1}{\sqrt{3}} = 0.577$$

$$\sin 30° = \frac{\text{side opposite}}{\text{hypotenuse}} = \frac{a}{2a} = \frac{1}{2} = 0.500$$

$$\cos 30° = \frac{\text{side adjacent}}{\text{hypotenuse}} = \frac{a\sqrt{3}}{2a} = \frac{\sqrt{3}}{2} = 0.866$$

3. Some applications

Now that we know the value of the tangent, sine, and cosine functions for the three angles 30°, 45°, and 60°, we shall solve some problems involving right triangles with these special angles.

Example 1. When the sun is 30° above the horizon, a tree casts a shadow of 40 feet (Fig. 46). Find the height of the tree.

Solution. We know that

$$\tan 30° = \frac{\text{side opposite}}{\text{side adjacent}} = \frac{h}{40}$$

We found that $\tan 30° = 0.577$, and we may write

$$0.577 = \frac{h}{40}$$

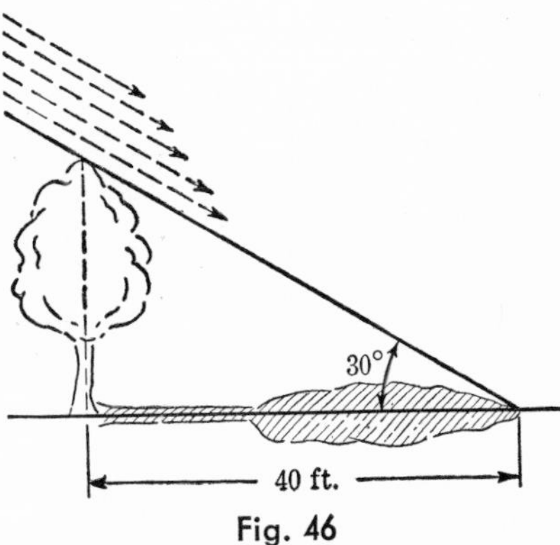

Fig. 46

and

$$h = 40(0.577) = 23.08 \text{ feet}$$

We were able to solve this problem easily without resorting to the graphical method. As a check, we can draw the triangle to scale and measure the height h.

Example 2. The angle of elevation of the top of a church spire is measured at a point A and found to be 30°. The angle of elevation is again measured at a point B which is 200 feet nearer to the church and found to be 60°. Find the height of the church.

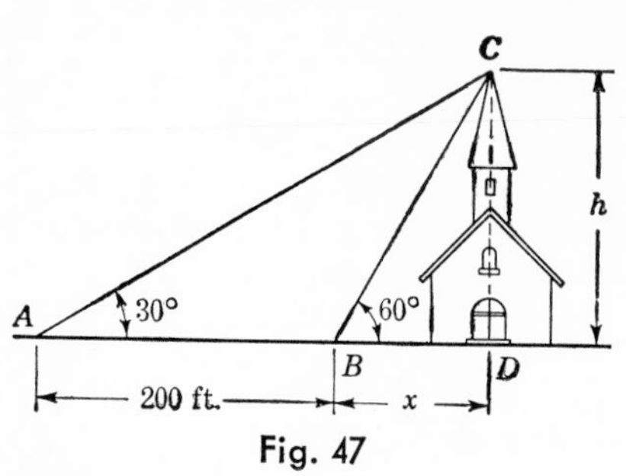

Fig. 47

Solution. A drawing is always helpful, so let's make one (Fig. 47). Using the triangle BCD, we may write

$$\tan 60° = \frac{\text{side opposite}}{\text{side adjacent}} = \frac{h}{x}$$

We look up the value of tan 60° and write

$$1.732 = \frac{h}{x}$$

Using triangle ACD, we may write

$$\tan 30° = \frac{\text{side opposite}}{\text{side adjacent}} = \frac{h}{200 + x}$$

Again we look up the value of tan 30°, and this equation becomes

$$0.577 = \frac{h}{200 + x}$$

or

$$h = 0.577(200 + x) = 115.4 + 0.577x$$

We have two linear equations containing two unknowns. We solve the first equation for $x = \frac{h}{1.732}$ and substitute this value into the second equation:

$$h = 115.4 + 0.577 \cdot \left(\frac{h}{1.732}\right)$$

$$h = 115.5 + \frac{h}{3}$$

$$h - \frac{h}{3} = 115.4$$

$$\frac{2h}{3} = 115.4$$

$$h = \frac{3(115.4)}{2} = 173.1 \text{ feet}$$

Having found the value of h, we can find the value of

$$x = \frac{h}{1.732} = \frac{173.1}{1.732} = 100 \text{ feet}$$

EXERCISES

Use the definitions of tangent, sine, and cosine and their values given previously to solve the following problems.

1. A boy flying a kite estimates that the angle of elevation of the kite is 60° when the kite is directly above a telephone pole which is 200 feet away. How high is the kite, and how many feet of string has the boy played out?

2. A certain hill has a 30° rise. How far has a boy traveled in the vertical and horizontal direction when he has climbed 300 feet up the slope?

3. Lots are laid out by lines perpendicular to Easy Street and running through to Primrose Path as shown in Fig. 48. If the angle between the streets is 30°, find the frontage on Primrose Path and the depth of each lot.

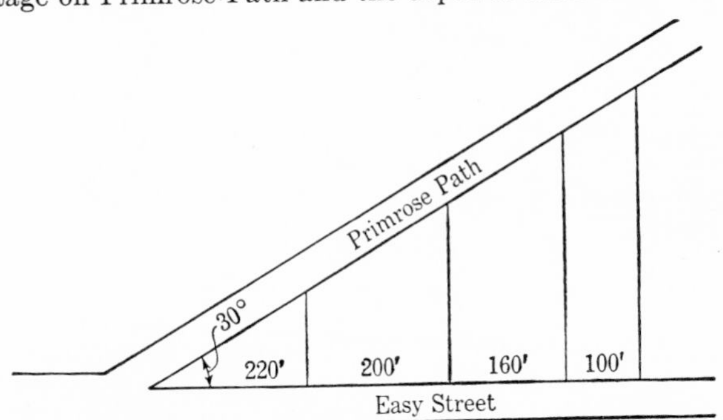

Fig. 48

4. A guy wire 300 feet long extends from the top of a radio tower to an anchor on the level ground. If the wire makes an angle of 45° with the ground, how high is the tower? How far from the base of the tower is the wire anchored?

5. The rafters of a house make an angle of 60° with the vertical. If 16-foot boards are used as rafters, find the height of the attic and the width of the house.

6. From a point 100 feet from a tower, the angle of elevation is 60°. Find the height of the tower.

7. From the top of a lighthouse 80 feet high, the angle of depression of a boat is 30°. How far is the boat from the lighthouse?

8. Two cars leave a highway junction at the same time. If the two roads are at right angles and one car travels west at a speed of 40 miles per hour and the other car travels north at a speed of 50 miles per hour, find the distance between the two cars after 2 hours have elapsed.

9. A 16-foot ladder standing against a wall makes an angle of 60° with the horizontal. How far up the wall does the ladder reach, and how far is the foot of the ladder from the wall?

10. If a man is standing on the ladder in Prob. 9, 10 feet above the ground, how far is he up the ladder and how far is he from the wall?

11. A pole 200 feet high is erected at the center of a circular circus tent. If the angle of elevation of the top of the pole from a point at the edge of the tent is 30°, find the diameter of the tent.

12. A flagpole is erected on top of a building. From a point on the ground 200 feet from the building, the angle of elevation of the top of the pole is 60° and of the bottom is 45°. Find the height of the flagpole.

13. From the foot of a mountain, the angle of elevation of the summit is found to be 45°. After walking 3 miles toward the summit up a 30° incline, a man finds the angle of elevation of the summit to be 60°. Find the height of the mountain.

14. A barn has a gambrel roof in which the lower rafters make an angle of 60° with the horizontal and the upper rafters make an angle of 60° with the vertical. If the two sets of rafters are equal in length and the width of the barn is 40 feet, find the length of the rafters and the height of the roof above the base of the roof.

15. An observer standing on top of a mountain found that the angle of depression of a town *A* was 45°, while that of town *B* directly beyond town *A* was 30°. If the two towns are on a level plain and are 1200 yards apart, find the height of the mountain.

??????????? PROBLEM JUST FOR FUN ???????????

Two men start walking toward each other from two points 10 miles distant. One man walks at the rate of 6 miles per hour and the other at the rate of 4 miles per hour. A bee leaves the nose of the first man as he starts and flies back and forth between the two at the rate of 25 miles per hour. When the two meet, how far has the bee flown?

???????????????? JUST FOR FUN ????????????????

CHAPTER

10

General Right Triangles

(How Far Is It from Here to There?)

> The utmost care must be taken to avoid errors, and that it is taken is proved by the wonderful accuracy with which the headings driven from opposite ends of the Musconetcony tunnel meet. The tunnel is about 5,000 feet long. When the headings met, the error in alignment was found to be only half an inch, and the error in level only about one-sixth of an inch.
>
> A. WILLIAMS

1. Tables and trigonometry

We must find the value of sine, cosine, and tangent for all values of the angle between 0° and 90°. If we have such a complete table we shall be able to solve completely any right triangle. If we are given one side and one acute angle of a right triangle, we can find the other two sides and the other acute angle. If we are given two sides of a right triangle, we can find the third side and the ratios of the sides. From the ratio of the sides we can find in the table the value of the angle for which this ratio corresponds. We shall discuss this idea in more detail shortly.

With such a table we have the means of solving any right triangle by analytical methods. The name of this mathematics is *trigonometry.* The word "trigonometry" comes from Greek words *trigonon,* which means "triangle," and *metron,* which means "to measure." From the meaning of the word, we see that trigonometry studies the relations between the sides and angles of the triangle and gives methods of deducing from the given parts the unknown sides and angles of a triangle. The early use of trigonometry was to measure indirectly inaccessible distances. We can use trigonometry to measure the heights of buildings and inaccessible mountains like Mount Everest, to determine the position of ships at sea, to navigate an airplane by the aid of stars, or to measure the length of a tunnel through a mountain or under a river.

Plane geometry enables us to *construct* the triangle, given three parts; while trigonometry enables us to *compute* these unknown parts of the triangle. From plane geometry we know that lengths of 3, 4, and 5 feet form a right triangle. But how large are the acute angles so formed? Geometry has no answer. We must turn to trigonometry for the solution.

While trigonometric functions were developed for and first used in the solutions of triangles, these functions have many uses in other branches of mathematics and fields of science. For example, any study of alternating-current machinery is full of trigonometric functions.

2. Constructing a table

Before we proceed farther, we must construct a table of sines, cosines, and tangents of all the angles between 0° and 90°. To make such a table, we shall use the method of Hipparchus (about 140 B.C.). We draw a right triangle in which one of the acute angles A is the desired angle. We measure the three sides and calculate the value of the three functions, sine A, cosine A, and tangent A, from the definition of these trigonometric functions. But we realize that the accuracy of our results will depend upon the care with which we draw the triangle and how accurately we can measure the length of the sides of the triangle.

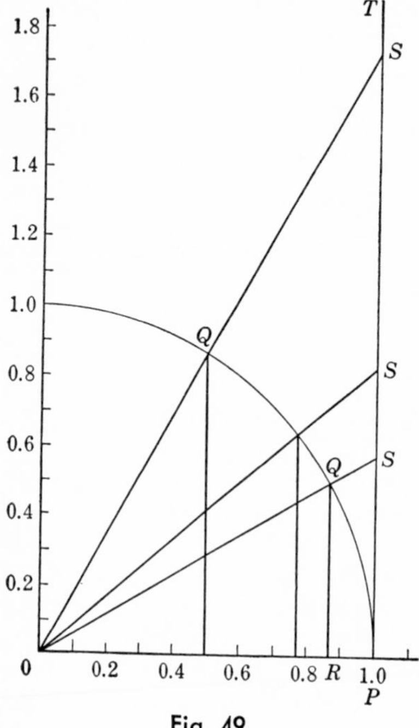

Fig. 49

Since we have at our disposal accurately constructed graph paper, we shall use it to aid us in measuring the length of the sides. Select a piece of graph paper. Using the lower left-hand corner as origin, carefully draw a circle with radius equal to 10 of the large divisions (see Fig. 49). If we consider each one of these divisions equal to $\frac{1}{10}$, the radius of the circle is equal to 1. We wish to find the value of the three trigonometric functions for an angle of 40°. We lay off this angle at 0 as carefully as possible and complete the right triangle QOR by drawing the vertical line QR. Triangle QOR is the right triangle with angle QOR equal to 40° and the hypotenuse OQ equal to 1. By definition.

$$\sin 40° = \frac{QR}{OQ} = \text{length of } QR$$

$$\cos 40° = \frac{OR}{OQ} = \text{length of } OR$$

Thus we see that in order to find the value of the sine and cosine for any acute angle, we draw with the aid of a protractor the angle POQ on the graph. The height of the point Q gives the value of the sine of the angle, and we see that $\sin 40° = 0.64$. The x coordinate of the point Q gives the value of the cosine of the angle, and we read from the graph, $\cos 40° = 0.76$.

At the point P draw the vertical line PT. Extend the line OQ to S, thus forming the right triangle POS in which the side PO is equal to 1. Then, using the right triangle POS, we may write

$$\tan 40° = \frac{PS}{OP} = PS = y \text{ coordinate of the point } S$$

From the graph we read $\tan 40° = 0.84$. Of course, we could find the tangent of the angle by dividing the ordinate of Q by the abscissa of Q, but it is easier to use a triangle so that the denominator is equal to 1.

EXERCISES

1. Use the method outlined above to find the value, correct to two decimal places, of sine, cosine, and tangent for the angles 10°, 20°, 30°, 40°, 50°, and 60°.

2. How do your values of the three functions for 30° and 60° compare with the values computed earlier?

3. What can you say about the size of the trigonometric functions for angles close to 0° and 90°?

4. What value would you assign to the following functions: sin 0°, cos 0°, tan 0°, sin 90° and cos 90°?

(Use the results of Prob. 1 to solve the following problems.)

5. When the sun's angle of elevation is 20°, a tree casts a shadow 132 feet long. How high is the tree?

6. From the top of a water tower, the angle of depression of a water hydrant is 50°. How high is the water tower if the hydrant is 300 feet from the base of the tower?

7. The diagonal of a rectangle makes an angle of 40° with the length of the rectangle. If the rectangle is 13.2 feet long, find its width and the length of the diagonal.

+ **8.** The top of a ladder makes an angle of 20° with a wall. If the base of the ladder rests on the level ground 6 feet from the wall, how long is the ladder and how high up the wall does it reach?

??????????? PROBLEM JUST FOR FÚN ???????????

Mr. Stupid did a division problem this way $\frac{1\not{6}}{\not{6}4} = \frac{1}{4}$. The answer is correct, but Teacher thought the method just suited Mr. Stupid. Can you find two other numbers which Mr. Stupid can divide and get the correct answer?

???????????????? JUST FOR FUN ????????????????

3. Early trigonometric tables

The scholars at the University of Alexandria started to make tables of the ratios of the sides of right triangles. Their values for these ratios were not too accurate, because they did not have an accurate table of square roots and a decimal system of fractions. We can say, however, that their development of trigonometry brought back measurement to geometry. As a need for greater accuracy developed, the mathematicians improved their tables to keep pace with the other sciences.

4. Functions of 0° and 90°

The value of the sine, cosine, and tangent of angles close to 0° and 90° are easily obtained from the definitions and Fig. 49. Now, if we make the angle ROS smaller and smaller until it is nearly zero, the point R is very near P. As $\cos ROS = OR$, we see that the cosine of a very small angle is nearly 1 and becomes closer as the angle gets smaller. Thus it seems natural to write

$$\cos 0° = 1$$

Similarly, as the angle approaches zero the distances QR and PS approach zero, and we define quite naturally

$$\sin 0° = 0 \qquad \cos 0° = 1 \qquad \tan 0° = 0$$

Likewise, if we make the angle larger and larger until it is almost 90°, the y coordinate of the point Q approaches 1, and the x coordinate of the point Q approaches zero, and we take

$$\sin 90° = 1 \qquad \text{and} \qquad \cos 90° = 0$$

Let us try to find a value for tan 90°. From Fig. 49 we see that the height of the point S as the angle gets close to 90° becomes larger and larger. In fact, when the angle becomes 90°, the line OQ is parallel to the line PT, and it is impossible to find the point of intersection of the two lines OQ and PT. We are not able to determine the distance PS. We conclude that $\tan 90° = PS$ does not exist. That is, we are not able to assign any definite value to tan 90°.

5. Functions of complementary angles

For the right triangle ABC shown in Fig. 50 we may write

$$\sin A = \frac{a}{c} \qquad \sin B = \frac{b}{c}$$

$$\cos A = \frac{b}{c} \qquad \cos B = \frac{a}{c}$$

$$\tan A = \frac{a}{b} \qquad \tan B = \frac{b}{a}$$

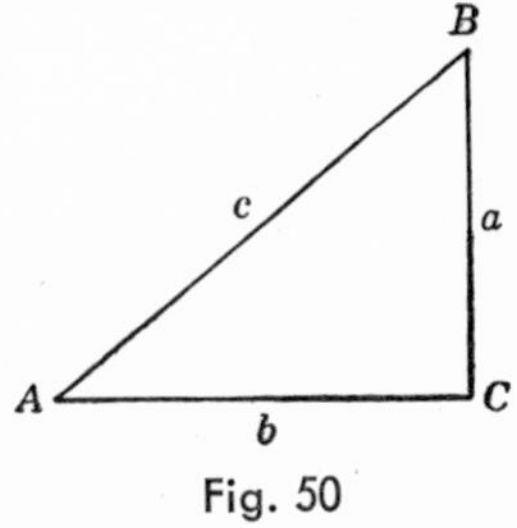

Fig. 50

We observe that $\sin A = \cos B$ and $\cos A = \sin B$. Also

$$\tan A = \frac{\sin A}{\cos A} \qquad \text{and} \qquad \tan A = \frac{1}{\tan B}$$

6. Four-place tables of trigonometric functions

The tables of trigonometric functions have been handed down from the Egyptians. As need for greater accuracy arose, methods were developed which gave better tables. The values of the sines, cosines, and tangents of angles between 0° and 90° were computed first for every degree, then for every 10 minutes, later for every minute, and at present we have tables for every second to four, eight and even twelve decimal places. These tables were computed by the use of special infinite series.

For our purpose, trigonometric tables giving the value of sine, cosine, tangent, and cotangent for every 10 minutes between 0° and 90° to four places will be accurate enough. Such a table will be found at the back of the book (Table II). Some time should be devoted to a study of this table in order to learn how to use it correctly and rapidly.

Looking at the table, we note that we can read from the top downward to get the sine, tangent, cotangent, or cosine of angles between 0° and 45°. Likewise, we can read from the bottom up to get the value of the same functions from 45° to 90°. We encounter no difficulty in finding that the $\sin 28°20' = 0.4746$ and $\cos 13°30' = 0.9724$. Check these results for yourself.

EXERCISES

Use the table to find the sine, cosine, and tangent of each of the following angles.

1. 20°40′
2. 57°10′
3. 86°30′
4. 8°50′
5. 65°20′
6. 72°

??????????? PROBLEM JUST FOR FUN ???????????

Arrange three 8's so that they equal 7.

???????????????? JUST FOR FUN ????????????????

7. To find the angle from the table

Sometimes we know the value of the trigonometric function and need to find the angle which has this value. For example, to find the value of angle A if $\sin A = 0.5495$, we look in the sine column of the table until we find the value 0.5495. We find that $\sin 33°20' = 0.5495$. Then angle A is equal to $33°20'$. In many cases we will not find the exact value in the table. For example, if we want the value of angle A for which $\tan A = 1.7596$, we look in the tangent column of the table and do not find the number 1.7596. However, we see that $\tan 60°20' = 1.7556$ and $\tan 60°30' = 1.7675$, and our value lies between these two values. We take $60°20'$ for the value of A because 1.7596 is closer to 1.7556 than to 1.7675. There are methods by which we can determine more closely the value of the angle. We will not discuss these methods here, because the accuracy of our measurements does not warrant the determination of an angle closer than 10 minutes.

EXERCISES

Find the angle to the nearest 10 minutes when the value of the trigonometric function is given.

1. $\sin A = 0.1132$ **2.** $\cos A = 0.9727$ **3.** $\sin A = 0.5195$
4. $\sin A = 0.9920$ **5.** $\tan A = 0.4210$ **6.** $\tan A = 1.3934$
7. $\cos A = 0.2720$ **8.** $\tan A = 2.7750$ **9.** $\cos A = 0.6614$

??????????? PROBLEM JUST FOR FUN ???????????

Three boats going upstream meet three boats coming downstream in a river with a channel so narrow that two boats cannot pass. However, at the point where they meet there is a side basin just large enough to hold one boat. Can you figure out how the six boats manage to pass one another?

???????????????? JUST FOR FUN ????????????????

8. A practical problem

Let us use the facts that we have learned about trigonometry to solve a practical problem.

Example. From the top of a lighthouse 100 feet above the water the angles of depression of two ships in the same straight line with the lighthouse are 15°30′ and 37°50′, respectively. What is the distance between the two ships, and how far are they from the point directly below the lighthouse?

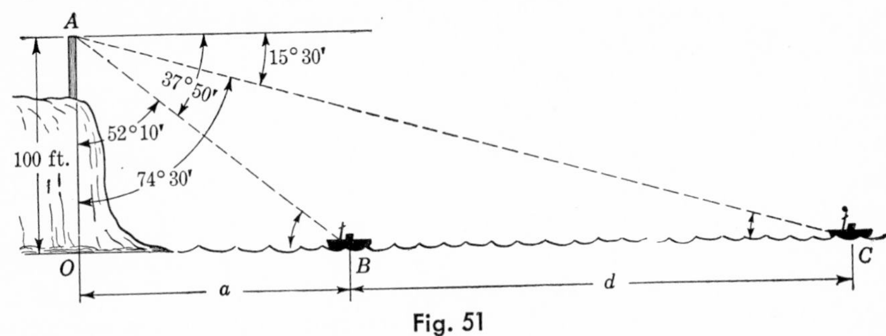

Fig. 51

Solution. First let us draw a diagram (Fig. 51).
From triangles OAB and OAC we get

$$\tan 52°10' = \frac{a}{100} \quad \text{and} \quad \tan 74°30' = \frac{a + d}{100}$$

From the first equation we find that

$$a = 100 \tan 52°10' = 100(1.2876) = 129 \text{ feet}$$

From the second equation we get

$$a + d = 100 \tan 74°30' = 100(3.6059) = 361 \text{ feet}$$

Then

$$d = 361 - a = 361 - 129 = 232 \text{ feet}$$

EXERCISES

Use the trigonometric tables to solve the following problems.

1. A tree 60 feet high casts a shadow of 70 feet. Find the angle of elevation of the sun.

2. How far is a surveyor from a building 700 feet high if the angle of elevation of the top of the building is 53°10′?

3. If a road rises steadily a distance of 210 feet in a horizontal distance of 1 mile, find the angle the road makes with the horizontal.

4. An iron wedge used for splitting trees has a base 3 inches wide and a vertex angle of 15°. Find the length of the edges of the wedge.

5. From a forest lookout tower perched on a cliff 200 feet above a lake, the angle of depression of a small blaze across the lake is 14°30′. How far is the blaze from the foot of the cliff? How far is the blaze from the ranger?

6. Find the area of a parallelogram if the angle between sides 8 inches and 12 inches long is 37°50′.

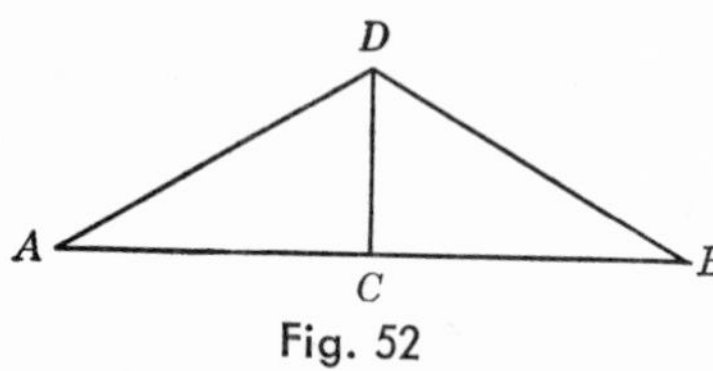

Fig. 52

7. The pitch of a roof gable is the ratio of its height to its entire width, i.e., CD/AB. If the pitch of the roof is $\frac{2}{3}$, what is the size of angle A?

8. Two ranger lookout stations are on hills which are the same height and 4.8 miles apart. When an airplane in level flight is directly above one station, the pilot finds the angle of depression of the second station to be 28°40′. How high is the airplane above the lookout stations?

9. A field-artillery gun has a range of 18 miles. If the gun is fired in the direction which is 20° north of west, how many miles north and how many miles west does the artillery shell go?

10. An airplane climbs 820 feet while traveling 1 mile west, then climbs 500 feet while traveling a second mile in the same direction. What angle of climb could the pilot have used in a steady climb to have gained the same total height of 1,320 feet in 2 miles?

11. A ship sails a distance of 50 miles in a direction 20° north of east and then sails 60 miles straight north. What is the distance of the ship from its starting point?

12. A 12-foot ladder rests against a wall at a point 10 feet above the ground. Find the angles the ladder makes with the wall and the ground.

13. If the ladder in Prob. 12 slips so that the top is 8 feet above the ground, find the angle of inclination of the ladder and the distance from the foot of the ladder to the wall.

14. How far must the foot of the ladder in Prob. 12 be pulled out if the angle of inclination of the ladder is to be 56°?

15. The summit of a mountain is seen at an angle of elevation of 23°20′ from a camp whose altitude is 5,280 feet. If the mountain is 11,450 feet, what is the air-line distance from the camp to the summit of the mountain?

16. Two guy wires are fastened to a vertical pole at a height of 40 feet. The longer wire is 80 feet long, and the shorter wire is 60 feet. If both wires are anchored in the ground in line with the pole, find the distance between the lower ends of the wires.

17. Two church steeples are 150 feet and 120 feet high and are 500 feet apart. If a line were drawn joining the tops of the steeples, what would be the angle of inclination of this line, and how far from the two churches would it meet the ground?

18. Two city streets meet at an angle of 30°. The fire department arrives at a fire which is 200 feet from the intersection and discovers that the only fire hydrant is around the corner on the other street 100 feet from the intersection. What is

the shortest length of hose needed, assuming that there are no buildings so that the hose can cut across lots?

??????????? PROBLEM JUST FOR FUN ???????????

Pete Smith, Sr., who was anxious to encourage Pete Smith, Jr., in this course, agreed to award him \$5 for every problem he solved correctly but fined him \$4 for every incorrect or unsolved problem. Junior did the preceding group of problems and found he had just broken even. How many did Junior solve correctly?

???????????????? JUST FOR FUN ????????????????

9. Distance of the moon from the earth

Aristarchus (310–250 B.C.) made the first estimate of the relative distances of the moon and the sun from the earth. Hipparchus (about 150 B.C.) made a table of sines and determined the distance of the moon from the earth. Hipparchus also made maps of the stars in latitude and longitude.

The method used by Hipparchus to calculate the distance of the moon from the earth is essentially as follows:

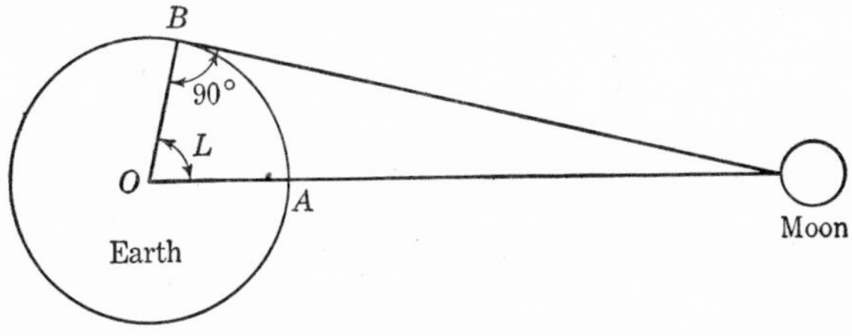

Fig. 53

An observer at A (Fig. 53) observes the moon when it is directly overhead, and at exactly the same instant an observer at B observes the moon when it rises on the horizon. If A and B are in the same latitude but are separated by L degrees of longitude, we may write

$$\cos L = \frac{OB}{OM} = \frac{\text{radius of the earth}}{\text{distance to the moon}}$$

If we know that $L = 89\frac{1}{16}°$ and find the value of $\cos 89\frac{1}{16}°$ from a table, we can solve for OM for the distance to the moon, which is approximately 245,000 miles.*

* Hogben, Lancelot, "Mathematics for the Million," p. 247, W. W. Norton & Company, New York, 1937.

Now, knowing the moon's distance, it is easy to determine its diameter and circumference. We need only measure the angle subtended by opposite spots on the boundary of a full moon when it is directly overhead (Fig. 54). We can write

$$\tan\frac{A}{2} = \frac{EM}{OM} = \frac{\text{radius of the moon}}{\text{moon's distance from the earth}}$$

If $A = \frac{1}{2}°$ and $\tan \frac{1}{4}° = 0.0044$, using $OM = 245{,}000$ miles, we find $EM = 1{,}078$ miles. The best modern measurements of the moon's radius give 1,081 miles. We can compute the circumference of the moon as 2π times the radius.

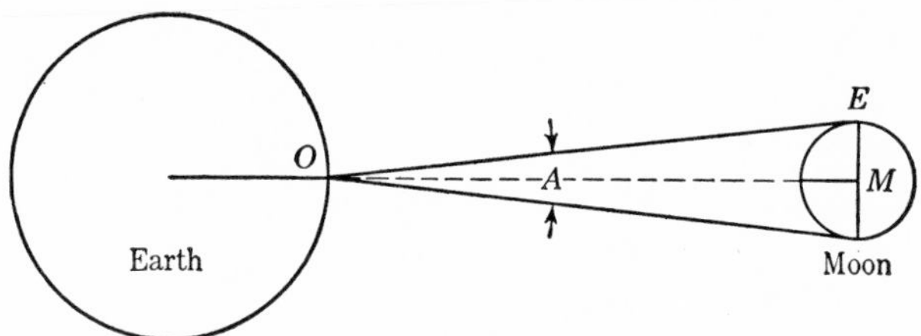

Fig. 54

It is now apparent that if we wish to measure astronomical distances, we are going to need tables of trigonometric functions for very small angles. Various formulas have been devised to obtain the values of sines, cosines, and tangents of angles close to zero.

10. Archimedes' method for finding the value of π

But how much did the ancients know about the value of π, which is the symbol in mathematics for the ratio between the lengths of the circumference and diameter of a circle? More than two centuries before Christ, the Greek scientist Archimedes (287–212 B.C.) developed a method for calculating the value of π to any desired accuracy.

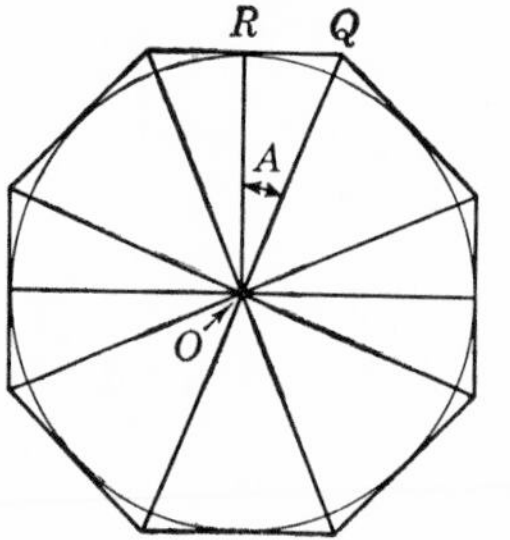

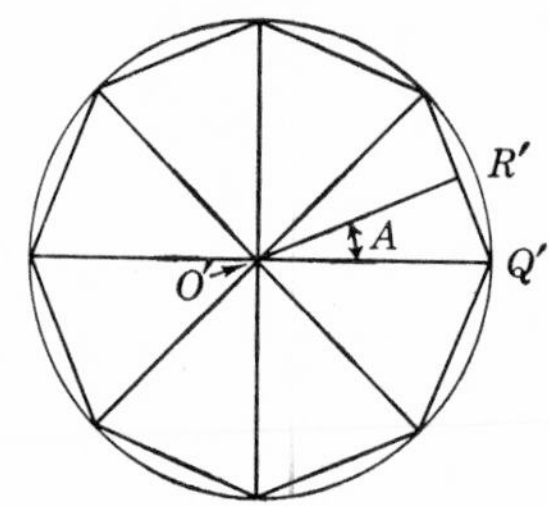

Fig. 55

Consider a circle of radius 1 with a regular polygon circumscribed about it (Fig. 55). From a triangle RQO we can write

$$\tan A = \frac{RQ}{RO} = RQ$$

because the radius of the circle is equal to 1. If the polygon has n sides, the angle $A = \dfrac{360°}{2n}$.

$$RQ = \tan \frac{360°}{2n}$$

The perimeter P of this circumscribed regular polygon becomes

$$P = 2n \tan \frac{360°}{2n}$$

Let us consider the regular polygon of n sides inscribed inside this circle with unit radius. For this case, we may write

$$\sin A = \frac{R'Q'}{O'Q'} = R'Q'$$

and $A = \dfrac{360°}{2n}$ so that

$$R'Q' = \sin \frac{360°}{2n}$$

In this case the perimeter P' of the inscribed regular polygon becomes

$$P' = 2n \sin \frac{360°}{2n}$$

It seems obvious that the circumference of the circle is less than P, the perimeter of the circumscribed polygon, and greater than P', the perimeter of the inscribed polygon. That is,

$$P > 2\pi \text{ radius} > P'$$

$$2n \tan \frac{360°}{2n} > 2\pi > 2n \sin \frac{360°}{2n}$$

or

$$n \tan \frac{360°}{2n} > \pi > n \sin \frac{360°}{2n}$$

If the polygon has six sides, this last inequality becomes

$$6 \tan 30° > \pi > 6 \sin 30°$$

$$6(0.577) > \pi > 6(\tfrac{1}{2})$$

$$3.462 > \pi > 3$$

We find that the value of π must be between 3.462 and 3. If we take the average of 3.462 and 3, we may write that the value is $\pi = 3.231$, with an error of at most 0.231.

It is clear that, if we increase n, the number of sides of the inscribed and circumscribed polygons, we may find the value of π as accurately as we wish. Archimedes used for π a number lying between $3\frac{1}{7}$ and $3\frac{10}{71}$. To get π more accurately, we see that Archimedes needed a table of sines and tangents. No record has been found that such a table existed before the tables compiled by Hipparchus.*

By modern methods the value of π has been computed to hundreds of decimal places. Below we give the value to 30 places, together with a little rhyme which has been used to remember these figures.

$$\pi = 3.141\ 592\ 653\ 589\ 793\ 238\ 462\ 643\ 383\ 279\ \ldots$$

3 1 4 1 5 9
Now I, even I, would celebrate

2 6 5 3 5
In rhymes inapt, the great

8 9 7 9
Immortal Syracusan, rivaled nevermore,

3 2 3 8 4
Who in his wondrous lore,

6 2 6
Passed on before,

4 3 3 8 3 2 7 9
Left men his guidance how to circles mensurate.

A. C. Orr

* For a table of values of π used by the Babylonians, Hebrews, Chinese, Egyptians, Hindus, Arabs, Japanese, and Europeans, see Hogben, *op. cit.*, p. 261.

CHAPTER

General Triangles

(*The Laws of Sines and Cosines*)

> The student of mathematics often finds it hard to throw off the uncomfortable feeling that his science, in the person of his pencil, surpasses him in intelligence—an impression which the great Euler confessed he often could not get rid of. ERNST MACH

1. A general triangle

If we reflect a bit, we realize that in the preceding chapters we have been solving problems that involved right triangles only. Of course, many problems involve triangles in which none of the angles are right angles. So we must roll up our sleeves and face this situation.

Suppose we have the following problem: Two towers at points A and B are viewed from a point C which is 100 feet from tower A and 400 feet from tower B. The angle ACB is 66°. How far are the towers apart? We make a rough sketch (Fig. 56), and we find that the triangle ABC is not a right triangle. Of course, we could make our drawing carefully and use the graphical method to determine the distance, but this is time-consuming and not very accurate.

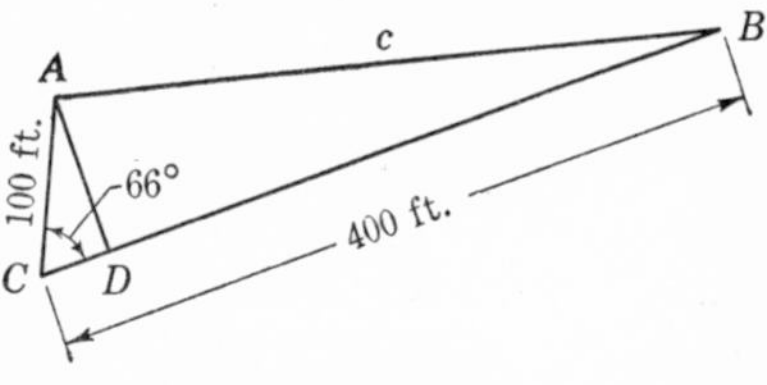

Fig. 56

Since we have been working with right triangles, it is natural to make two right triangles CAD and ADB by dropping the perpendicular AD upon the side CB. From the right triangle ACD we can easily determine the distances AD and CD. Subtracting the length of CD from 400 will give us BD, and we can find the length AB in the right triangle ABD by the *square of the hypotenuse* method. But this is also tedious and we hope to find a way or a formula that will shorten the work.

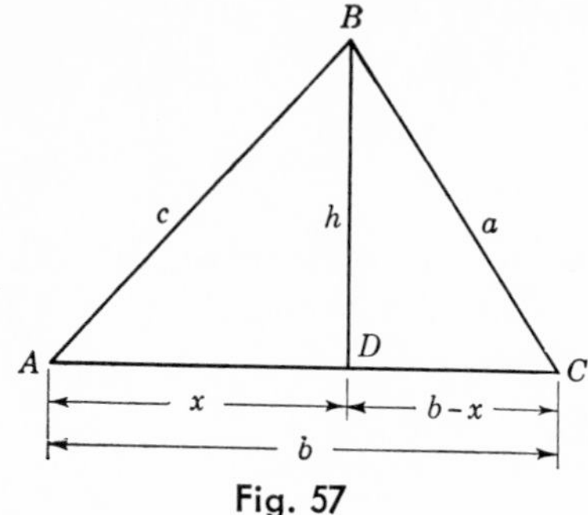

Fig. 57

2. The law of cosines

Let us consider the triangle ABC, where angles A and C are acute (Fig. 57). From the vertex B drop the perpendicular BD upon the side AC, forming the two right triangles ABD and BCD. Let $BD = h$ and $AD = x$. Then $DC = b - x$. From triangle ABD, we may write

$$h^2 = c^2 - x^2$$

From triangle BCD, we may write

$$h^2 = a^2 - (b - x)^2 = a^2 - b^2 + 2bx - x^2$$

Equating these two values for h^2, we obtain

$$c^2 - x^2 = a^2 - b^2 + 2bx - x^2$$

Solving for a^2, we get

$$a^2 = b^2 + c^2 - 2bx$$

In the triangle ABD we see

$$\cos A = \frac{x}{c} \qquad \text{or} \qquad x = c \cos A$$

If we replace x by this value, we obtain one of the equations which is known as the *law of cosines*,

$$a^2 = b^2 + c^2 - 2bc \cos A$$

The other two equations are

$$b^2 = a^2 + c^2 - 2ac \cos B$$

and

$$c^2 = a^2 + b^2 - 2ab \cos C$$

These are obtained in a similar manner if the perpendicular h is dropped from angles A and C, respectively.

These three equations are easy to remember in words as follows: *The square of one side of a triangle is equal to the sum of the squares of the other two sides minus twice the product of the two sides times the cosine of the included angle.*

We can use one of these equations to determine the unknown side of a triangle if we know the length of two sides and the included angle. This is exactly the situation in the preceding tower problem, and we can find the distance c between the two towers.

$$\begin{aligned} c^2 &= 100^2 + 400^2 - 2(100)(400) \cos 66^\circ \\ &= 10{,}000 + 160{,}000 - 80{,}000(0.4067) \\ &= 137{,}464 \\ c &= \sqrt{137{,}464} = 370 \text{ feet} \end{aligned}$$

Thus far we have not defined the cosine of an angle greater than 90°. This will be done in the next chapter. With this extended definition the law of cosines holds in triangles containing an obtuse angle.

If the angle A is a right angle, $\cos A = \cos 90^\circ = 0$; then the last term of the law of cosines disappears, leaving

$$a^2 = b^2 + c^2$$

which is our familiar Pythagorean theorem. It seems natural to think of the law of cosines as being the Pythagorean theorem for general triangles.

3. Law of sines

Returning to the triangle ABC of Fig. 57, we shall develop another useful formula. Using triangle ABD, we may write

$$\sin A = \frac{h}{c} \text{ or } h = c \sin A$$

From triangle BCD, we may write

$$\sin C = \frac{h}{a} \text{ or } h = a \sin C$$

Equating these two values of h, we get

$$c \sin A = a \sin C$$

or

$$\frac{a}{\sin A} = \frac{c}{\sin C}$$

In exactly the same way, we may drop a perpendicular line from A to the side BC, forming two triangles. We follow the same line of reasoning and obtain

$$\frac{c}{\sin C} = \frac{b}{\sin B}$$

We combine these two equations into one statement, which is known as the *law of sines*,

$$\frac{a}{\sin A} = \frac{b}{\sin B} = \frac{c}{\sin C}$$

This statement is also easy to remember, for it says that *the ratio of a side of a triangle to the sine of the angle opposite that side is the same for all three sides.*

Like the law of cosines, the law of sines is valid for any triangle. Notice that it reduces to the usual form for the sine of an angle in a right triangle if $A = 90°$. It is used when we know the angles and one side and need to find the other sides of the triangle. Also, if we know two sides and an angle opposite one of them, the law of sines does the job for us.

Suppose we want to know the angle at tower B in Fig. 56. We write

$$\frac{c}{\sin C} = \frac{AC}{\sin B}$$

or

$$\frac{370}{\sin 66°} = \frac{100}{\sin B}$$

$$\sin B = \frac{100 \sin 66°}{370} = 0.2469$$

and

$$B = 14°20'$$

EXERCISES

Use the laws of sines and cosines to solve the following problems.

1. When 200 feet of string has been played out, the angle of elevation of a kite is 43°. Find the height of the kite above the ground.

2. Find the length of the shorter diagonal of a parallelogram if the angle between two sides is 43° and the sides are 8 and 12 feet.

3. A triangular lot has sides 100 feet, 80 feet, and 60 feet. Find the angles at the corners and the area of the lot.

4. Two piers, A and B, are on opposite sides of a lake. The point C on land is taken a distance of 120 feet from A and 190 feet from B, and the angle between BC and AC is found to be 57°. Find the distance between the two piers.

5. A 10-foot pole placed vertically on a hillside casts a shadow 15 feet straight down the hill. The angle formed by the hill and the line joining the top of the pole with the tip of the shadow is 25°. Find the angle of elevation of the sun. What is the angle between the horizontal and the hill?

6. An observer in a lighthouse notices that one ship is 20 miles in a direction 67° north of west and another ship is 26 miles in a direction 33° north of east. How far apart are the ships?

7. In what direction must an observer on the second ship in Prob. 6 look to see the first ship?

8. Two angles of a triangular lot are 60° and 63°30′. If the largest side is 102 feet, find the value of the other two sides.

9. A man walks 10 miles in a direction 20° north of west and then 5 miles in a direction 30° east of north. How far is he from the starting point?

10. In what direction should the man in Prob. 9 have walked to have reached the same point without changing his course?

??????????? PROBLEM JUST FOR FUN ???????????

Eight coins lie in a straight row. In any one move we may jump a coin over *exactly* two others, stacked or not, onto the top of the next one. How do you make the moves so that you end with four stacked pairs?

???????????????? JUST FOR FUN ????????????????

CHAPTER

12

General Angles

(The Angle Goes 'Round and 'Round)

> No more impressive warning can be given to those who would confine knowledge and research to what is apparently useful, than the reflection that conic sections were studied for eighteen hundred years merely as an abstract science, without regard to any utility other than to satisfy the craving for knowledge on the part of mathematicians, and that then at the end of this long period of abstract study, they were found to be the necessary key with which to attain the knowledge of the most important laws of nature.
>
> A. N. WHITEHEAD

1. Functions of general angles

Suppose the man in Prob. 9 on page 107 had walked 10 miles in a direction 20° north of west and then 5 miles in a direction 40° north of west. How far is he from the starting point? If we make a sketch (Fig. 58), we see that the desired distance $CA = b$ from the starting point A is opposite an angle of 160°. Using the appropriate form of the law of cosines derived in Sec. 2 of the previous chapter, we write

$$b^2 = 10^2 + 5^2 - 2(5)(10) \cos 160°$$

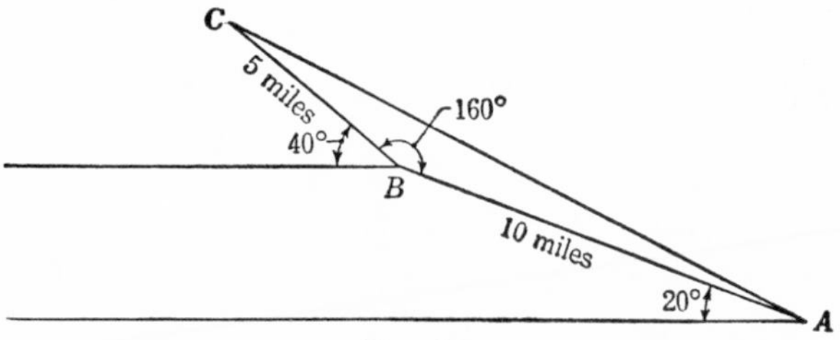

Fig. 58

We can easily find the value of b if we are able to find the value of cos 160°. If we look in our tables, we find that they stop at 90°. We do not want to resort to the graphical method or to break the triangle ABC into two right triangles by dropping a perpendicular from the vertex B upon AC. The simplest thing to do is to find the value of the cosine of 160°.

2. Angles of any magnitude

First, we must extend our idea of angles. Let us draw a set of rectangular axes. We will consider an angle as being in standard position if its vertex is placed at the origin, with one side OP on the positive x axis, the other side OQ falling as shown in Fig. 59.

Now let a line OQ' start coincident with the line OP and rotate about O, coming to rest coincident with OQ. This line generates an angle whose magnitude is determined by the amount of rotation. If the line rotates counterclockwise, the angle is taken as positive; if the line rotates clockwise, the angle is taken to be negative. To obtain positive angles of 70°, 150°, and 250°, start with the line OQ' along the x axis and rotate it counterclockwise 70°, 150°, and 250°, respectively (Fig. 60). To obtain negative angles of 70°, 150°, and 250°, rotate the line OQ' in the clockwise direction. An arc is usually drawn connecting the initial and terminal sides of the angle. An arrow is placed on the arc to denote the direction of rotation.

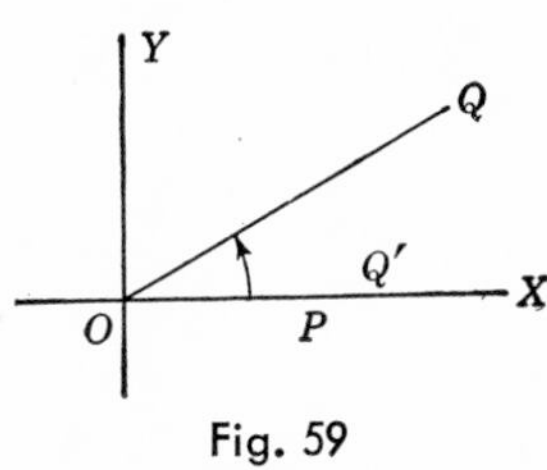

Fig. 59

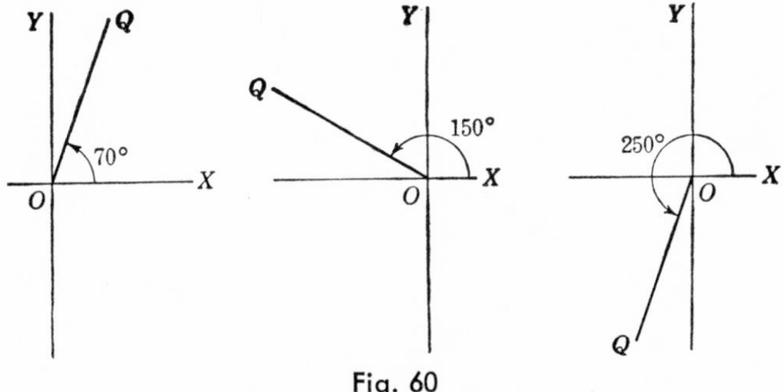

Fig. 60

We have replaced the idea of an angle being an opening between two lines by an angle being an "amount of rotation." As the line OQ' rotates about O, the angle will increase up to 360° in one revolution. We need not stop with one revolution. If the line rotates through two revolutions, the angle generated is 720°, or twice 360°. In this way we can determine an angle of any size.

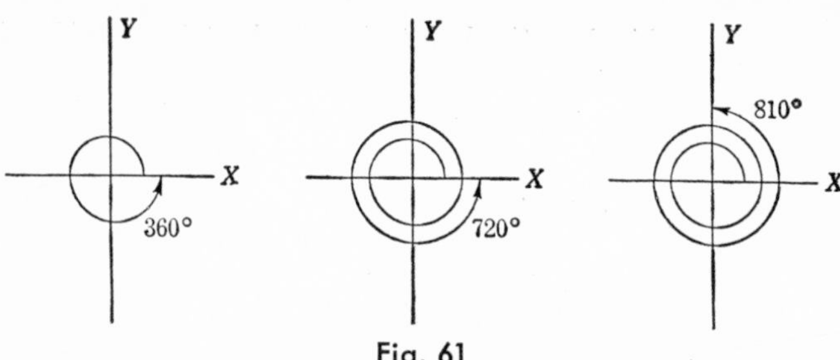

Fig. 61

Such large angles may appear to be unnecessary, but our modern machinery contains many rotating parts (airplane propellers, flywheels, electric fans, etc.), and we often need to know the angle that a part turns through in a minute, which may be many revolutions.

We recall that the values of the trigonometric functions sine, cosine, and tangent for angles between 0° and 90° were found by evaluating the ratios $\frac{\text{side opposite}}{\text{hypotenuse}}$, $\frac{\text{side adjacent}}{\text{hypotenuse}}$, and $\frac{\text{side opposite}}{\text{side adjacent}}$, respectively. In order to extend these definitions to angles greater than 90°, we shall have to decide what is meant by hypotenuse, side opposite, and side adjacent for such angles. We shall agree arbitrarily to call x, y, and r (see Fig. 62) the side adjacent, the side opposite, and the hypotenuse. We shall always regard the distance r as positive, but we see from the figures that the distances x and y may be positive or negative, depending upon the position of the terminal side of the angle.

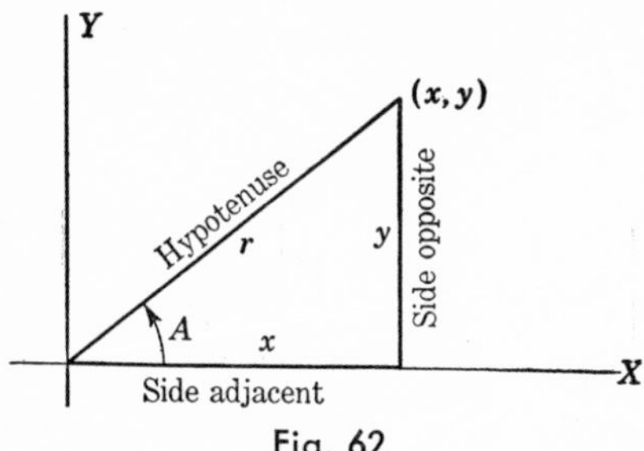

Fig. 62

In order to find the value of the trigonometric functions for angles

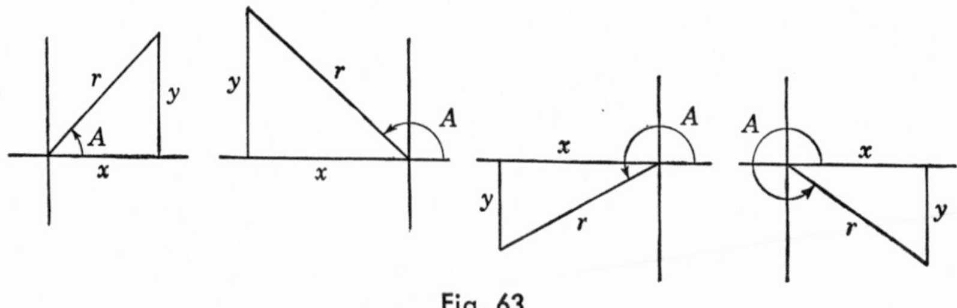

Fig. 63

greater than 90°, we draw the angle carefully and measure its sides x, y, and r (Fig. 63). Then

$$\sin A = \frac{\text{side opposite}}{\text{hypotenuse}} = \frac{y}{r}$$

$$\cos A = \frac{\text{side adjacent}}{\text{hypotenuse}} = \frac{x}{r}$$

$$\tan A = \frac{\text{side opposite}}{\text{side adjacent}} = \frac{y}{x}$$

For example, if angle $A = 210°$, its terminal side lies in the third quadrant, and we draw the diagram as in Fig. 64 and measure the sides x, y, and r. Using the values from the figure and the definitions of the trigonometric functions, we write

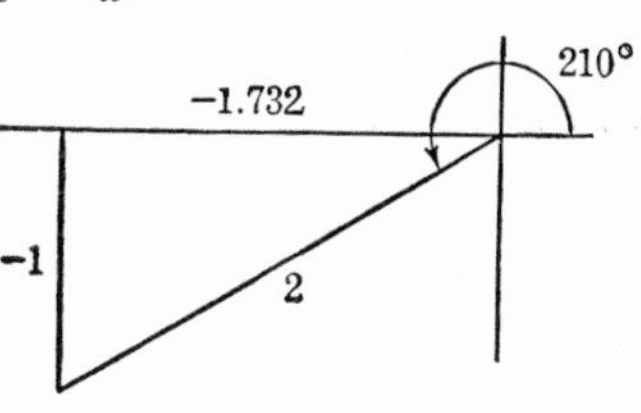

Fig. 64

$$\sin 210° = -\frac{1}{2} = -0.500$$

$$\cos 210° = \frac{-1.732}{2} = -0.866$$

$$\tan 210° = \frac{-1}{-1.732} = 0.577$$

EXERCISES

1. Write out the value of sine, cosine, and tangent for the angles shown in Fig. 65. Be careful about signs.

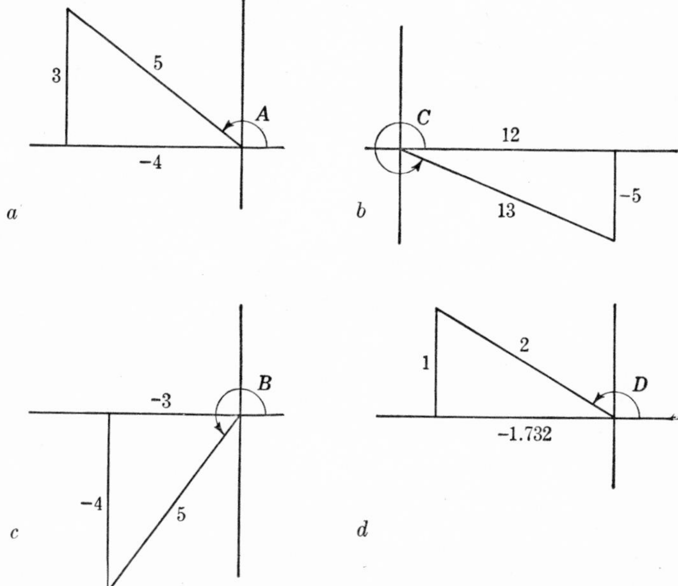

Fig. 65

2. Given each of the following functions, draw each possible angle which is less than 360°, and write by inspection the value of the two remaining trigonometric functions, sine, cosine, or tangent.

a. $\cos A = \frac{12}{13}$ *b.* $\sin A = -\frac{1}{3}$
c. $\sin A = \frac{4}{5}$ *d.* $\cos A = \frac{1}{2}$
e. $\tan A = -\frac{3}{2}$ *f.* $\tan A = \frac{4}{3}$

??????????? PROBLEM JUST FOR FUN ???????????

Mike and Pat between them won one glass of beer from Jake on a bet. Jake paid off but insisted that Mike and Pat divide the one glass of beer equally without the aid of any measuring device. How was this division accomplished, assuming that the glass was clear, with perfectly vertical sides?

??????????????? JUST FOR FUN ???????????????

3. More about general angles

We could calculate a table of the trigonometric functions for all angles between 90° and 360° in the same way that we calculated the values of functions for angles between 0° and 90°. This would be too much work. Since the values of the trigonometric functions have not been tabulated for angles greater than 90°, there must be some simple way to get the value of these functions for large angles.

Perhaps we have overlooked some clues that might be hidden in the above examples. Let us look carefully at the angle of 210° (Fig. 66). When we measured the sides x, y, and r, we found that $r = 2$, $y = -1$, and $x = -1.732$. Since the hypotenuse is twice the opposite side, a 30° angle must be involved. Inspection of the figure confirms our suspicions, since angle ROQ is 30°. If we draw a 30° angle in standard position, we obtain the triangle in Fig. 67. By comparing these two figures, we find

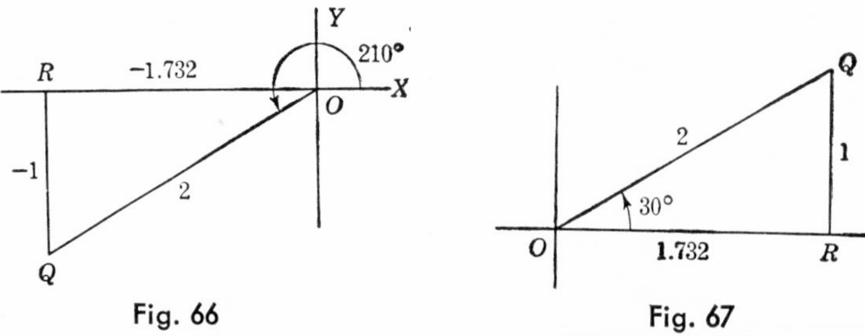

Fig. 66 Fig. 67

that the hypotenuse, side opposite, and side adjacent of the two angles 30° and 210° are equal except for sign. Thus

$$\sin 210^\circ = -\frac{1}{2} \qquad \sin 30^\circ = \frac{1}{2}$$

$$\cos 210^\circ = \frac{-1.732}{2} = -0.866 \qquad \cos 30^\circ = \frac{1.732}{2} = 0.866$$

$$\tan 210^\circ = \frac{-1}{-1.732} = 0.577 \qquad \tan 30^\circ = \frac{1}{1.732} = 0.577$$

We see that the values of sin 210°, cos 210°, and tan 210° are numerically the same as sin 30°, cos 30°, and tan 30°, respectively. Since the terminal side of 210° lies in the third quadrant, we expect the sine and cosine to be negative. We conclude that in order to find the sine, cosine, and tangent of 210°, we look up the sine, cosine, and tangent of 30° and assign the proper sign.

If we have any angle A whose terminal side lies in the third quadrant (Fig. 68), we determine the size of the acute angle ROQ and find the value of its trigonometric functions from the table. The sine, cosine, and tangent of angle A is then obtained by assigning the proper sign + or − to the sine, cosine, or tangent of the acute angle ROQ.

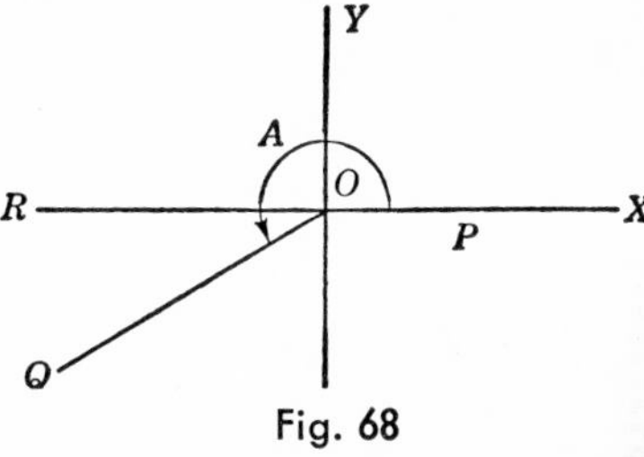

Fig. 68

If the terminal side of angle A lies in the second or fourth quadrants, the acute angle ROQ is as shown in Fig. 69. The sine, cosine, and tangent of angle A have the same numerical value as the sine, cosine, and tangent of the acute angle ROQ. All we need to do is attach the proper + or − sign. We can determine the proper sign by picturing the angle mentally and noticing whether the sides x and y are negative or positive.

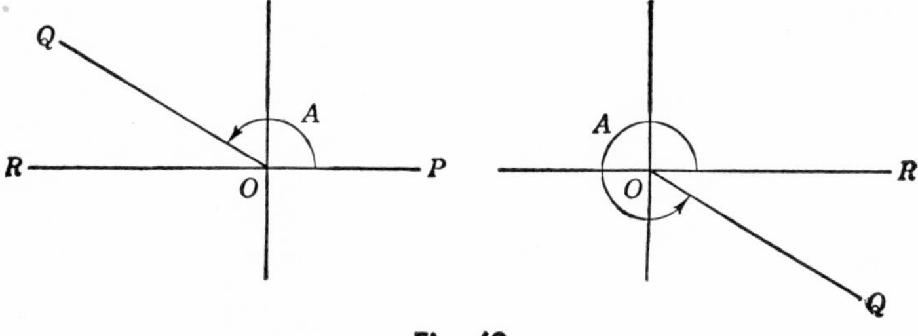

Fig. 69

We are now in a position to finish the problem mentioned at the beginning of the chapter. In order to find the cos 160°, we look up the value for cos 20° and, since 160° is in the second quadrant, we find that cos 160° = −0.9397. Then

$$b^2 = 10^2 + 5^2 - (2)(5)(10)(-0.9397)$$
$$= 100 + 25 + 93.97 = 218.97$$
$$b = \sqrt{218.97} = 14.8 \text{ miles}$$

EXERCISES

1. Determine the value for the following functions:

a. sin 150° *b.* sin 300° *c.* cos 160°
d. cos 225° *e.* cos 210° *f.* sin 248°
g. tan 330° *h.* tan 110° *i.* tan 200°

2. For each of the following functions, draw each possible angle which is less than 360° and determine the value of the angle:

a. $\cos \theta = -\frac{3}{4}$ *b.* $\tan \theta = -\frac{4}{10}$
c. $\tan \theta = \frac{1}{2}$ *d.* $\cos \theta = \frac{2}{3}$
e. $\sin \theta = -\frac{7}{10}$ *f.* $\sin \theta = \frac{1}{3}$

3. A road runs up a hill at an angle of 18°. When a hiker has climbed 800 feet from the bottom of the hill, he observes another man who is approaching the hill. If the angle of depression is 8°, how far is the man from the base of the hill?

4. One man walks 5 miles directly east, while another man walks 10 miles in a direction 35° north of west. How far apart are the men if they started at the same point?

5. A telephone pole 100 feet high was knocked out of a vertical position during a windstorm. A guy wire 150 feet long attached at the top of the pole and at a point 95 feet from the base kept the pole from falling. What angle did the pole make with the horizontal?

6. A tree which stands erect upon a hillside which has an inclination of 20° is viewed from two points A and B which are farther down the hill, 400 feet apart, and in line with the tree. If the angles subtended by the tree at A and B are 8° and 14°, respectively, find the height of the tree.

??????????? PROBLEM JUST FOR FUN ???????????

A lake boat carries a rock ballast. The ballast is thrown overboard, and this tends to raise the water level of the lake. On the other hand, the boat, being empty, now displaces less water. Will the level of the lake rise or fall as a result of the unloading of the rock ballast?

???????????????? JUST FOR FUN ????????????????

CHAPTER

13

Graphs of the Trigonometric Functions

(*Waves but No Water*)

> Trigonometry contains the science of continually undulating magnitude: meaning magnitude which becomes alternately greater and less, without any termination to succession of increase and decrease.
>
> A. DE MORGAN

1. Graph of the sine function

In the circle with radius 1, we see from Fig. 70 that the opposite side QP of angle A increases from 0 to 1 as A changes from 0° to 90°; decreases from 1 to 0 as A changes from 90° to 180°; decreases from 0 to -1 as A changes from 180° to 270°; and increases from -1 to 0 as A changes from 270° to 360°. Since the value of sin A starts at 0 for $A = 0°$ and

$$\sin A = \frac{\text{opposite side}}{\text{hypotenuse} = 1} = \text{opposite side}$$

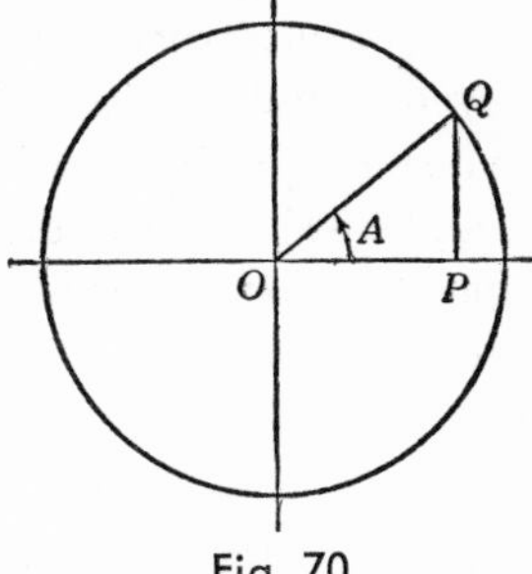

Fig. 70

builds up to a maximum value of 1 for $A = 90°$, then its value decreases from 1 to 0 for $A = 180°$. As A changes from 180° to 270°, the value of sin A changes from 0 to a minimum value of -1 for $A = 270°$. Then, as A changes from 270° to 360°, the value of the sin A increases from -1 to 0.

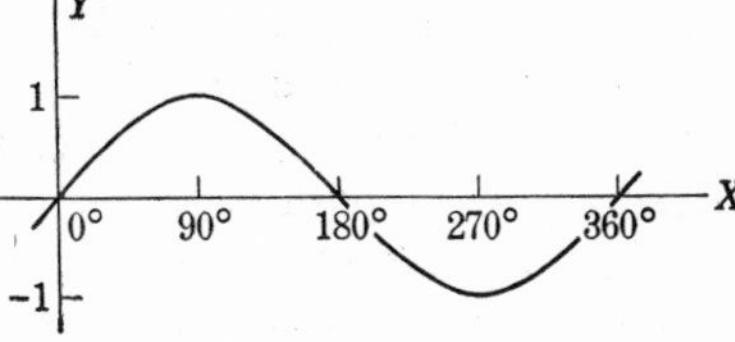

Fig. 71

If we plot the values of sin A for angles between 0° and 360°, we get the graph in Fig. 71. As angle A increases from 360° to 720°, the values for sin A will repeat themselves, and we get the curve shown in Fig. 72. Also, we can extend this curve to the left of the origin, because sin $(-A) = -\sin A$. Why?

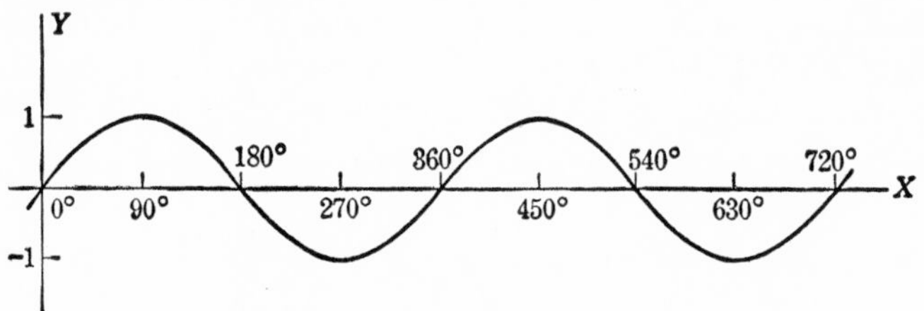

Fig. 72

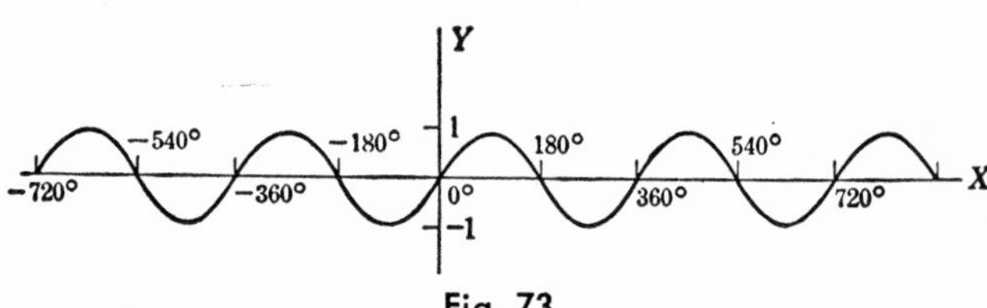

Fig. 73

We see (Fig. 73) that the function sin A, when plotted, yields a wavy curve which has a maximum value of 1 at 90° and a minimum value of -1 at 270°. The curve repeats itself every 360°. That is, sin x takes on the same value when x is increased by 360° or multiples of 360°and is said to be periodic, with period of 360°. Because this curve represents sin A, it is called a *sine curve.*

If we study this curve, we can readily understand why it is necessary only to tabulate the values of sin A for angles between 0° and 90°. If we become familiar with that portion of the sine curve for angles between 0° and 360°, we will have no trouble determining the sign to use. Sin A is positive for angles between 0° and 180° and negative for those between 180° and 360°.

EXERCISES

1. Discuss the values of cos A for values of A between 0° and 360°.

2. Draw the curve for cos A for angles between $-540°$ and 720°.

3. Is the cosine curve periodic? If periodic, what is the period?

4. Compare the sine and cosine curves.

5. Is there any way to change the sine curve into the cosine curve? How would you accomplish this?

6. Did you expect to find this relation between the two curves?

7. From the portion of the cosine curve between 0° and 360°, determine the range of angles for which the cosine is positive and negative.

??????????? PROBLEM JUST FOR FUN ???????????

A truck and a car meet one foggy night on a bridge that is so narrow they cannot pass each other or turn. The car is twice as far on the bridge as the truck. But it has taken the truck twice as long as the car to reach this meeting point. Both car and truck can back at only half their forward speed. Which of them should back up to allow both to cross the bridge in the shortest time?

???????????????? JUST FOR FUN ????????????????

2. More general sine curves

When data from certain physical measurements are plotted, a curve of the sine or cosine type is obtained, and the function which the data represents is said to be a *sine or cosine function.* Just knowing that the function is a sine function is very informative, because we know that such a function starts with a 0 value, builds up to a maximum value, falls to zero again, and then falls to a minimum value before coming back to zero. This process is repeated again and again, and we can reduce the study of the whole process to a study of this one period, knowing that whatever is true for this one period will also be true for any other period.

When a light jump rope is attached to a post and the end moved up and down in a vertical path with the right frequency, the rope assumes the shape shown in Fig. 74. We notice that the portion of the curve between the points AB, BC, and CD is the same and that this curve looks like the sine curve. The vertical displacement y at any point x is given by the equation $y = A \sin kx$.

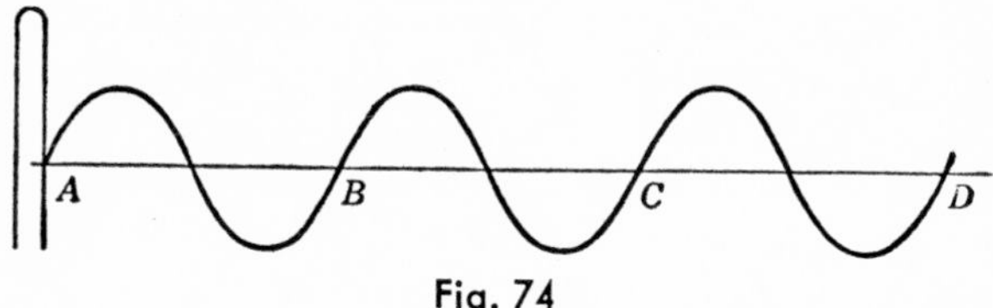

Fig. 74

Pictures of vibrating strings have been taken. The shape assumed by the string is similar to that of the rope, and we say that the vertical displacement is a sine function of the horizontal distance along the string.

Since sound and light are propagated by wave motion, the physicist uses the sine function to help explain and understand the behavior of the phenomena. In fact, the physicist loses no opportunity to use the trigonometric function of sine or cosine to describe mathematically a motion which is periodic.

The alternating current used to light our homes starts with a value of zero, builds up to a maximum value, then decreases to zero. After this, the current increases up to a maximum value in the opposite direction and then falls to zero again. The whole process takes a very short time and then is repeated again and again. This alternating current as a function of time is represented by the sine function,

$$I = A \sin kt$$

The above uses of the trigonometric function of sine give some insight into the important role played by such functions in the solution of problems in fields other than mathematics. Because of this wide use, we shall spend some time studying this more general sine function.

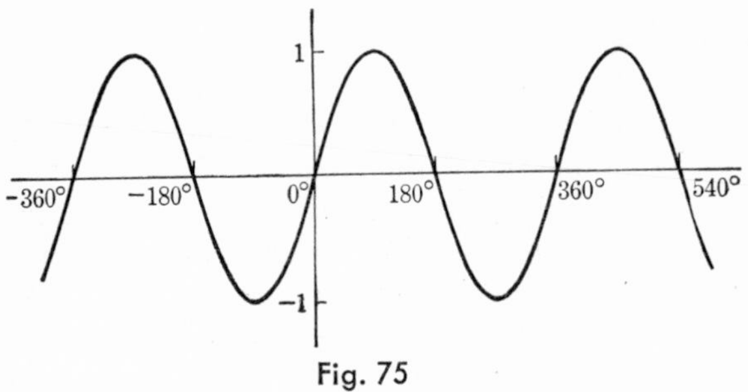

Fig. 75

From the graph of $y = \sin x$ (Fig. 75), we see that $\sin x$ is zero when $x = -540°, -360°, -180°, 0°, 180°, 360°, 540°, \ldots$. The maximum value of 1 is obtained when $x = -270°, 90°, 450°, \ldots$, and the minimum value of -1 is obtained when $x = -90°, 270°, 630°, \ldots$. We observe that each maximum and minimum repeats itself every 360°.

Now let us see what happens when we introduce a constant A. That is, how does the graph of $y = A \sin x$ compare with that of $y = \sin x$? For a given x, $\sin x$ will be the same in both cases. Thus the height y of the new curve will be A times the other. The ordinate y will still be equal to zero when $x = -180°, 0°, 180°, 360°, \ldots$, but its maximum value will be $A \cdot 1 = A$ and occurs when $x = -270°, 90°, 450°, \ldots$. The minimum value will be $A \cdot (-1) = -A$ at $-90°, 270°, \ldots$ (Fig. 76).

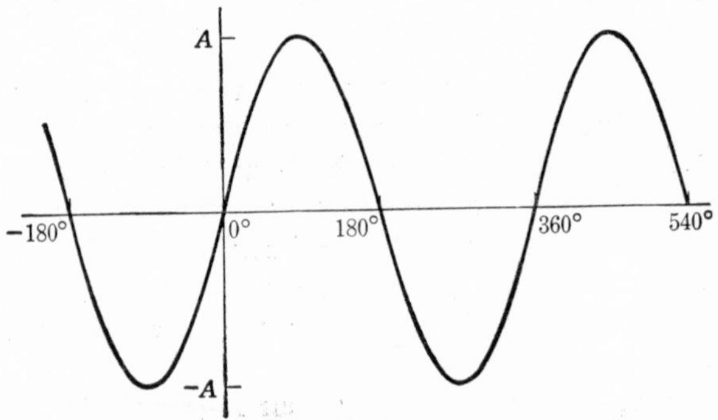

Fig. 76

We learn that multiplying $\sin x$ by a constant merely stretches or contracts the curve for $\sin x$ in the vertical direction, depending on whether the constant A is greater or less than 1.

What change is made in the curve $y = \sin x$ if we multiply x by a constant to get $y = \sin kx$? In order to be specific, let us discuss $y = \sin 2x$. We observe that the maximum and minimum values will still be 1 and -1. The zeros will occur at the points where $2x = -180°$, 0°, 180°, 360°, 540°. Then

$$x = \frac{-180}{2}, 0, \frac{180}{2}, \frac{360}{2}, \frac{540}{2}$$

or

$$x = -90°, 0°, 90°, 180°, 270, \ldots$$

The maximum value of 1 occurs at points where $2x = -270°$, 90°, 450°, . . . , or

$$x = -135°, 45°, 225°, \ldots$$

Likewise, the minimum values occur at points where

$$2x = -90°, 270°, 630°, \ldots$$

or

$$x = -45°, 135°, 315°, \ldots$$

From the above discussion we can quickly sketch the curve $y = \sin 2x$ since it has the general shape of the sine curve, but the zeros, maximum, and minimum values occur at different points. We see that the curve (Fig. 77) is compressed in the horizontal direction by a factor of ½. The period for $y = \sin 2x$ is 180°, which is one-half the period for $y = \sin x$.

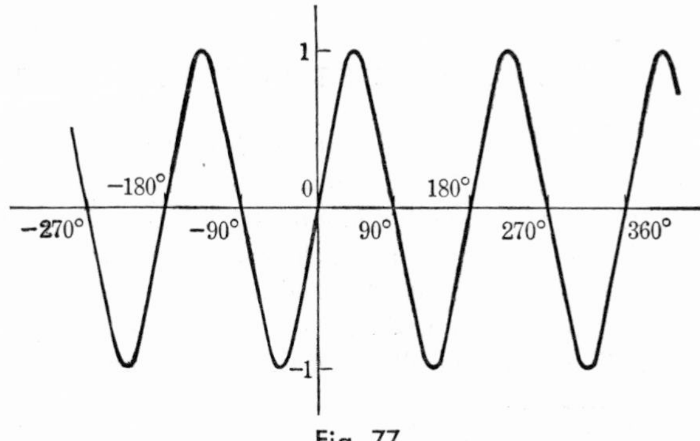

Fig. 77

We can conclude that the curve represented by the general equation $y = A \sin kx$, where A and k are constants, has the shape of the sine curve, $y = \sin x$.

The effect of the constant A, which is called the *amplitude* of the wave, is to stretch or compress the curve in the vertical direction. The effect of the constant k is to stretch or compress the curve in the horizontal direction.

You need not plot the curve $y = A \sin kx$ point by point. The shape of the curve is that of $y = \sin x$, which you can readily sketch, and all that is needed is to make the proper changes as made necessary by the constants A and k.

EXERCISES

1. What change is made in the cosine curve (Fig. 78) if $y = \cos x$ is multiplied by a constant A, giving $y = A \cos x$?

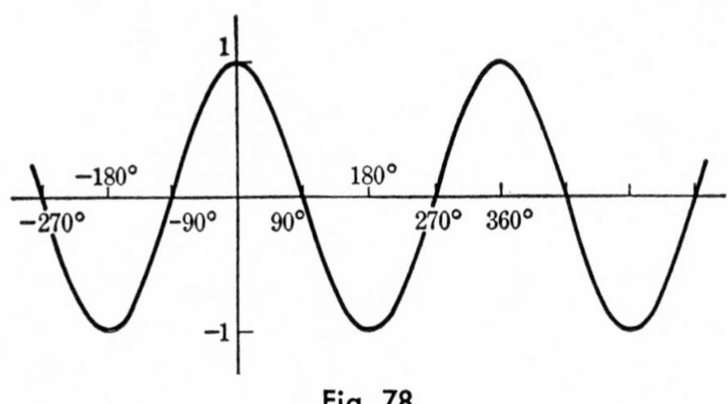

Fig. 78

2. What change is made in the cosine curve $y = \cos x$ if the x is multiplied by a constant k?

??????????? PROBLEM JUST FOR FUN ???????????

The natives of a remote South Sea island are all members of two tribes, Abel and Babel. To a stranger they look exactly alike. But the members of the Abel tribe always tell the truth, while those of Babel blood always lie.

To this island came an explorer and met three natives.

"Of what tribe are you?" the explorer asked the first.

"Chsz cinth cstrm," replied the native.

"What did he say?" asked the explorer of the second and third natives, both of whom spoke some English.

"He say he Abel," said the second.

"He say he Babel," said the third.

To what tribes did the second and third natives belong?

???????????????? JUST FOR FUN ????????????????

3. Make sketches for Prob. 1 and Prob. 2.

4. Sketch the following curves and discuss them by noting the amplitude and period:

a. $y = \sin \frac{x}{2}$ *b.* $y = 3 \cos 2x$ *c.* $y = 5 \cos \frac{x}{3}$

d. $y = 4 \sin 3x$ *e.* $y = \cos \frac{x}{2}$ *f.* $y = -2 \sin \frac{x}{2}$

CHAPTER

14

Finance

(*Pocketbook Mathematics*)

There is no problem in all mathematics that cannot be solved by direct counting. But with the present implements of mathematics many operations can be performed in a few minutes which without mathematical methods would take a lifetime.

ERNST MACH

1. A bit of history

In 1626 Peter Minuit purchased Manhattan Island from the Indians for about $24. Suppose the Indians had put the money in the bank at compound interest from that date. Interest rates in new countries are higher, so we will assume a rate of 7%. This would have amounted to more than *four billion dollars* by the beginning of this century, or more than the assessed value of *all* the real estate of the borough of Manhattan.*

2. Percentage in business

The business world uses percentage in many ways. For example, a firm's or bank's balance sheet is usually given both in dollars and in per cent of total figures. Profit and loss statements show both dollars and per cent of net sales. Expressing each asset or liability of a concern as a per cent of the total assets facilitates a comparison of different firms. Merchants use percentage to indicate discounts and markups. Percentage is used to give interest rates and tax rates.

Percentage, or per cent, was defined in Sec. 3, page 4. Let us apply this definition to a few problems, some from the field of finance and some from other fields.

* White, W. F., "A Scrapbook of Elementary Mathematics," pp. 47–48, Open Court Publishing Co., Chicago, 1908.

Example 1. A grocer sells a certain brand of peas for 25 cents a can, but offers a 10% discount if they are bought in lots of a dozen or more. How much will 18 cans of this brand of peas cost?

Solution.

$$\text{Cost without discount} = \$0.25 \times 18 = \$4.50$$
$$\text{Amount of discount} = {}^{10}\!/_{100} \times \$4.50 = \$0.45$$
$$\text{Cost of peas} = \$4.50 - \$0.45 = \$4.05$$

Example 2. A dealer in photographic supplies finds that he must mark up cameras $33\frac{1}{3}\%$ to cover overhead and earn a reasonable profit. In addition there is a 20% Federal tax on cameras. What will be the cost to a purchaser of a camera that the dealer obtains from the manufacturer for $60?

Solution.

$$\text{Dealer's price} = \$60$$
$$\text{Dealer's markup} = 33\tfrac{1}{3}\% \times \$60 = \$20$$
$$\text{Price of camera without Federal tax} = \$60 + \$20 = \$80$$
$$\text{Federal tax on camera} = {}^{20}\!/_{100} \times 80 = \$16$$
$$\text{Purchase price of camera} = \$80 + \$16 = \$96$$

Example 3. A merchant tells a salesman that he has decided to discontinue the handling of a certain magazine and that he is returning 85 magazines. If this number represents 17% of the original consignment, how many magazines did the merchant have at the start?

Solution.

$$17\% \text{ or } {}^{17}\!/_{100} \times \text{total number of magazines} = 85$$
$$\text{Number of magazines} = 85 \times {}^{100}\!/_{17} = 500$$

EXERCISES

1. The cost of an article plus the cost of shipping is $472.20. The shipping cost is 8% of the billed price. What is the cost of the article?

2. A worker's monthly wage of $200 was raised to $232. What per cent increase did he receive?

3. A worker received a 15% raise in his wages. What were his wages before the raise, if his monthly wages were $285 after the raise?

4. A factory turned out 1,890 machines instead of the planned 1,800 machines. What was the per cent of overproduction?

5. A ruler 1 yard long is allowed a 0.01 inch margin of error. What is this per cent of error?

6. Coffee beans lose 12.5% of their weight in roasting. How many pounds of coffee beans must be roasted in order to obtain 250 pounds of coffee?

7. A bricklayer found that he had laid 3,532 bricks, which was 82% of the number of bricks needed for the job. How many bricks were used?

8. An alloy consists of 64% copper, 31% zinc, and 5% lead. How many pounds of each metal was used in 2,000 pounds of the alloy?

9. If a 25% markdown on a hat amounted to \$3.30, determine the original and reduced price of the hat.

10. A person's monthly salary was \$350. On Jan. 1, he received a 20% increase in salary, but on July 1, the employer was forced to cut this person's salary by 20%. What was the monthly salary after the cut?

11. A tailor bought some woolen cloth for \$1.75 per yard. He priced the cloth to allow him a profit and later reduced this selling price by one-third for a clearance sale. The tailor found that he made a 20% profit on the cost price of the cloth. What was the original selling price of the woolen cloth?

12. What percentage of profit did the tailor in Prob. 11 originally intend to make on his woolen cloth?

13. A farmer sells 400 pounds of cream. The cream tests 38% butterfat. The farmer gets 68 cents per pound of butterfat for sweet cream and 56 cents per pound of butterfat for sour cream. How many pounds of sweet cream did the farmer have if he received \$88.37 for the cream?

??????????? PROBLEM JUST FOR FUN ???????????

Smith can run around the indoor track in the Michigan Fieldhouse in 30 seconds, and Black can run around the same track in 40 seconds. If the two men start together, how many minutes will it take for Smith to be one lap ahead of Black?

???????????????? JUST FOR FUN ????????????????

3. Interest

It is a rare individual who will never have need for some understanding of the fundamentals of simple and compound interest, depreciation, and periodic payments. We shall discuss a few of the fundamental principles basic to the growth of money by accumulation of interest and their application to installment buying and amortization of mortgages.

4. Definition of terms

Most of us have had some experience, either directly or indirectly, with the terminology we shall use.

Interest, I, is an amount of money paid for the use of invested capital.

Principal, P, is the amount of capital invested.

Interest rate, r, is the per cent of the principal that is to be paid at stated intervals for the use of the money. An interest rate of 4% means that 4 cents will be paid for the use of each dollar of the principal for a period of 1 year. Each state has laws which specify the highest rate of interest that may legally be charged. At present most banks pay about $1\frac{1}{2}\%$ interest on savings accounts, and the interest rate paid by the United States government on Series E bonds held to maturity is about 2.9%. Interest rates are quoted per year, and the interest is frequently calculated for each month or fraction of a month the principal is kept.

The investor and the borrower first agree on the interest rate and the type of interest to be paid. The amount to be paid is computed on this basis. The two types of interest are *simple* and *compound.*

5. Simple interest

Simple interest is equal to the product of the principal, interest rate, and time:

$$I = Prt$$

Simple interest is computed on the original principal only.

The amount A repaid is equal to the principal plus the interest:

$$A = P + Prt = P(1 + rt)$$

Example 1. A merchant borrowed \$1,500, agreeing to repay the principal with 5% simple interest at the end of 3 years. Find the amount of interest and the total sum which must be paid.

Solution. The amount of interest I to be paid is

$$I = Prt = (1{,}500)(5/100)(3) = \$225$$

The amount the merchant must pay is

$$A = P + I = 1{,}500 + 225 = \$1{,}725$$

Example 2. Find the time required for a loan of \$1,800 to earn \$36 if the simple interest rate is 3%.

Solution. Since

$$\begin{aligned} I &= Prt \\ 36 &= 1800(3/100)t \\ t &= 36/54 = 2/3 \text{ year, or 8 months} \end{aligned}$$

EXERCISES

1. A man borrows \$500 for 6 months at a simple interest rate of 6%. How much interest does he pay, and what amount is paid at the end of the 6 months?

2. What amount will \$2,500 earn at $2\frac{1}{2}\%$ simple interest in 3 years? In 3 months?

3. Find the time required for \$3,500 to earn \$150 at 4% simple interest.

4. Find the simple interest rate that is necessary for \$2,000 to earn \$90 in 9 months.

5. What principal will yield a total of \$1,500 in 2 years at $2\frac{1}{2}$% simple interest?

6. How long must \$1,000 be kept at 4% simple interest to become \$1,200?

7. What school tax rate must be paid by a community whose total assessed valuation is \$74,800,000, if \$800,000 is needed for the schools?

8. Find the assessed valuation of a city if \$750,000 is to be raised by a tax at the rate of 25 mills. $\left(1 \text{ mill} = \frac{1}{10} \text{ cent} = \frac{1}{\$1,000} \text{ dollars.}\right)$

9. A man has \$10,000 and invests \$3,000 for one year at 8% interest. At what rate of interest should the remainder be invested if the income from the \$10,000 is to be \$660?

10. A firm invested \$30,000 for 1 year at simple interest. One portion was invested at 6% and the remainder at 3%. How much money was invested at each rate of interest if the total return was the same as if all the money had been invested at 4%?

11. A man has \$4,000 invested at 4.4% simple interest. How much money must he invest at 7% simple interest to make the total investment yield 6% interest each year?

12. Find the total amount a man must pay if he borrows \$1,000 and agrees to pay at the end of each month \$100 on the principal and simple interest at 6% per year on the principal outstanding during each month.

Hint: The interest due with the first payment is

$$1,000(6/100)1/12 = \$5$$

The interest due with the second payment is

$$900(6/100)1/12 = \$4.50$$

13. If the lender in Prob. 12 had lent the use of the entire principal for 10 months, what simple interest rate would have yielded the same amount of interest?

14. A loan of \$2,400 is to be repaid in monthly installments of \$200 plus simple interest at the rate of 4% per annum on the principal outstanding during each month. Find the amount of interest and the total amount paid.

15. If the lender in Prob. 14 had lent the use of the entire principal for 1 year, what simple interest rate would have yielded the same amount of interest?

??????????? PROBLEM JUST FOR FUN ???????????

Two men agree to saw a pile of logs which are 3 feet long into 1-foot lengths for \$5. How much would these men have charged to cut the same number of logs into 1-foot lengths if the logs had been 6 feet long?

???????????????? JUST FOR FUN ????????????????

6. Compound interest

In most transactions where money is loaned for more than 1 year, simple interest is not used. If the interest due at the end of a stated period of time is added to the principal, that is, converted into principal which earns interest, the sum by which the original principal has been increased at the end of the period is called *compound interest.* An illustration of compound interest is a savings account when the depositor does not withdraw the interest he is entitled to but lets the interest be converted into principal on which interest must be paid by the bank.

Interest period, k, is the time between successive additions of interest to the principal.

Compound amount, A, is equal to the original principal plus the compound interest.

An example will best illustrate compound interest. We deposit \$1,000 in a bank at 4% interest which is to be compounded yearly, and we calculate the value of the account at the end of 10 years. At the end of 1 year, the amount is given by

$$A_1 = \$1{,}000 + \$1{,}000(4/100) = \$1{,}040$$

If we were dealing with simple interest, the amount at the end of 2 years would be

$$A_2 = \$1{,}000 + (\$1{,}000)(4/100)(2) = \$1{,}080$$

But since we loaned the money at compound interest, the \$40 interest earned the first year becomes principal and also earns 4% interest during the second year. At the end of the second year the amount would be

$$A_2 = \$1{,}040 + \$1{,}040(4/100) = \$1{,}040 + \$41.60 = \$1{,}081.60$$

The principal which draws interest during the third year is \$1,081.60, and hence at the end of the third year the amount would be

$$A_3 = \$1{,}081.60 + \$1{,}081.60(4/100) = \$1{,}124.86$$

We can continue this process and find the amount in the account at the end of 10 years.

The procedure outlined above is tedious to carry out, and we shall develop a formula which will give the compound amount A at the end of n years.

Let P = the original principal and r = interest rate, and let the compounding take place annually. Then at the end of 1 year the amount A_1 will be

$$A_1 = P + Pr = P(1 + r)$$

At the end of the second year the amount A_2 will be

$$A_2 = A_1 + A_1r = A_1(1 + r) = P(1 + r)(1 + r) = P(1 + r)^2$$

At the end of the third year the amount A_3 will be

$$A_3 = A_2 + A_2r = A_2(1 + r) = P(1 + r)^2(1 + r) = P(1 + r)^3$$

At the end of the fourth year the amount A_4 will be

$$A_4 = P(1 + r)^4$$

If we continue this procedure, we shall find that the amount A_n at the end of n years will be

$$A_n = P(1 + r)^n \tag{1}$$

This formula connects four quantities, A, P, r, and n. If any three of them are known, the fourth may be found.

For the problem discussed previously in this section, the amount due at the end of 10 years on \$1,000 loaned at 4% interest rate compounded annually would be

$$A_{10} = \$1{,}000(1 + 0.04)^{10} = \$1{,}000(1.04)^{10}$$

In order to calculate A_{10}, we need to know the value of $(1.04)^{10}$. We shall use tables to find $(1.04)^{10}$. Table III at the back of the book gives the values of $(1 + r)^n$ for values of n from 1 to 50 years and interest rates of 1½%, 2%, 2½%, 3%, 4%, 5%, and 6%. Using this table, we find that $(1.04)^{10} = 1.4802$ and

$$A_{10} = \$1{,}000(1.4802) = \$1{,}480.20$$

7. Interest compounded semiannually

Let the original principal P be compounded semiannually (at the end of each half year) at an annual interest rate r. Since r is the annual interest rate, the interest due at the end of one-half year is $Pr(\frac{1}{2}) = Pr/2$, and the amount at the end of the first half year would be

$$A_{\frac{1}{2}} = P + \frac{Pr}{2} = P\left(1 + \frac{r}{2}\right)$$

The amount at the end of the first year, the second half-year period, would be

$$A_1 = A_{\frac{1}{2}} + A_{\frac{1}{2}}\left(\frac{r}{2}\right) = A_{\frac{1}{2}}\left(1 + \frac{r}{2}\right) = P\left(1 + \frac{r}{2}\right)^2$$

and the amount at the end of 1½ years would be

$$A_{1\frac{1}{2}} = A_1 + A_1\left(\frac{r}{2}\right) = A_1\left(1 + \frac{r}{2}\right) = P\left(1 + \frac{r}{2}\right)^3$$

In general, if the interest is compounded semiannually, the amount at the end of n years would be

$$A_n = P\left(1 + \frac{r}{2}\right)^{2n} \tag{2}$$

Example. If \$1,000 is placed at 4% interest for 20 years and the interest is compounded semiannually, find the amount due at the end of the 20 years.

Solution. Using equation (2), we get

$$A_{20} = \$1,000\left(1 + \frac{0.04}{2}\right)^{40} = \$1,000(1.02)^{40}$$

From Table III we find that $(1.02)^{40} = 2.2080$ and

$$A_{20} = \$1,000(2.2080) = \$2,208.00$$

8. Interest compounded k times a year

The amount A_n at the end of n years of any investment P with interest at an *annual rate* of r, compounded k times a year, will be

$$A_n = P\left(1 + \frac{r}{k}\right)^{kn} \tag{3}$$

When $k = 2$, equation (3) becomes equation (2). Equation (3) can be developed following the procedure used in developing equations (1) and (2).

EXERCISES

1. The sum of \$5,000 is invested at 6% interest. If the interest is compounded annually, find the value of the investment at the end of 4 years.
2. Work Prob. 1 if the interest is compounded four times a year.
3. Work Prob. 1 if the interest is compounded semiannually.
4. The sum of \$200 is deposited in each of four banks, each paying 6% interest per annum. The first bank compounds interest annually, the second bank semiannually, the third bank quarterly, and the fourth pays simple interest. If no further deposits or withdrawals are made, how much is in each account at the end of 10 years?
5. A young man is to inherit \$30,000 at the age of 30. If he is now 12, how much money must his father invest at 3% interest, compounded semiannually, in order to have \$30,000 when his son is 30?

6. Find the approximate time for a sum of money to double itself if the sum is invested at 6% interest, compounded quarterly.

7. On the tenth birthday of his daughter a man deposits $2,000 to his daughter's account in a bank that pays 4% interest compounded annually. How much money will the daughter have on her eighteenth birthday, assuming no withdrawals or deposits are made during this time?

8. How much will $125 amount to in 15 years if the interest rate is 5% compounded semiannually?

9. A man makes deposits of $500 on Mar. 1 for 5 years in a bank whose interest rate is 4% compounded semiannually. What will be the value of this account just after the last deposit is made?

10. Find the value of the account in Prob. 9, 5 years after the last deposit is made, if no withdrawals or further deposits are made.

??????????? PROBLEM JUST FOR FUN ???????????

Here you see the nine digits arranged in such a way that the number in the second column reading down is twice the number in the first column, and the number in the third column is three times the number in the first column.

1	3	5
9	8	7
2	4	6

Can you find another arrangement of the nine digits to produce the same results?

??????????????? JUST FOR FUN ???????????????

9. Present value of deferred payments

If a person is to receive a series of n payments, each of amount A, the first being due a year from today, he might wish to find the present value of these payments if money is worth r% compounded annually. For example, on selling a house it is agreed that $5,000 in cash shall be paid at once and $1,000 payments shall be made annually for 5 years. What is the present value of these payments if money is worth 4% compounded annually?

The present value is the sum of the cash payment plus the present value of the five deferred payments. In order to find the present value of the five deferred payments, we must determine the principal P that must be set aside now at 4% interest, compounded annually, to yield $1,000 at the time the payments are due. Since

$$A = P(1 + r)^n, \text{ or } P = \frac{A}{(1 + r)^n}$$

we should need to set aside (see Table IV at end of book)

$$P_1 = \frac{\$1{,}000}{(1.04)^1} = \$961.54$$

to yield $1,000 one year hence, and this is the present value of the $1,000 which will be paid as the first installment. Also,

$$P_2 = \frac{\$1{,}000}{(1.04)^2} = \$924.56$$

which is the present value of the $1,000 which will be paid as the second installment. We continue in this way to find

$$P_1 = \frac{\$1{,}000}{(1.04)^1} = \$961.54$$
$$P_2 = \frac{\$1{,}000}{(1.04)^2} = \$924.56$$
$$P_3 = \frac{\$1{,}000}{(1.04)^3} = \$889.00$$
$$P_4 = \frac{\$1{,}000}{(1.04)^4} = \$854.80$$
$$P_5 = \frac{\$1{,}000}{(1.04)^5} = \$821.93$$
$$P_1 + P_2 + P_3 + P_4 + P_5 = \$4{,}451.83$$

Since the present value of the deferred payments is $4,451.83 and the down payment was $5,000, the present value of the house is $9,451.83.

Since the process outlined above involves a division, it is tedious to carry out, and tables which reduce the labor have been prepared. Table VI gives the present value of one dollar per year for n years for an interest rate r. Thus

$$\text{Present value} = \text{yearly payment} \times a_{n/r}$$

where $a_{n/r}$ is the value obtained from Table VI; r is the interest per year and n is the number of years that the payments are made.

To apply this to the previous problem, we have $n = 5$, $r = 4$. If we look in the 4% column in Table VI for the entry opposite $n = 5$, we find $a_{5\frac{1}{4}} = 4.4518$. This is the present value of five payments of \$1 each. As the payments are of \$1,000, we multiply by 1,000 to obtain the present value, \$4,451.80. Then the present value of the house is \$5,000 + \$4,451.80 = \$9,451.80. The difference of 3 cents between this figure and the one obtained by the other method results from Table VI being rounded off at five figures. If it were carried to six figures, the two results would be identical.

If the payments are made oftener than once a year, for example, k times a year, the interest rate per period is r/k and the number of periods is kn. If \$100 is to be paid four times a year for 3 years and money is worth 6%, we may wish to determine the present value of these 12 payments of \$100. We use Table VI again. The interest rate is 6% ÷ 4, or 1½% per period. There are 12 periods, so we look for the entry in the 1½% column opposite 12 and read $a_{12/1.5} = 10.9075$. Then present value = $\$100a_{12/1.5} = 100(10.9075) = \$1{,}090.75$.

EXERCISES

1. A man buys a house and lot and pays \$3,000 down and agrees to pay \$800 a year for 10 years. What is the equivalent cash price if money is worth 3% compounded annually?

2. If annual sewer assessments on a piece of property amounted to \$43.35, and 8 years intervened between the first and last payments, what was the equivalent cash payment on a 3% basis at the time the first payment was made?

3. In order to purchase a secondhand car, a man pays \$36 down and \$36 a month thereafter until 12 payments, including the down payment, have been made. If the interest rate is 1½% per month, what is the cash price (present value of the payments) of the car?

4. A young man 18 years of age is to receive from an estate the sum of \$10,800 when he reaches the age of 27. Assuming that the man will live to receive his inheritance, what is the present value of his interest in the estate if money is worth 4% compounded annually?

??????????? PROBLEM JUST FOR FUN ???????????

On a shopping trip, Mary Jane spent one-half the money that was in her pocketbook. When she got home she had just as many cents as she had had dollars and half as many dollars as she had had cents when she left home. How much money did Mary Jane have at the start of the shopping trip?

???????????????? JUST FOR FUN ????????????????

10. Amortization of a debt

It is a common practice to pay off an interest-bearing debt by means of a series of payments which are usually of equal amounts. Each payment must be larger than the interest on the original debt, and the amount of payment in excess of the current interest for any period is used to decrease the principal, which thus becomes smaller and is finally reduced to zero. A debt paid off in this manner is said to be *amortized.*

Example. A debt of $1,000 is to be paid, principal and interest, in five equal annual payments. What is the amount of each payment if the rate of interest is 4%?

Write up a schedule showing the yearly condition of this debt.

Solution.

The present value of the debt is $1,000, and since

$$\text{Present value} = \text{yearly payment times } a_{n/r}$$

we have

$$\$1{,}000 = \text{yearly payment times } a_{5/4}$$

$$\text{Yearly payment} = \frac{1{,}000}{4.4518} = \$224.63$$

Table 37 shows the operation of the payments.

TABLE 37

Year	*Principal outstanding at beginning of year*	*Interest at 4%*	*Payment*	*Principal repaid*
1	$1,000.00	$40.00	$224.63	$184.63
2	815.37	32.62	224.63	192.01
3	623.36	24.94	224.63	199.69
4	423.67	16.95	224.63	207.68
5	215.99	8.64	224.63	215.99

EXERCISES

1. A man pays off a $5,000 mortgage, interest and principal, by equal payments made at the end of each year for 10 years. What is the annual payment if interest is paid at 4% per annum compounded annually? Make a schedule showing the part of each payment which goes for interest and principal, respectively.

2. An electric range costs $345.90. The down payment is $50.00, and the balance is to be paid in 15 equal monthly payments. If the interest rate on the unpaid balance is 18% per annum, determine the monthly payment. Make a schedule showing the part of each payment which goes for interest and principal, respectively.

3. A mortgage of $6,000 is paid off, interest and principal, by equal payments, made at the end of each year, for 20 years. What is the annual payment if interest is paid at 4% per annum on the unpaid balance?

4. A standard-quality washing machine may be purchased for $86.95 cash or a down payment of $8.70 and the remainder to be paid in 10 monthly installments. Find the amount of each installment if the interest rate is 24% per annum on the unpaid balance.

5. A washing machine may be purchased for $89.35 cash or a down payment of $11.10 and the remainder to be paid in 12 monthly installments of $7.18. Find the interest rate that is being paid on the unpaid balance at any time.

6. An electric refrigerator may be purchased for $275.00 cash or a down payment of $27.50 and the remainder to be paid in 15 monthly installments of $19.25. Find the interest rate that is being paid on the unpaid balance at any time.

7. Determine the total amount of interest paid for the refrigerator in Prob. 6.

8. A company takes $500,000 from its surplus to construct an addition to the plant. How much cash must be put back into surplus each year, if the total amount is to be paid back in 10 years and if the interest rate is 3% compounded annually?

9. The amount charged against one piece of property for erecting a sewage-disposal system is $2,296.30. The owner may pay this amount in cash or extend the payments over 15 years, at 3% interest compounded annually. If the owner uses the installment plan, what are his annual payments? How much additional money will he pay for the privilege of spreading the payments over 15 years?

??????????? PROBLEM JUST FOR FUN ???????????

When asked the time, an old gentleman replied, "If you add one-quarter of the time from noon until now to one-half the time from now until noon tomorrow, you will get the exact time." What was the time?

??????????????? JUST FOR FUN ???????????????

CHAPTER

15

Exponents and Logarithms

(*Mighty Are the Powers of Numbers*)

The miraculous powers of modern calculation are due to three inventions: the Arabic Notation, Decimal Fractions and Logarithms.

F. CAJORI

1. Multiplication by exponents

Archimedes (287–212 B.C.), who used the complicated Greek number system which did not enable mathematicians to write large numbers, was handicapped because he was unable to multiply large numbers together. However, he did notice that some numbers could be multiplied together by using exponents. That is,

$$a \cdot a = a^1 \cdot a^1 = a^2 = a^{1+1}$$

$$a^2 \cdot a^3 = (a \cdot a) \cdot (a \cdot a \cdot a) = a^5 = a^{2+3}$$

and in general,

$$a^m \cdot a^n = a^{m+n}$$

Thus we observe that the product of two numbers which are expressed as some powers, m and n, of the same number a, called the *base*, is given by the base a raised to the $m + n$ power. For example,

$$9 \cdot 81 = 3^2 \cdot 3^4 = 3^6 = 729$$

Also,

$$9 \cdot 81 \cdot 27 = 3^2 \cdot 3^4 \cdot 3^3 = 3^{2+4+3} = 3^9 = 19{,}683$$

2. Division by exponents

Exponents may also be used in division. For example,

$$\frac{625}{25} = \frac{5^4}{5^2} = \frac{5 \cdot 5 \cdot 5 \cdot 5}{5 \cdot 5} = 5^2 = 5^{4-2}$$

$$\frac{a^6}{a^4} = \frac{a \cdot a \cdot a \cdot a \cdot a \cdot a}{a \cdot a \cdot a \cdot a} = a^2 = a^{6-4}$$

and we see that in general

$$\frac{a^m}{a^n} = a^{m-n}$$

That is, the quotient of two numbers expressed as powers of the same base is the base raised to the difference of the powers.

Hence, we are led to the general principle: when we *multiply* numbers which are powers of the same base, we *add* the exponents; and when we divide, we *subtract* exponents:

$$10^7 \cdot 10^4 = 10^{11} \quad \text{and} \quad 10^7 \div 10^4 = 10^3$$

EXERCISES

1. Find the value of

a. 3^3 | *b.* 5^4
c. 2^2 | *d.* 2^7
e. 2^4 | *f.* 3^5
g. 3^4 | *h.* 4^3

2. Express the following numbers as some base raised to a power n:

a. 27 | *b.* 125
c. 32 | *d.* 81
e. 49 | *f.* 3,125
g. 100 | *h.* 128

3. Find the result of the following operations:

a. $a^2 \cdot a^4 \cdot a^7$ | *b.* $3^{10} \cdot 3^2$
c. $\dfrac{x^4 \cdot x^6}{x^3}$ | *d.* $\dfrac{10^5 \cdot 10^7}{10^9}$
e. $\dfrac{a^3 \cdot a^9}{a \cdot a^4}$ | *f.* $\dfrac{b^3 \cdot b \cdot b^5}{b^2 \cdot b^4}$
g. $\dfrac{10^{10}}{10^3 \cdot 10 \cdot 10^4}$ | *h.* $\dfrac{2^3 \cdot 2^5 \cdot 2^{12}}{2^6 \cdot 2^4 \cdot 2^7}$

4. Perform the following operations by using exponents:

a. $\dfrac{1{,}000 \cdot 1{,}000}{100}$ | *b.* $\dfrac{64 \cdot 128}{16 \cdot 256}$
c. $\dfrac{27 \cdot 9}{81}$ | *d.* $\dfrac{4 \cdot 32 \cdot 64}{256 \cdot 8}$
e. $\dfrac{16 \cdot 8 \cdot 4}{32}$ | *f.* $\dfrac{81 \cdot 243}{27 \cdot 27}$

??????????? PROBLEM JUST FOR FUN ???????????

Mr. Commuter catches the 5 o'clock train from the city each day and is met at the station by Mrs. Commuter. One day he caught the 4 o'clock train and, on arriving at his station, started walking toward home. Mrs. Commuter started for the station at the usual time, met her husband on the way, and returned home with him. They arrived home 20 minutes before their usual time. How long did Mr. Commuter walk?

???????????????? JUST FOR FUN ????????????????

3. Negative and zero exponents

If we blindly follow our rule for division by the subtraction of exponents, we are led directly to the proper intepretation of negative and zero exponents. For example, we see that $x^9/x^9 = 1$, but following our general principle, we find that $x^9/x^9 = x^{9-9} = x^0$. Thus it seems natural to write $x^0 = 1$ and to say that any number (except zero) raised to the zero power is equal to 1. (The exception is not surprising, since we know that division by zero is not possible.) We also know that

$$\frac{a^4}{a^6} = \frac{a \cdot a \cdot a \cdot a}{a \cdot a \cdot a \cdot a \cdot a \cdot a} = \frac{1}{a^2}$$

and the general principle gives

$$\frac{a^4}{a^6} = a^{4-6} = a^{-2}$$

Thus we see that our general principle applies providing we understand that $a^{-2} = \frac{1}{a^2}$. In general, we define $a^{-n} = \frac{1}{a^n}$.

Examples.

$$\frac{3^2 \cdot 3^4}{3^9} = 3^{2+4-9} = 3^{-3} = \frac{1}{3^3} = \frac{1}{27}$$

$$2^5 \cdot 2^{-11} \cdot 2^4 = 2^{5-11+4} = 2^{-2} = \frac{1}{2^2} = \frac{1}{4}$$

4. Raising to powers

If we look at the operation

$$(a^2)^4 = a^2 \cdot a^2 \cdot a^2 \cdot a^2 = a^8 = a^{2\times 4}$$

we see that we obtain the correct result by multiplying the two exponents 2 and 4 together. In general, we find that $(a^m)^n = a^{mn}$. We must be careful to distinguish between

$$(a^2)^4 = a^8 \qquad \text{or} \qquad (a^m)^n = a^{mn}$$

and

$$(a^2)(a^4) = a^6 \qquad \text{or} \qquad a^m \cdot a^n = a^{m+n}$$

Let us restate the three general principles of exponents involved when we combine numbers which are expressed as the same base raised to powers:

1. When we wish to *multiply* the numbers, we *add* the exponents.
2. When we wish to *divide* the numbers, we *subtract* the exponents.
3. When we wish to *raise* to a power, we *multiply* the two exponents.

5. Fractional exponents

If we compare $\sqrt{a^4} = \sqrt{a^2 \cdot a^2} = a^2$ with $(a^4)^{1/2} = a^{4 \cdot 1/2} = a^2$ and $\sqrt{x}\sqrt{x} = x$ with $x^{1/2}x^{1/2} = x^{1/2+1/2} = x$, we see that in both cases the square root behaves like the fractional exponent $\frac{1}{2}$. In the same manner, we observe that the cube root behaves exactly like operations with the exponent $\frac{1}{3}$, and fourth roots like the exponent $\frac{1}{4}$. It is much easier to use our general principles and to work with fractional exponents than to work with roots. So we always change roots to fractional exponents.

Examples.

$$\sqrt{a^8} = (a^8)^{1/2} = a^4$$
$$\sqrt[3]{64} = (2^6)^{1/3} = 2^2 = 4$$
$$\sqrt[4]{x^2} = (x^2)^{1/4} = x^{1/2} = \sqrt{x}$$
$$\sqrt{32} = (2^5)^{1/2} = 2^{5/2} = 2^2 2^{1/2} = 4\sqrt{2}$$

EXERCISES

Find the results of the following operations.

1. $\dfrac{x^{11} \cdot x^4 \cdot x^3}{x^{12} \cdot x^{10}}$
2. $\dfrac{2^4 \cdot 4^2}{2^6}$
3. $\dfrac{a^5 \cdot a^2 \cdot a^3}{a^6 \cdot a^4}$
4. $\dfrac{(2^2)^5}{(2^3)^4}$
5. $(a^2)^3$
6. $\sqrt{a^{10}}$
7. $\sqrt{\sqrt{a^8}}$
8. $\sqrt[3]{16}$
9. $\dfrac{\sqrt{2^{16}}}{\sqrt{4^4}}$
10. $\sqrt{10^{-6}}$
11. $\dfrac{x^2 \cdot x^5}{x^3 \cdot x^4}$
12. $9 \cdot 3^3$

13. $\dfrac{b^4 \cdot b^7}{b^5 \cdot b^3 \cdot b^6}$

14. $(x^3)^4 \cdot x^2$

15. $\dfrac{(10^2)^3 \cdot 100}{(10^3)^3}$

16. $\sqrt[3]{x^{15}}$

17. $(x^6)^{1/3}$

18. $\sqrt{128}$

19. $\dfrac{(a^4)^{1/2}}{\sqrt{a^{-2}}}$

20. $\sqrt{10^4 \cdot 10^{-6}}$

??????????? PROBLEM JUST FOR FUN ???????????

Given 5 coins arranged as shown.

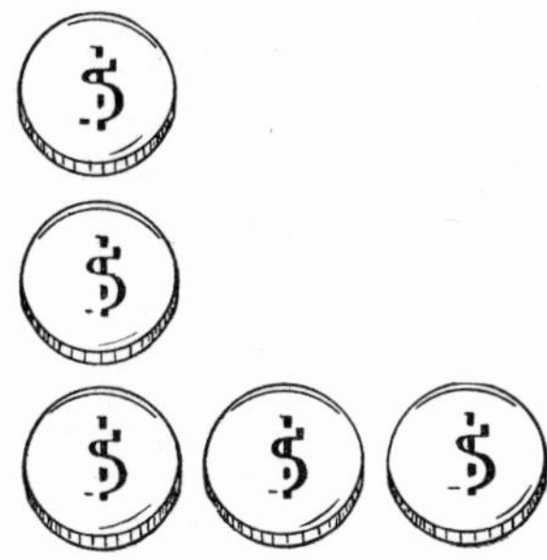

There are three coins on each side. Rearrange the five coins so that there are four on one side and three on the other side.

???????????????? JUST FOR FUN ????????????????

6. Powers of 10

We wish to compute 10^x for various values of x in order to study the equation $y = 10^x$. If x is any whole number, we can easily find the value of 10^x.

$$
\begin{array}{ll}
x = 0 & 10^0 = 1 \\
x = 1 & 10^1 = 10 \\
x = 2 & 10^2 = 100 \\
x = 3 & 10^3 = 1000 \\
x = -1 & 10^{-1} = 0.1 \\
x = -2 & 10^{-2} = 0.01 \\
x = -3 & 10^{-3} = 0.001
\end{array}
$$

We can also compute 10^x for many other values of x. For example,

$$
\begin{array}{ll}
x = \frac{1}{2} & 10^{1/2} = \sqrt{10} = 3.16 \\
x = \frac{3}{2} & 10^{3/2} = 10\sqrt{10} = 31.62 \\
x = \frac{1}{3} & 10^{1/3} = \sqrt[3]{10} = 2.15
\end{array}
$$

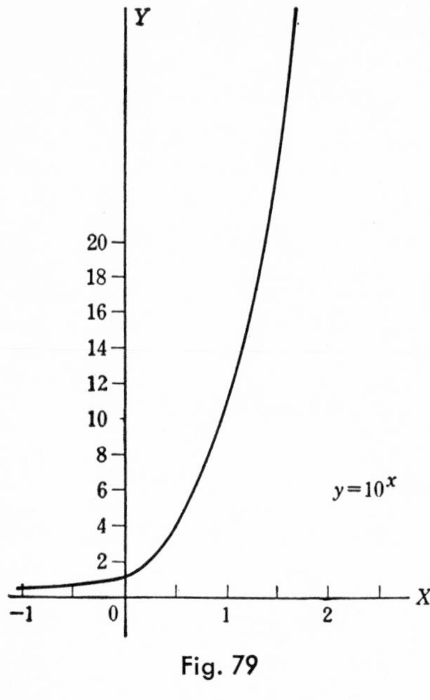

Fig. 79

Let us plot our values and draw a smooth curve through these points, as in Fig. 79. This curve represents $y = 10^x$, and we see that it indicates a value of 10^x for each value of x. If $x = 0.8$, we wish the value of $10^{0.8}$. Since $10^{1/2} = 3.16$ and $10^1 = 10$, we expect a value between 3.16 and 10. From the graph of $y = 10^x$, we find that the approximate value of $10^{0.8}$ is 6. Within the limitations of the figure, we can use the graph of $y = 10^x$ to find the value 10 raised to a positive power x. Of course, the accuracy is limited. We can also use the graph of $y = 10^x$ to find the power x to which 10 must be raised to give a particular value of y. For example, for $y = 5 = 10^x$, how much is x? From Fig. 79 we find that x is approximately equal to 0.7.

We conclude that every positive number can be expressed as some power of 10. We can reason that, since each number can be expressed as a power of 10, we can multiply two numbers together by changing each number to the number 10 raised to the proper power and adding the exponents, that is,

$$A \cdot B = 10^m \cdot 10^n = 10^{m+n}$$

Archimedes was the first to discover this clever method of multiplying and dividing numbers by using exponents. He suggested that all numbers be expressed in powers of another number, and that such a table be made. Archimedes did not make such a table, and it was not until the seventeenth century that such a table was made. A Scotsman named John Napier desired a table similar to that suggested by Archimedes that would end the laborious work of multiplying and dividing large numbers. Briggs, in collaboration with Napier, published the first table giving x in the relation $y = 10^x$ for all values of y from 1 to 1,000, correct to 14 decimal places. Such tables are known as logarithm tables.

Using logarithm tables, we can multiply two numbers A and B together. We find the power a to which 10 must be raised to give A, and the power b to which 10 must be raised to give B. Then $A \cdot B = 10^a \cdot 10^b = 10^{a+b}$. Finally, we find from the tables the number that corresponds to 10 raised to the $a + b$ power.

The task of computing a table of logarithms, that is, the power to which 10 must be raised to give the number, appears hopeless. However, it is not so great a task as it first appears, if we observe that we may write all numbers as a number between 1 and 10 multiplied by 10 to a whole number power. For example,

$$
\begin{aligned}
13.27 &= 1.327 \times 10^1 \\
132.7 &= 1.327 \times 100 = 1.327 \times 10^2 \\
1{,}327 &= 1.327 \times 1{,}000 = 1.327 \times 10^3 \\
0.1327 &= \frac{1.327}{10} = 1.327 \times 10^{-1} \\
0.01327 &= \frac{1.327}{100} = \frac{1.327}{10^2} = 1.327 \times 10^{-2}
\end{aligned}
$$

7. Scientific notation

In scientific work, numbers which are very small or very large are expressed in the form used above instead of being written out in full. In this way we avoid operations with long rows of zeros. For example,

1. The estimated age of the earth is $694{,}000{,}000{,}000 = 6.94 \times 10^{11}$ years.
2. The approximate distance that light travels in 1 year is

$$5{,}870{,}000{,}000{,}000 = 5.87 \times 10^{12} \text{ miles}$$

3. The diameter of a certain molecule is $0.0000005 = \frac{5}{10^7} = 5 \times 10^{-7}$ centimeters.
4. The mass of an electron is 9.11×10^{-28} grams.

It is apparent that it is much easier to multiply two numbers together when they are written in the above form, which is sometimes called the *scientific notation.* If one desires to find the cross-sectional area of the molecule whose diameter is given in the third example above, one proceeds as follows:

$$
\begin{aligned}
\text{Area} = \frac{\pi d^2}{4} = \frac{\pi}{4}(5 \times 10^{-7})^2 = \frac{\pi}{4} 25 \times 10^{-14} &= 19.6 \times 10^{-14} \\
&= 1.96 \times 10^{-13} \text{ square centimeters}
\end{aligned}
$$

It is easy to write large or small numbers in scientific notation. Move the decimal point to the right or left, obtaining a number between 1 and 10. Multiply this number by 10 with an exponent numerically equal to the number of places the decimal point has been moved. The exponent is positive if the decimal point has been moved to the left, and negative if the decimal point has been moved to the right.

EXERCISES

1. Write the following numbers in scientific notation, that is, a number between 1 and 10 multiplied by 10 to a whole number power:

a. 0.00073 *b.* 0.123
c. 0.0035 *d.* 52,800
e. 0.0000000068 *f.* 8,370,000
g. 687,000,000,000 *h.* 0.0000013
i. 3,620 *j.* 146,000

2. Write the following numbers in ordinary form:

a. 5.63×10^4 *b.* 3.22×10^{-4}
c. 4.6×10^{-24} *d.* 1.69×10^{-9}
e. 8.32×10^{-7} *f.* 7.83×10^{10}
g. 3.27×10^6 *h.* 2.73×10^3
i. 1.43×10^{-3} *j.* $6,163 \times 10^{22}$

3. If the velocity of light is 1.86×10^5 miles per second, how far does light travel in 1 hour?

4. If the sun is 9.3×10^7 miles from the earth, how long does it take light from the sun to reach the earth?

5. If a molecule weighs 4.3×10^{-24} grams, how many molecules are there in 1 gram of the substance?

??????????? PROBLEM JUST FOR FUN ???????????

Three men and their wives came to a river which they wished to cross. There was one small rowboat which could only carry two persons at a time. The husbands were jealous, so no woman could be with any man unless her husband was also present. How do they manage to cross the river? No fair building bridges or drying up the river!

???????????????? JUST FOR FUN ????????????????

8. Tables for $N = 10^x$

We have seen that all numbers may be expressed as 10 to some power x. We need tables only for the numbers between 1 and 10, since all numbers may be expressed as a number between 1 and 10 multiplied by 10^n, where n is a positive or negative integer. Such tables are known as logarithm tables. We shall use four-place tables, which are accurate enough for our work. If greater accuracy is needed, one can use a larger table.

If we wish to find the power x to which 10 must be raised to give the number 1,060, we first write $1,060 = 1.060 \times 10^3 = 10^a \times 10^3$. Then we look in the table of logarithms to find the power a to which 10 must be raised to give 1.060, using Table VII at the end of the book. We find that $a = 0.0253$. Then $1{,}060 = 10^a \times 10^3 = 10^{0.0253} \times 10^3 = 10^{3.0253}$. Likewise $425 = 4.25 \times 10^2 = 10^{0.6284} \times 10^2 = 10^{2.6284}$. The exponent 0.6284 is obtained from the table. All the numbers a obtained from the table are between 0 and 1. *One must remember to place the decimal point in front of each such number.*

EXERCISES

Find the power x to which 10 must be raised to give the following numbers:

1. 7,320
2. 0.523
3. 268
4. 9.73
5. 1.73
6. 10.20
7. 0.00542
8. 37,900
9. 0.0685
10. 0.000497

??????????? PROBLEM JUST FOR FUN ???????????

```
    X X X
      X X
    -----
    X X X
  X X 4
  -------
  X X X 1 7
```

In the above multiplication problem the X's are numbers to be found. Find these numbers. There are exactly two solutions.

???????????????? JUST FOR FUN ????????????????

9. Finding the number if its logarithm is given

If the exponent x of 10 is known and we want to find the number N which corresponds to this number, we proceed as follows:

$$N = 10^{2.6284} = 10^2 \times 10^{0.6284}$$

Then we look in the body of the table of logarithms until we find the number 0.6284. We then look in the left-hand column to find the number, 4.25, which corresponds to $10^{0.6284}$. The number $N = 10^2 \times 4.25 = 425$. This process is just the reverse of finding the power x of 10.

If N is given by $10^{-2.3716}$ and we desire to find the corresponding N, we proceed as follows:

$$10^{-2.3716} = \frac{10^3}{10^3} \times 10^{-2.3714} = \frac{10^{0.6284}}{10^3} = 10^{-3} \times 10^{0.6284}$$

Since

$$10^{0.6284} = 4.25$$

we find that

$$10^{-2.3716} = 10^{-3} \times 10^{0.6284} = 10^{-3} \times 4.25 = 0.00425$$

EXERCISES

Find the number which corresponds to each of the following powers of 10:

1. $10^{2.8281}$
2. $10^{1.4368}$
3. $10^{3.6652}$
4. $10^{0.5228}$
5. $10^{-3} \times 10^{0.9048}$
6. $10^{-2.8416}$
7. $10^{-1.3139}$
8. $10^{4.9175}$
9. $10^{0.8281}$
10. $10^{1.9854}$

??????????? PROBLEM JUST FOR FUN ???????????

In the wee small hours after a not-on-the-up-and-up poker game, the boys decided to do some plain and fancy tradin'.

Jones gave Black a no-good \$10 bill and in exchange got a no-good \$5 bill and a good \$5 bill.

Black gave Gray a bad \$20 bill and got back good \$10 and \$5 bills and a phony \$5 bill.

Gray gave Smith a good \$20 bill and got back one good and one phony \$10 bill.

Smith gave Jones a good \$10 bill and got back a homemade \$5 bill and a good \$5 bill.

Who were the winners and losers? By how much in good United States currency?

???????????????? JUST FOR FUN ????????????????

10. Calculations using logarithms

Using the idea of scientific notation, we have seen that the task of determining a table of logarithms is simplified. We need only determine the logarithms of the numbers from 1 to 10. Then we may express all numbers as some power of 10. For example,

$$132 = 1.32 \times 10^2 = 10^a \times 10^2 \text{ where } 10^a = 1.32$$

From the table, we find the number a to which 10 must be raised to give 1.32. Thus

$$10^{0.1206} = 1.32 \qquad 132 = 10^{0.1206} \times 10^2 = 10^{2.1206}$$

Likewise, $173 = 10^2 \times 1.73 = 10^2 \times 10^{0.2380} = 10^{2.2380}$. If we desire to find the product of 132 and 173, we proceed as follows:

$$132 \times 173 = 10^{2.1206} \times 10^{2.2380} = 10^{4.3586} = 10^4 \times 10^{0.3586} = 2.28 \times 10^4 = 22{,}800$$

That $2.28 = 10^{0.3586}$ is obtained from a table. Check the extent of the accuracy by multiplying 173 by 132 in the usual manner. If we wish to obtain the quotient of 173 and 132, we proceed as follows:

$$\frac{173}{132} = \frac{10^{2.2380}}{10^{2.1206}} = 10^{2.2380-2.1206} = 10^{0.1174} = 1.31$$

The accuracy of our results depend upon the completeness of the table of logarithms. We can see that such tables greatly reduce the labor of multiplication and division. We can also use these tables to extract roots of numbers and raise numbers to powers. Between 1614 and the first quarter of the twentieth century when calculating machines were invented, logarithms were used in making all difficult calculations. They greatly shortened the calculations of astronomers and other scientists.

11. Multiplication and division using tables of logarithms

Let us perform the following multiplication:

$$1{,}060 \times 425 \times 8.76$$

We proceed as follows:

$$1{,}060 = 10^3 \times 1.060 = 10^3 \times 10^{0.0253} = 10^{3.0253}$$
$$425 = 10^2 \times 4.25 = 10^2 \times 10^{0.6284} = 10^{2.6284}$$
$$8.76 = 10^{0.9425}$$

We now add these exponents of 10, and we find that the product

$$10^{6.5962} = 10^6 \times 10^{0.5962} = 10^6 \times 3.95 = 3{,}950{,}000$$

Let us perform the following division:

$$\frac{1{,}060}{425} = \frac{10^{3.0253}}{10^{2.6284}} = 10^{3.0253-2.6284} = 10^{0.3969} = 2.49$$

EXERCISES

Perform the following operations using logarithms.

1. $143 \times 1760 \times 0.26$
2. $98 \times 7.63 \times 37.6$
3. $0.015 \times 0.0076 \times 1578$
4. $\dfrac{6.89 \times 1732}{132 \times 102}$
5. $\dfrac{0.0432 \times 21.8}{0.056 \times 0.00327}$

??????????? PROBLEM JUST FOR FUN ???????????

Three men met in a hobo jungle. The first had three loaves of bread and the second two loaves, and the third had \$1 but no bread. The third offered to buy bread from the other two. After the transaction all three had the same amount of bread, and the third had spent all of his dollar. How much money did he give to each of the other hoboes?

???????????????? JUST FOR FUN ????????????????

CHAPTER

16

Growth

(*Mighty Oaks from Tiny Acorns*)

> Mathematics is a science continually expanding; and its growth, unlike some political and industrial events, is attended by universal acclamation.
>
> H. S. White

1. How quantities grow

Changes are continually taking place, and we have observed changes which have been produced by motion, temperature changes, chemical reactions, etc. Probably the most important and interesting of all the changes due to natural phenomena is that of growth—the growth of a tree, plant, or person, of the amount of radioactive emanation from a small amount of radium, etc. The growth of the population of a country or the growth of invested capital also makes an interesting study.

Growth takes place in many ways. Sometimes the changes are extremely complicated and depend upon many factors. In such cases no one is able to describe fully and explain the growth. Sometimes a quantity grows in a manner that is comparatively simple, and we can understand and interpret the process. It is this latter type of growth that we wish to study.

We all have some ideas—perhaps hazy—about growth. For example, the more money we have invested at compound interest, the greater the amount that accumulates; the larger the population of a state, the greater the expected yearly increase in population; the better the climatic conditions, the faster the growth of a plant or a tree; etc. But we know that in order to apply mathematics to a problem, we must state and interpret the problem more carefully.

We have previously studied the variation or growth processes which can be expressed by the relations

$$y = kx \qquad \text{and} \qquad y = kx^2$$

Two examples of growth expressed by the first relation are

(*a*) the price of a meat roast increases with the weight in pounds; and (*b*) the paycheck of a person who has a fixed hourly rate of pay increases with the number of hours worked. Two examples of growth expressed by the second relation are (*a*) the surface area of a balloon increases with the square of the diameter; and (*b*) the distance a stone falls from rest increases with the square of the time of fall.

2. Interest compounded continuously

We have studied the way a sum of money grows when invested at simple interest and at compound interest. We found that when a principal P was invested at an interest rate r compounded k times a year, the amount A due at the end of n years was given by the formula

$$A = P\left(1 + \frac{r}{k}\right)^{nk} \tag{1}$$

Now let us see what change is made in the amount A if the money is compounded exceedingly often, that is, if the value of k becomes very large. When k becomes very large, for example a trillion, the compounding must be done every trillionth of a year, or about every 0.00004 seconds. That is, if k becomes large without limit, then we say that the money is compounded continuously.

Let us see how a dollar invested at 100% interest grows during 1 year if the number of times k that interest is compounded is increased. The amount A due on $1 at the end of 1 year is given by

$$A = \left(1 + \frac{1}{k}\right)^{k} \tag{2}$$

Table 38 gives the value of A for different values of k.

TABLE 38

k	1	10	100	1000	10,000	100,000
A	2.000	2.594	2.704	2.717	2.718	2.718

We notice that k increases very rapidly, but the amount A, while it increases, does not increase very rapidly and appears to be approaching a limiting value of about 2.718. In fact, mathematicians have proved that as k increases indefinitely, the value of A correct to eight decimal places is equal to 2.71828183.

Since this limiting value of $\left(1 + \frac{1}{k}\right)^{k}$ as k increases indefinitely is encountered in many branches of mathematics, it is denoted by the letter e. Thus

$$e = 2.71828183 = \text{limiting value of } \left(1 + \frac{1}{k}\right)^k$$

as k becomes very large. For our purposes, we will take $e = 2.718$. Thus the amount due on \$1 at the end of 1 year if the interest is compounded continuously at 100% is \$2.72. As depositors, we wish our savings bank would pay interest compounded continuously.

3. Effect of compounding continuously

Equation (1) gives the amount due at the end of n years when the interest is compounded k times a year.

$$A = P\left(1 + \frac{r}{k}\right)^{nk} \tag{1}$$

In the preceding section we found $A = 2.718$ when k increases indefinitely and $P = 1$, $r = 100\%$, $n = 1$. Now, what will be the effect on this equation if k is increased indefinitely but we do not give special values to P, n, and r?

If we let $r/k = 1/z$, then $k = rz$, and equation (1) becomes

$$A = P\left(1 + \frac{1}{z}\right)^{nrz} = P\left[\left(1 + \frac{1}{z}\right)^z\right]^{nr} \tag{3}$$

If k increases indefinitely, z will also increase indefinitely. We have just seen above that the limit of $\left(1 + \frac{1}{k}\right)^k$ as k becomes very large is e. Therefore, when k, and hence z, become exceedingly large, equation (3) becomes

$$A = Pe^{nr} \tag{4}$$

This equation (4) gives the amount A of any principal P after n years if the interest is *compounded continuously* at an annual rate r. That is, the amount A is equal to the principal P invested, multiplied by the number $e = 2.718$ raised to the nr power.

4. The exponential functions e^{kx} and e^{-kx}

When any quantity y varies with another quantity x in such a way that the rate of change in y is constantly proportional to the value of y, it is said to vary in a manner similar to the continuous-interest law. The functional relation between y and x is given by

$$y = Ae^{kx} \tag{5}$$

where A and k are constants.

This relation (5) is important and is known as the *law of continuous growth.* It is commonly found in problems of finance, growth of timber, growth of bacteria, etc. If the exponent is negative, the relation

$$y = Ae^{-kx} \tag{6}$$

is called the *law of decay.*

This law of decay is used to determine the altitude when the atmospheric pressure is given, the healing of the surface area of a wound, the decomposition of radium, transmission of light through various media, damped vibrations of a pendulum, loss of heat or electrical energy, etc.

The two functions given by equations (5) and (6) are called *exponential functions.* Whenever the nature of the functional dependence between two variables is known to be exponential, the exact dependence is given by one of these equations.

5. The graph of the functions $y = e^x$ and $y = e^{-x}$

The values of e^x and e^{-x} are defined for all values of x and have been determined for many values of x. These values may be found in tables. Let us plot each of these functions (Fig. 80).

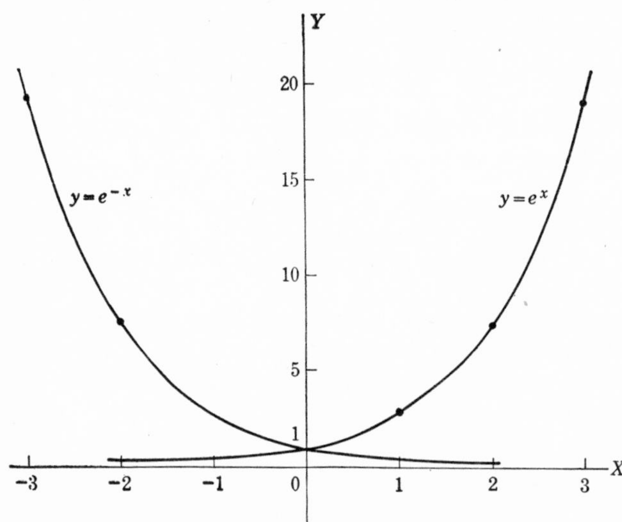

Fig. 80

The two curves in Fig. 80 are known as the *standard exponential curves.* We observe that each curve crosses the y axis at the point $y = 1$. The curve for $y = e^x$ rises very rapidly as x increases and approaches the x axis as x decreases. The curve for $y = e^{-x}$ rises very rapidly as x

decreases and approaches the x axis as x increases. Neither curve crosses the x axis.

EXERCISES

1. Using the same coordinate axis and scale, plot the curves for the following functions:

a. $y = x + 1$ *b.* $y = x^2 + 1$
c. $y = x^3 + 1$ *d.* $y = 2^x$
e. $y = e^x$

2. Compare the five curves in Prob. 1.

3. By means of Table VIII at the end of the book, find the value of

a. $e^{1.2}$ *b.* $e^{7.5}$
c. $e^{2.5}$ *d.* $e^{-0.4}$
e. $e^{-2.5}$ *f.* $e^{-1.1}$
g. $e^{-2.1}$ *h.* $e^{4.5}$

??????????? PROBLEM JUST FOR FUN ???????????

At exactly 12 o'clock, two bacteria are placed in a growing medium. One minute later there are 4 bacteria, in another minute they have increased to 8, in another to 16, etc. At exactly 1 o'clock the growing mass of bacteria measures 1 gallon. At what time will there be 1 quart of bacteria?

???????????????? JUST FOR FUN ????????????????

6. Growth in nature

In nature many quantities grow or increase in a manner similar to the way a sum of money grows when the interest is compounded very often or continuously. If the rate of growth is proportional to itself, a physical quantity P grows to a value Q after t units of time, where Q is given by the relation

$$Q = Pe^{rt} \tag{7}$$

In many instances there is a continuous decrease in the quantity instead of an increase. A quantity P which decreases continuously at a constant rate r per unit of time has decayed to a value Q after t units of time, where Q is given by the relation

$$Q = Pe^{-rt} \tag{8}$$

Example 1. The number of bacteria in a culture of yeast increases continuously at a rate per minute which is always 12% of the number of bacteria then present. If the original number of bacteria is 1,000, how many bacteria are in the culture at the end of 10 minutes?

Solution. The number Q of bacteria present at any time is given by the relation

$$Q = 1{,}000e^{0.12t}$$

When $t = 10$, $Q = 1{,}000e^{1.2} = 1{,}000(3.32) = 3{,}320$. The value

$$e^{1.2} = 3.32$$

is obtained from the table.

Example 2. In a treated culture, the number of bacteria present was 1,000 to start with, and 5 minutes later the number of bacteria was 670. If the bacteria decreased continuously at a rate $r\%$ per minute, find the rate r and the time it takes the number of bacteria to decrease to 100.

Solution. The number Q of bacteria present at any time is given by the relation

$$Q = 1{,}000e^{-rt} \tag{9}$$

When $t = 5$, $Q = 670$. Hence

$$670 = 1{,}000e^{-5r} \qquad \text{and} \qquad e^{-5r} = 0.67$$

From the tables, we find that $e^{-x} = 0.67$ when $x = 0.4$, and

$$r = \frac{0.4}{5} = 0.08 = 8\%$$

Equation (9) becomes

$$Q = 1{,}000e^{-0.08t}$$

When $Q = 100$, we have

$$100 = 1{,}000e^{-0.08t} \qquad \text{and} \qquad e^{-0.08t} = 0.1$$

From the table, we find that $e^{-x} = 0.1$ when $x = 2.3$. Hence $0.08t = 2.3$ and $t = 28.75$ minutes, which is the time for the number of bacteria to decrease to 100.

Example 3. A snowslide is started by a snowball which weighs 5 pounds. As the snowball descends, it increases its weight continuously at the rate of 80% every 400 feet. What will be the weight of the moving snow mass after the original ball has traveled ½ mile down a mountain?

Solution. This is a problem in growth, but the units involved are distance rolled rather than time. The equation

$$Q = Pe^{rt}$$

applies if we choose t to mean distance rolled. Since we are given the gain every 400 feet, we choose t to be measured in units of 400 feet, that is, $t = 1$ means 400 feet rolled, $t = 2$ means 800 feet rolled, etc. A half mile is 2,640 feet, or $t = 6.6$. From our problem we have $P = 5$ pounds, $r = 0.8$. Then

$$Q = 5e^{0.8 \times 6.6} = 5e^{5.28}$$

In Table VIII we find $e^5 = 148$ and $e^{5.5} = 245$, so we estimate $e^{5.28}$ to be about 200. This gives us Q equal to about 1,000 pounds.

EXERCISES

1. The number of bacteria in a certain culture increases at a rate per hour equal to 25% of the number. If the original number of bacteria was 200, find the number after 2 hours and after 10 hours.

2. The growth of a certain type of tree is such that its cross-sectional area increases continuously at an annual rate of 10%. Find the cross-sectional area of the tree at the end of 12 years, if the original cross-sectional area was 4 square inches.

3. Find the amount that would be produced by $1,000 if it could be invested at 6% interest compounded continuously for 10 years.

4. Compare the answer for Prob. 3 with the amount received from $1,000 invested at 6% compounded semiannually for 10 years.

5. A building depreciated continuously at a constant rate of 6% per year. If the original value was $50,000, what is the formula for its value after t years? What was the value of the building after 20 years?

6. Sunlight transmitted down into deep water loses its intensity continuously and is approximately 50% for each 100 feet of depth. Find the depth at which the intensity of the light will be 20% of its intensity at the surface.

7. The pressure P as measured by the height of a mercury column in inches is given by the equation

$$P = 29.92e^{-h/26,200}$$

where h is the elevation above sea level expressed in feet. Find the pressure in inches of mercury at the following altitudes:

a. Sea level, $h = 0$ feet
b. $h = 2{,}620$ feet
c. $h = 29{,}000$ feet
d. $h = 10$ miles

8. If a metal ball is cooled by a moving stream of air, the difference in temperature between the ball and the air decreases continuously at a rate of k degrees per second, where k depends on the radiation qualities of the metal. If $k = 0.002$, how long will it take for the difference in temperature between the ball and the air to drop from 38 to 23°C.?

9. Radium disintegrates continuously with a half life of 1,600 years. Find the amount of radium remaining in 1 gram after 3,200 years and after 5,000 years.

10. Radioactive sodium disintegrates continuously with a half life of 15 hours. If 10 milligrams of radioactive sodium is administered to a patient, how much of the sodium remains at the end of 1 hour? After 5 hours? After 30 hours?

??????????? PROBLEM JUST FOR FUN ???????????

Arrange the nine digits in the following square to make a perfect square in which the rows and columns add to the same number.

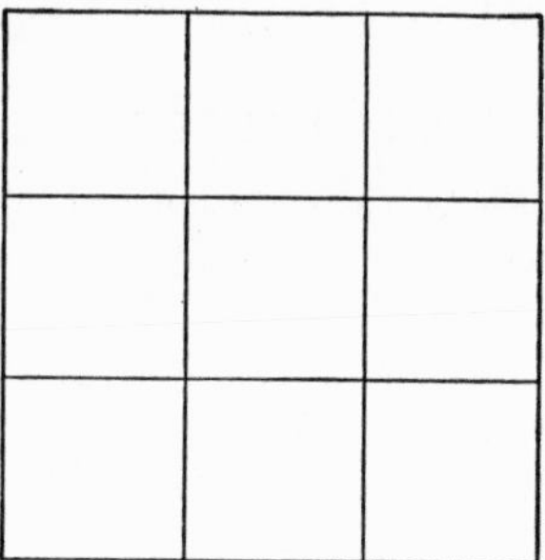

??????????????? JUST FOR FUN ???????????????

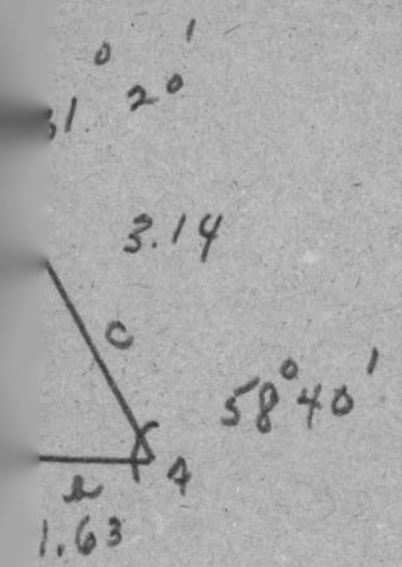

31° 20'

3.14

c

58° 40'

A

a

1.63

$\tan 58°40' = \frac{a}{1.63}$

a = 1.63 × 1.6426

.2122 + .2148

a = .5270

a = 3.37

$\sin 31°20' = \frac{1.63}{c}$

$c = \frac{1.63}{.5200}$ = log .2122
colog .2840
.4962

c = 4962

c = 3.14

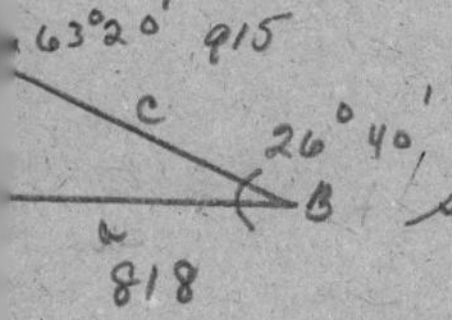

63° 20' 915

c

26° 40'

B

a

818

$\sin B = \frac{411}{915}$ log 2.6138
colog -3.0386
-1.6524

B = .4490

B = 26° 40'

$\tan 63°20' = \frac{a}{411}$

a = 411 × 1.9912

2.6138 + .2989

a = 2.9127

a = 818

David Brubaker

(1)

B 61°30′, .753, c, .359, a, C, b, .661, 28°30′, A

$\tan A = \frac{.359}{.661}$ log -1.5551
colog $.1798$
-1.7349

A = .5430

A = 28°30′

$\sin A = \frac{.359}{c}$

$c = \frac{.359}{.4772}$ = log -1.5551
colog $.3215$
-1.8766

c = .753

(2)

B 60°20′, .685, B, 339, A, C, b, .595, 29°40′, A

$\sin A = \frac{a}{.685}$

a = .685 × .4950

$-1.8357 + -1.6946$

a = -1.5303

a = .339

$\sin B = \frac{b}{.685}$

b = .685 × .8689

$-1.8357 + -1.9390$

b = -1.7747

b = .595

(3)

B 47°40′, 8.52, c, 5.73, a, C, b, 6.29, 42°20′, A

$\tan A = \frac{5.73}{6.29}$ log .7582
colog -1.2013
-1.9595

A = .9110

A = 42°20′

$\sin 42°20′ = \frac{5.73}{c}$

$c = \frac{5.73}{.6734}$ log .7582
= colog .1720
.9302

c = .9302

c = 8.52

CHAPTER

17

Probability

(*Gambler's Mathematics*)

It is remarkable that a science [probability] which began with the consideration of games of chance, should have become the most important object of human knowledge. LAPLACE

1. Probability, or chance

One of the most interesting topics with which men have been concerned throughout the ages is the prediction of future events. Whether or not any individual has the power to foretell the things which are going to happen does not particularly concern us. But we are concerned with more or less subjective statements of opinion with regard to some event. For example, "What are our chances of winning the ball game tomorrow?" "Do you think it will rain?" "In all probability I will go to town tomorrow." Such statements illustrate the everyday meaning of probability, or chance. Our opinions as to the outcome of such questions may change from hour to hour as our dispositions change, and two similarly informed men may have radically different opinions.

Any mathematical definition of probability must be objective and convey the same meaning to everyone who uses it. We need to study mathematical probability, because the probability of an event is fundamental in many lines of science, for example, statistical studies of physics, biological and social phenomena, theory of errors of measurements, etc. Important applications of the theory of probability are found in fire and life insurance, the Mendelian law in genetics, the making of a good pension or retirement program, the military science of bombing and artillery fire, etc.

The insurance business, one of the largest businesses in the world, is based upon the ability to establish the likelihood of the occurrence of certain events. On the basis of past records, the life insurance company establishes the average life expectancy of a person and bases its premiums upon the probability of his reaching a certain age.

In order to develop a good pension or retirement fund, we need to know the probability that we will live 5, 10, or 15 years after retirement. After the amount of money expected to be needed after retirement is determined, we simply calculate the amount needed to be set aside each month at a given interest rate to yield the desired sum at retirement.

2. Historical development of probability

Historically the theory of probability had its origin in games of chance. Apart from a few casual remarks on the subject by Galileo (1564–1642), we find the origin of the science of probability in the personal correspondence between two great men, Blaise Pascal (1623–1662) and Pierre de Fermat (1601–1665). Chevalier de Méré, a French nobleman and a man of great experience in gambling, asked Pascal to explain an apparent contradiction between his theoretical reasoning and his observations gathered from the gambling tables. Pascal solved the problem for the nobleman, and Fermat became interested in this problem and in those of similar nature. In their private correspondence these two men laid the foundation of the science of probability.

3. Basic ideas of chance

The basic ideas of chance underlying the study of probability are familiar to everyone, as the following example will illustrate.

Example 1. If we toss a coin into the air, what is the chance, or probability, that it will fall "heads"?

Solution. We know that a tossed coin will fall in one of two ways, that is, with heads or tails showing. We regard either way as equally probable, and we say that the chance of falling "heads" is $\frac{1}{2}$. This means that if a coin were tossed thousands of times, we should expect it to fall "heads" about half the time and "tails" about half the time.

Example 2. If we toss a die, which is a cube that has spots one through six on its six faces, what is the chance that a four spot will come up?

Solution. The total number of ways a cube can fall is six, all of which we assume to be equally probable, or that the die is not "loaded." We expect that each face will come up about one-sixth of the time if the die is tossed thousands of times. Therefore the chance that a four spot will come up on each toss of the die is $\frac{1}{6}$.

Example 3. If we name a date at random, what is the chance that this date falls on Sunday?

Solution. If the date selected is one falling after the present calendar was established and accepted, the chance that this date falls on Sunday is $1/7$. Since there are seven days in a week, there is no reason to assume that we are more or less likely to select a Sunday.

Example 4. If one card is drawn from an ordinary deck of bridge cards, what is the chance of drawing a heart?

Solution. There are 52 cards in a deck, of which 13 are hearts, and it appears that any one card is as likely to be drawn as another. Out of the 52 cards there are 13 equally likely ways of drawing a heart. The chances of drawing a heart, then, are 13 out of 52, or $13/52 = 1/4$. That is, if we take a deck of cards and draw thousands of cards in succession, each time replacing the drawn card and reshuffling, we should expect to draw a heart one-quarter of the time.

4. Definition of probability

If, on any one trial, an event can happen in a different ways and can fail to happen in b different ways, and if all the $a + b$ ways are equally likely, the ratio

$$p = \frac{a}{a + b}$$

of the favorable to the total number of ways is called the probability p that the event will occur on a particular trial. The ratio

$$q = \frac{b}{a + b}$$

of the ways the event can fail to happen to the total number of ways the event may happen is called the probability q that the event will fail to occur on the trial. That is, the probability of an event equals the number of ways it can occur divided by the total number of ways it can occur and fail to occur.

Notice that

$$p + q = \frac{a}{a + b} + \frac{b}{a + b} = \frac{a + b}{a + b} = 1$$

If an event is certain to happen, its probability is 1, for in this case there are no ways in which it can fail, and $p = a/a = 1$. If an event is certain to fail, $a = 0$ and $p = 0$, but $q = 1$. In all other cases, a is greater than zero and less than $a + b$, so that the probability p is a positive fraction whose value is never less than 0 nor greater than 1.

Example 1. An ordinary die is thrown. What is the probability that an even number, that is, 2, 4, or 6, will turn up?

Solution. In all dice problems it is assumed that each die is a cube, with faces numbered 1 to 6. Any one of the six numbers 1, 2, 3, 4, 5, or 6 is as likely to appear as another. Of the six possible events, three results, 2, 4, or 6, are favorable. Hence the probability of an even number coming up on each throw of the die is $3/6 = 1/2$.

Example 2. A number from 1 to 10 is selected at random. What is the probability that it is divisible by 4?

Solution. There are 10 numbers, of which 2 are divisible by 4, namely, 4 and 8. Hence the probability is $2/10 = 1/5$.

EXERCISES

1. What is the probability (*a*) of throwing a 4 when rolling a single die? (*b*) Of drawing a club from an ordinary deck of 52 playing cards? (*c*) Of naming at random a date that falls on Tuesday?

2. If two quarters are tossed, what is the probability of getting (*a*) two heads? (*b*) Two tails? (*c*) One head and one tail?

3. If three coins are tossed, what is the probability of getting (*a*) three heads? (*b*) Three tails? (*c*) Two heads and one tail?

4. If two dice are thrown, what is the probability of throwing (*a*) two 1's? (*b*) Two 3's?

5. If a number between 1 and 12, inclusive, is selected at random, what is the probability that it is not divisible by any number except itself and 1?

??????????? PROBLEM JUST FOR FUN ???????????

What part of the day has disappeared if the time left is twice two-thirds of the time passed away?

???????????????? JUST FOR FUN ????????????????

5. More problems on probability

In order to determine the probability that a certain event will happen, often we need to know the number of possible choices or arrangements which can be made from a group of objects. It is desirable to enumerate these arrangements, because we get a better idea of the probability and the factors which affect it. The following problems will serve as illustrations.

Example 1. If two balls are drawn at random from a bag containing five red balls and two black balls, what is the chance that (*a*) two red balls will be drawn? (*b*) That two black balls will be drawn? (*c*) That one red and one black ball will be drawn?

Solution. The two red balls must be drawn from the five red balls, and this can be done in 10 different ways. Let us designate the five red balls by R_1, R_2, R_3, R_4, and R_5 and the two black balls by B_1 and B_2. The possible ways of drawing two red balls from the five red balls are

$R_1 R_2$	$R_2 R_3$	$R_3 R_4$	$R_4 R_5$
$R_1 R_3$	$R_2 R_4$	$R_3 R_5$	
$R_1 R_4$	$R_2 R_5$		
$R_1 R_5$			

The total number of possible ways of selecting two balls out of the seven balls is 21, and these ways are

$R_1 R_2$	$R_2 R_3$	$R_3 R_4$	$R_4 R_5$	$R_5 B_1$	$B_1 B_2$
$R_1 R_3$	$R_2 R_4$	$R_3 R_5$	$R_4 B_1$	$R_5 B_2$	
$R_1 R_4$	$R_2 R_5$	$R_3 B_1$	$R_4 B_2$		
$R_1 R_5$	$R_2 B_1$	$R_3 B_2$			
$R_1 B_1$	$R_2 B_2$				
$R_1 B_2$					

The chance of selecting two red balls out of the seven balls is $10/21$.

The chance of selecting two black balls out of the seven balls is $1/21$.

The chance of selecting one red and one black ball out of the seven balls is $10/21$.

Example 2. Three different pairs of gloves are placed in a box. If two gloves are drawn at random from the box, what is the chance of drawing a matched pair? Drawing a glove for the right and left hand? Drawing 2 gloves for the right hand? For the left hand? For the same hand?

Solution. Let us use R_1,L_1, R_2,L_2 and R_3,L_3 to represent the three pairs of gloves. The possible ways of drawing two gloves are

R_1,L_1	R_2,L_1	R_3,L_1	L_1,L_2	L_2,L_3
R_1,L_2	R_2,L_2	R_3,L_2	L_1,L_3	
R_1,L_3	R_2,L_3	R_3,L_3		
R_1,R_2	R_2,R_3			
R_1,R_3				

There are 15 ways of selecting 2 gloves and only 3 ways of obtaining a matched pair. Hence the probability of obtaining a matched pair is $3/15 = 1/5$.

There are 9 ways of selecting a glove for the right and left hand. Hence the chance of drawing a glove for each hand is $9/15 = 3/5$.

There are 3 ways of obtaining a glove for the right hand and 3 ways of obtaining a glove for the left hand. But there are 6 ways of drawing a glove for one hand. Hence the probability of drawing two gloves for the right hand is $3/15 = 1/5$, for the left hand is $1/5$, and for one hand is $6/15 = 2/5$.

EXERCISES

1. If a number is drawn at random from the integers 1 to 20, inclusive, what is the probability that it will (*a*) end in 5? (*b*) Be even? (*c*) Be divisible by 3? (*d*) Be divisible by 4?

2. What is the probability that a single throw of a die will result in a number under 4? Under 5?

3. What is the probability of throwing an odd number with one die?

4. What is the probability of throwing a pair of even numbers with two dice?

5. If two dice are thrown, what is the chance of throwing the dice so that faces add to (*a*) 2, (*b*) 3, (*c*) 4, (*d*) 5, (*e*) 6, (*f*) 7, (*g*) 8, (*h*) 9, (*i*) 10, (*j*) 11?

6. If three balls are drawn from a bag containing four black and three red balls, what is the probability that (*a*) all will be black? (*b*) Two will be red and one black? (*c*) All will be red?

7. If three dice are thrown, what is the probability of getting (*a*) all 1's? (*b*) All alike? (*c*) A sum of 8?

??????????? PROBLEM JUST FOR FUN ???????????

Three natives made a raid on a neighboring village and stole some bananas. It became dark before they reached their own village, so they decided to sleep and divide the loot the following morning. The thieves posted a pet monkey nearby as lookout and went to sleep. The first thief woke up and, not trusting the others, divided the large pile into three equal piles and had one banana left over. He fed the extra banana to the monkey, hid his pile, and left the remainder. A short time later the second thief woke up, divided the bananas that remained into three equal piles, and found that there was an extra banana, which he fed to the monkey. This thief hid his pile and went back to sleep. The third thief awoke and divided the remaining pile into three equal piles, with one banana left over, which he gave to the monkey. He hid his share and went back to sleep. In the morning the three thieves divided the small remaining pile into three equal piles with one banana left over, which they fed to the monkey. How many bananas did the thieves steal?

???????????????? JUST FOR FUN ????????????????

6. The problem of choice

In determining the probability that a certain event will happen, we determine the number of choices, or arrangements, which can be made from a group of objects. If the number of arrangements is small, we are able to enumerate all the possibilities. But as the number of possible arrangements increases, it takes too long to enumerate all the possible arrangements. For example, to how many patrons can a telephone company give telephone numbers having four digits if the first number cannot be zero? How many code "words" can one form by using any six different letters of the alphabet? How many car licenses can a state have if the license consists of one letter followed by five numbers?

We shall first discuss situations in which it is possible to enumerate the choices, arrangements, or selections which can be made from various groups of objects. Then we shall try to generalize in order to determine the number of possible arrangements. We shall use simple examples to illustrate these principles of selection.

Example 1. If we wish to ascend a certain mountain, we may go by car, by foot, or by a cograil car from a town at the foot of the mountain to a point A part way up the mountain, but to reach the top of the mountain from there, we must either walk or ride the cograil car. In how many ways is it possible to reach the top of the mountain?

Solution. First let us make a simple sketch showing the ways it is possible to reach the point A and the top of the mountain. By observing the drawing (Fig. 81), we can write down all the possible ways of ascending the mountain.

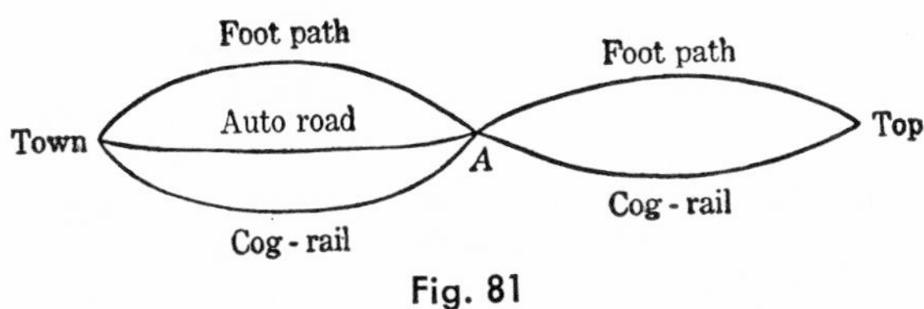

Fig. 81

1. Foot path—foot path
2. Foot path—cograil
3. Auto road—foot path
4. Auto road—cograil
5. Cograil—foot path
6. Cograil—cograil

We find that there are six, and only six, ways of ascending this mountain. Notice that the answer of six ways can be obtained by multiplying 3, the number of ways of going from the town to point A, by 2, the number of ways of going from point A to the top of the mountain.

We might obtain this solution in another way. For each of the three ways of going from the town to the point A, there are two ways of going from A to the top of the mountain. Hence the number of ways to climb the mountain is $2 + 2 + 2 = 6$.

Example 2. Our friend the milkman dresses in the dark so as not to awaken his wife. If he has four pairs of shoes, in how many ways is it possible for him to leave the house with a left and a right shoe from different pairs?

Solution. He may select any one of four left shoes. With the left shoe which he may select, he may choose any one of three right shoes from the remaining pairs of shoes. Hence the number of ways of selecting a left and a right shoe not from the same pair is

$$3 + 3 + 3 + 3 = 4 \times 3 = 12$$

We can check this answer by actually enumerating all possible choices. Let the pairs of shoes be designated by

$$L_1,R_1 \qquad L_2,R_2 \qquad L_3,R_3 \qquad L_4,R_4$$

where L_1 means the left shoe and R_1 means the right shoe belonging to the first pair of shoes and similarly for the other pairs. The solution above states that with L_1 the milkman can select R_2, R_3, or R_4. Proceeding in this way, we can write down the 12 possible selections

$$\begin{array}{cccc} L_1,R_2 & L_2,R_1 & L_3,R_1 & L_4,R_1 \\ L_1,R_3 & L_2,R_3 & L_3,R_2 & L_4,R_2 \\ L_1,R_4 & L_2,R_4 & L_3,R_4 & L_4,R_3 \end{array}$$

Example 3. Three flags are to be placed in a vertical row on a mast as a signal. If there are seven different flags, how many signals are possible?

Solution. We can select the first, or top, flag in seven different ways. Having selected the top flag, there remain six ways of selecting the second flag. Having selected the top two flags, the bottom flag can be selected in five ways from the remaining flags. We see that for each way of selecting the top flag there are six ways of selecting the second flag, and hence there are $7 \times 6 = 42$ ways of selecting the first two flags. Likewise, for every way of selecting the first two flags there are five ways of selecting the bottom flag. Hence there are $7 \times 6 \times 5 = 210$ ways of selecting the three flags, and 210 signals can be arranged.

7. Fundamental principle of choice

In order to help us solve problems similar to the examples above, we now state a fundamental principle.

Fundamental principle of choice: If one selection can be made in any one of n ways, and if, after one of the n ways has been selected, a second selection can be made in any one of m ways, then the two selections can be made together, in that order, in $n \times m$ ways. If, in addition, a third selection can be made in k independent ways, the three selections can be made together in $n \times m \times k$ ways.

Proof. Corresponding to the first one of the n ways of making the first selection, there are m ways of making the second selection. For the second one of the ways of making the first selection, there are m ways of making the second selection, and so on—for each of the n ways of making the first choice, there are m ways of making the second choice. There are then

$$\underbrace{m + m + m + m + \cdots + m}_{n \text{ terms}} = n \times m$$

ways that the two selections can be made together in that order.

EXERCISES

1. If a nickel, a dime, and quarter are tossed into the air together, in how many ways may they fall?

2. Between Milwaukee, Wis., and Chicago there are two steam railroads, one electric railroad, a boat line, a bus line, and an airplane line. In how many different ways can one make a round trip between the two cities?

3. From a group of nine students, a president, a vice-president, and secretary are to be elected. How many sets of officers are possible?

4. If a die is tossed, in how many ways can it fall?

5. Five people enter a bus at the same time. If there are three vacant seats, in how many ways may these people be seated?

6. How many signals can be made using two different flags if each flag can be held in any one of five different positions? Each different position of the two flags (except together) represents a signal.

7. If one coin and one die are thrown, in how many ways can they fall?

8. How many mixtures can be made using one of three spices and one of four flavoring extracts?

9. Ten men compete in a race in which the first five places win prizes. If there are no ties, in how many ways may the prizes be awarded?

10. How many straight lines are determined by 5 distinct points on a given circle? By 10 points? By 20 points?

??????????? PROBLEM JUST FOR FUN ???????????

A man and his wife, who weigh 150 pounds apiece, have two sons, each of whom weighs 75 pounds. They own a boat which is capable of carrying only 150 pounds. If this family wishes to cross a river, how can they do it?

??????????????? JUST FOR FUN ???????????????

8. Permutations

Let us now determine the number of ways that two letters can be selected from the four letters a, b, c, and d. We know that there are 4 ways of selecting the first letter, and after this choice there are 3 ways of making the second selection. Hence the number of ways of selecting two letters from four letters is

$$4 \times 3 = 12 \text{ ways}$$

We can easily list all the possible arrangements.

ab	*ba*	*ca*	*da*
ac	*bc*	*cb*	*db*
ad	*bd*	*cd*	*dc*

Each arrangement, or order, such as *ab*, is called a *permutation*. Hence there are twelve different permutations possible from 4 letters taken 2 at a time.

The number of permutations of n objects taken r at a time is denoted by the symbol $P_{n,r}$. Thus, in the example above, the permutations possible from 4 letters taken 2 at a time are denoted by $P_{4,2}$, which we know is equal to 4×3. Hence

$$P_{4,2} = 4 \times 3 = 12$$

Let us reconsider the examples in Sec. 6. From Example 3, there are 7 different flags to be selected 3 at a time. Hence the number of permutations possible is

$$P_{7,3} = 7 \times 6 \times 5 = 210$$

These examples suggest that the number of permutations of n objects taken r at a time is the product of r factors whose first term is n, second term is $n - 1$, third term is $n - 2$, etc., until there are r factors. That is,

$$P_{n,r} = n(n-1)(n-2)(n-3) \cdots (n-r+1) \qquad (1)$$

To prove this formula for $P_{n,r}$, we can reason as follows: Since the number of ways of selecting the first object is n, the number of ways that the second object may be selected is 1 less than n, or $n - 1$ ways. The third object may then be selected in $n - 2$ ways. We continue in this way, and the rth object can then be selected in n minus the previous $r - 1$ ways, that is, in $n - (r - 1) = n - r + 1$ ways. The fundamental principle of choice, in Sec. 7, tells us that the total number of ways of selecting r objects at a time from n objects is the product of the ways of selecting each object. That is,

$$P_{n,r} = n(n-1)(n-2)(n-3) \cdots (n-r+1)$$

Example 1. Twelve boys compete in a race in which the first five places win prizes. If there are no ties, in how many ways may the prizes be awarded?

Solution. We have 12 objects, and we want to find the number of arrangements, or permutations, that are possible if the objects are taken 5 at a time. We want the value of $P_{12,5}$. Using equation (1), we find that

$$P_{12,5} = 12 \times 11 \times 10 \times 9 \times 8 = 95{,}040 \text{ ways}$$

Example 2. How many possible ways are there to arrange 10 books which just fit on a shelf 18 inches long?

Solution. We have 10 objects, and these 10 objects are to be taken 10 at a time. Hence the number of permutations is $P_{10,10}$. From equation (1) we find that

$$P_{10,10,} = 10 \times 9 \times 8 \times 7 \times 6 \times 5 \times 4 \times 3 \times 2 \times 1 = 3{,}628{,}800$$

9. Factorial notation

A convenient way of expressing the products of n consecutive numbers, such as

$$n(n-1)(n-2) \cdots 5 \cdot 4 \cdot 3 \cdot 2 \cdot 1$$

is the factorial notation $n!$, and we call this product *factorial n*. That is, we use $n!$ to represent the product

$$n! = n(n-1)(n-2) \cdots 5 \cdot 4 \cdot 3 \cdot 2 \cdot 1 \tag{2}$$

We observe that

$$\begin{aligned}
1! &= 1\\
2! &= 2 \cdot 1 = 2\\
3! &= 3 \cdot 2 \cdot 1 = 6\\
4! &= 4 \cdot 3 \cdot 2 \cdot 1 = 24\\
5! &= 5 \cdot 4 \cdot 3 \cdot 2 \cdot 1 = 120\\
&\cdots\cdots\cdots\cdots\\
10! &= 10 \cdot 9 \cdot 8 \cdot 7 \cdot 6 \cdot 5 \cdot 4 \cdot 3 \cdot 2 \cdot 1 = 3{,}628{,}800
\end{aligned}$$

It is easy to see that

$$(n+1)! = (n+1)n! \tag{3}$$

for

$$(n+1)! = (n+1)(n)(n-1)(n-2) \cdots 4 \cdot 3 \cdot 2 \cdot 1 = (n+1)n!$$

Since $(n+1)! = (n+1)n!$, we can use this equation to define $0!$ If we let $n = 0$, we obtain

$$(0+1)! = (1)0!$$

or

$$1 = 0!$$

Thus equations (2) and (3) define the factorial of all positive integers and zero 0, 1, 2, 3, ...

We can use this factorial notation to write $P_{n,r}$ in a different form. We may write

$$P_{n,r} = n(n-1)(n-2) \cdots (n-r+1) \cdot \frac{(n-r)(n-r-1) \cdots 5 \cdot 4 \cdot 3 \cdot 2 \cdot 1}{(n-r)(n-r-1) \cdots 5 \cdot 4 \cdot 3 \cdot 2 \cdot 1}$$

because the last quotient is 1 and does not alter the value of the expression for $P_{n,r}$. We notice that the numerator is $n!$ and that the denominator is $(n-r)!$ We may write

$$P_{n,r} = n(n-1)(n-2) \cdots (n-r+1) = \frac{n!}{(n-r)!}$$

The number of permutations of n objects taken r at a time is usually expressed by the equation

$$P_{n,r} = \frac{n!}{(n-r)!} \tag{4}$$

The solution to Example 1 of Sec. 8 is

$$P_{12,5} = \frac{12!}{7!} = 95{,}040$$

The solution to Example 2 of Sec. 8 is

$$P_{10,10} = \frac{10!}{0!} = 10!$$

since $0! = 1$

The values of factorial m have been tabulated, but they are easily worked out for small numbers, so we shall not use tables.

EXERCISES

1. Evaluate

$$P_{10,6} \qquad P_{8,4} \qquad P_{6,6} \qquad P_{3,3}$$

2. Simplify

$$\frac{P_{5,3}}{P_{3,3}} \qquad \frac{P_{n,r}}{P_{r,r}}$$

3. Write out all permutations of the letters a, b, and c taken two at a time.

4. Write out all permutations of the letters a, b, and c taken three at a time.

5. A shelf will hold only 10 of 15 books which are the same size. In how many ways may the shelf be filled?

6. A man has a combination lock with 50 numbers on it. He forgets the combination but remembers that it required four different numbers to open it. Would he be wise to try all the combinations in order to find the one which opens the lock?

7. How many numbers of four digits can be made using the digits 1, 4, 7, and 9 if no numeral is used twice in a number? How many numbers of three digits from the same four numerals?

8. An automobile manufacturer has 10 different colors available. He uses different colors for fenders, body, and wheels of each car. How many color combinations can he produce?

9. A boy has two suits of clothes, three shirts, four ties, and two hats. In how many ways may this lad dress by changing suits, shirts, ties, and hats?

10. In a football game, how many different signals can the quarterback call using the numbers 4, 5, 6, 7, and 8 if he uses four numbers at a time?

11. How many batting orders are possible for a baseball team?

12. If 15 men turn out for the basketball team, in how many ways can the team be selected?

??????????? PROBLEM JUST FOR FUN ???????????

At the bottom of a well which is 45 feet deep is a snail which starts crawling toward the top in a vertical line. The snail climbs 3 feet each day but slides back 2 feet every night. How many days does it take the snail to get out of the well?

???????????????? JUST FOR FUN ????????????????

10. Restricted arrangements

Whenever an arrangement is to be made which is subject to some restriction, the restricted group must be considered first. An example will illustrate.

Example 1. A bus has 20 seats on each side. In how many ways can 40 people be seated if 12 of them insist upon sitting on the shady side?

Solution. We must first assign 12 of the 20 shady seats to the 12 restricted people in some order, and the number of ways this can be done is $P_{20,12}$. The other 28 people may sit any place in the remaining 28 seats, and the number of ways they may be seated is $P_{28,28}$. For each seating arrangement of the 12 restricted persons on the shady side, there are $P_{28,28}$ seating arrangements for the other 28 people. Hence, the number of ways for seating all 40 people is

$$P_{20,12} \times P_{28,28} = \frac{20!}{8!} \times 28!$$

Warning. *In working any problem, it is necessary to analyze it and not try merely to fit it into a special type or formula.*

EXERCISES

1. In how many ways can a baseball team be selected from 15 players if 3 of the men can only pitch and the rest can play any of the other positions?

2. In how many ways can a baseball team be selected from 15 players if 3 men can only pitch and 2 can only catch, but the rest of the players can play any of the other positions?

3. How many five-place numbers can be formed from the digits 1, 2, 3, 4, and 5 if 3 is always to occupy the middle place?

4. In how many ways can eight books be arranged on a shelf if two of the books must be kept side by side?

5. In how many ways can five men and four women be seated in a row if a man is always seated at each end?

6. In how many ways can 11 football players be arranged if 3 of the men can play in a 7-man line only, and 2 of the players can play only in the backfield?

??????????? PROBLEM JUST FOR FUN ???????????

A fastidious dresser wakes in the middle of the night with the house on fire and the lights out. He has three pairs of brown socks and four pairs of black socks in his drawer, but they are loose rather than tied in pairs. How many individual socks must he grab to be sure to be able to dress later with two socks of the same color?

???????????????? JUST FOR FUN ????????????????

11. Combinations

In the previous example of Sec. 8, the possible permutations of the letters a, b, c, and d taken two at a time were found to be

ab	ba	bc	cb	cd	dc
ac	ca	bd	db		
ad	da				

We considered the permutation ab as being distinct and different from the permutation ba. But considered as a group or combination, there is no difference between ab and ba. Likewise, when considered as a combination, there is no difference between ac and ca, ad and da, bc and cb, bd and db, or cd and dc. Hence, if we disregard order, there are only six possible combinations of the letters a, b, c, and d taken two at a time, namely:

ab	bc	cd
ac	bd	
ad		

We often need to know the different groups or combinations that can be chosen from n objects taken r at a time. *A combination is regarded as different if a single individual of the group is changed, but the different orders or permutations that can be made within the group do not change the combination.*

Example 1. How many committees consisting of a chairman, a secretary, and a committeeman may be chosen for a group of six people?

Solution. Since all the positions are different, order must count, and hence this is a problem in permutations. The number of ways of selecting this committee is

$$P_{6,3} = \frac{6!}{3!} = 120$$

Example 2. In how many ways can a committee of 3 members be selected from 6 people?

Solution. We have just found that the number of permutations of 6 objects taken 3 at a time is $P_{6,3} = 120$. But our solution does not depend entirely upon the number of possible arrangements, because a person is on the committee regardless of whether he is the first, middle, or last man. That is, order or arrangement within the groups of three has no meaning. Since the arrangement within each group of three is 3! or 6 ways, the number of permutations of the 6 people selected 3 at a time is 6 times too large. Hence the number of combinations or possible ways of selecting a committee of 3 people from 6 people is $^{120}/_{6} = 20$.

12. A way of calculating the number of combinations

We denote the number of combinations of r objects that can be selected from n objects by

$$C_{n,r}$$

We know that the number of permutations possible using n objects r at a time is

$$P_{n,r} = \frac{n!}{(n-r)!}$$

We have also seen that within a group or combination the arrangements or orders are not important and are not considered. That is, *abcd* is the same group as *bdca* or *dcab*. Since the number of possible arrangements within each combination or group of r objects is $r!$, the number of permutations $P_{n,r}$ is $r!$ times the number of combinations. That is,

$$P_{n,r} = r!C_{n,r}$$

And we may write

$$C_{n,r} = \frac{P_{n,r}}{r!} = \frac{n!}{r!(n-r)!} \tag{5}$$

Example 1. Find the number of straight lines that may be drawn through 10 points no 3 of which lie on the same line.

Solution. Since a line is determined by two points, and since the order of the choice of the points is immaterial, the problem is clearly one of finding the number of combinations of 10 objects taken 2 at a time. Thus we need to find the value of

$$C_{10,2} = \frac{P_{10,2}}{2!} = \frac{10!}{8!2!} = \frac{1 \cdot 2 \cdot 3 \cdot 4 \cdot 5 \cdot 6 \cdot 7 \cdot 8 \cdot 9 \cdot 10}{1 \cdot 2 \cdot 3 \cdot 4 \cdot 5 \cdot 6 \cdot 7 \cdot 8 \cdot 1 \cdot 2} = 45$$

Example 2. In how many ways can a hand of 13 cards be drawn from the usual pack of 52 cards so as to contain precisely 5 spades?

Solution. Any 5 of the 13 spades might be drawn, and this can be done in $C_{13,5}$ ways. But the other 8 cards may be any 8 of the 39 clubs, diamonds, or hearts. These 8 cards can be drawn in $C_{39,8}$ ways. Each set of 5 spades can go with any set of the 8 other cards. Hence the total number of hands possible is

$$C_{13,5} \times C_{39,8} = \frac{13!}{8!5!} \times \frac{39!}{31! \times 8!} = 71{,}843{,}726{,}136$$

—an enormous number!!

EXERCISES

1. Calculate

$$C_{25,4} \qquad C_{10,3} \qquad C_{7,3} \qquad C_{8,8} \qquad C_{5,5}$$

2. What is the essential difference between permutations and combinations?

3. How many straight lines are determined by five points on a circle? Check by actually counting the number.

4. A club has 12 members. How many committees of 4 members may be chosen?

5. On an examination, a student is asked to answer any 10 questions out of 12 questions. In how many ways may the student choose the questions?

6. If you were to choose any three pictures from a collection of nine, all different, how many choices would you have?

7. A box contains 10 different colored balls. How many sets of 3 can be taken from the box?

8. If a student must answer 10 questions true or false, how many combinations of answers to the 10 questions are possible?

9. How many different recitation schedules could a student make if he registered for three out of five elective subjects which meet at different times?

10. Find the number of different poker hands of 5 cards that one can draw from a deck of 52 cards.

11. How many different bridge hands can be dealt? Express your answer and estimate the magnitude of your answer.

12. If one draws 5 balls at random from a bag containing 11 red and 6 white balls, in how many ways may one get 3 red and 2 white balls?

13. If one draws 8 cards from a pile containing 12 spades and 9 hearts, in how many ways may he get 3 spades and 5 hearts?

14. A committee to consider labor-management problems is to be made up of 3 outsiders, 3 employers, and 3 workers and is to be selected from 10 employers, 40 workers, and 7 outsiders. In how many ways can this committee be made up?

15. How many batting orders for a baseball team are possible if the pitcher bats last and the three outfielders bat at the head of batting order?

??????????? PROBLEM JUST FOR FUN ???????????

Farmer Brown owns a farm which is 20 acres in area and is a square. Near each corner stands a large oak tree which is on a neighbor's land. Mr. Brown desires to add to his farm so as to have a farm of 40 acres which is a square, but he does not want to buy the land upon which the four trees stand. How may he accomplish this?

???????????????? JUST FOR FUN ????????????????

13. More problems on probability

We have learned a method for determining the number of arrangements that can be made from a group of objects without enumerating these arrangements. We are now ready to solve problems in probability when the number of ways that an event can happen or fail to happen is large.

Example 1. If 5 balls are drawn at random from a bag containing 7 red and 6 black balls, what is the chance of drawing precisely 3 red balls?

Solution. Any one of the 7 red balls can be drawn, and the number of different sets of 3 red balls that can be drawn from the 7 red balls is $C_{7,3}$. The other 2 (out of the 5 drawn) must be black, and these black balls can be drawn from the 6 black balls in $C_{6,2}$ ways. The total number of ways we can draw 5 balls, 3 of which are red and 2 of which are black, is $C_{7,3} \times C_{6,2}$. The total possible number of ways of drawing 5 balls from the 13 balls is $C_{13,5}$. Using the definition of probability, we find that the probability of drawing to produce 3 red balls is

$$p = \frac{C_{7,3} \times C_{6,2}}{C_{13,5}} = \frac{\dfrac{7!}{3!4!} \times \dfrac{6!}{2!4!}}{\dfrac{13!}{5!8!}} = \frac{175}{429} = \frac{2}{5} \text{ approximately}$$

There are approximately 2 chances in 5 to pick the 5 balls so that 3 are red.

Example 2. Three cards are drawn from a suit of 13 cards.

a. What is the chance that neither king nor queen is drawn?

b. What is the chance that a king or queen is drawn, one or both?

Solution.

a. The total number of ways of drawing 3 cards from a suit of 13 cards is

$$C_{13,3}$$

There are 11 cards in the suit other than the king or queen. Hence, there are $C_{11,3}$ ways of drawing 3 cards which include neither the king nor the queen. Therefore the chance of drawing neither the king nor the queen is

$$p = \frac{C_{11,3}}{C_{13,3}} = \frac{15}{26}$$

b. This event can occur when the event described in (*a*) fails to occur. Hence the required probability is

$$1 - {}^{15}\!/_{26} = {}^{11}\!/_{26}$$

EXERCISES

1. What is the probability of drawing five hearts from an ordinary deck of playing cards?

2. What is the chance of selecting a man when choosing one person by lot from a group of seven men and five women?

3. In selecting 5 persons for a committee out of a group of 15 men and 10 women,

a. What is the probability that four men and one woman will be selected?

b. What is the probability that three men and two women will be selected?

4. If a person draws 5 cards from a deck of 52 cards, what is the chance that

a. All will be red?

b. All will be hearts?

c. Three will be red and two black?

d. Three will be hearts and two spades?

e. Precisely three will be hearts?

??????????? PROBLEM JUST FOR FUN ???????????

"When you toss a coin to decide who is going to pay the check, let your companion do the calling. 'Heads' is called seven times out of ten. The simple law of averages gives the man who listens a tremendous advantage." (Henry Hoyns, quoted by Bennett Cerf in *The Saturday Review of Literature*.)

Is Mr. Hoyns correct?

???????????????? JUST FOR FUN ????????????????

14. Compound probabilities

Most complex problems in probability are solved by determining the probabilities of their simpler parts. We can see the ideas easily by considering two questions when dice are cast. We ask "What is the probability that in two throws a 5 will show both times?" There are six possible cases on the first throw, and one shows a 5, so the probability of a 5 on the first throw is $1/6$. Similarly the probability of a 5 on the second throw is $1/6$. How may we combine these two simple probabilities to answer our question? As we demand that both happen, the probability is $1/6 \times 1/6 = 1/36$. Each of the six possible throws on the first die may be followed by any one of the six on the second throw, so there are a total of 36 equally probable throws. Only the throw of 5, followed by a throw of 5, is a success for our problem. Thus $1/36$ is the correct probability. We may also see this by writing out the cases:

1,1	1,2	1,3	1,4	1,5	1,6
2,1	2,2	2,3	2,4	2,5	2,6
3,1	3,2	3,3	3,4	3,5	3,6
4,1	4,2	4,3	4,4	4,5	4,6
5,1	5,2	5,3	5,4	**5,5**	5,6
6,1	6,2	6,3	6,4	6,5	6,6

We may ask "What is the probability of an even number on one throw?" This may occur with a 2, 4, or 6. The probability of each one is $1/6$. Any one gives an even number, or a success. Then the probability of an even number on one throw is $1/6 + 1/6 + 1/6 = 1/2$. We may verify this by counting cases.

These two types of compound probabilities are stated as theorems:

Theorem I. The probability that two independent events will both happen is equal to the product of their separate probabilities.

Theorem II. The probability that one or the other of two mutually exclusive events will happen is equal to the sum of their separate probabilities.

Example 1. Two equally matched tennis players, Smith and Jones, play three sets. What is the probability that Smith will win all three sets?

Solution. The probability that Smith will win any given set is $1/2$. Then the probability that Smith will win all three sets is

$$1/2 \times 1/2 \times 1/2 = 1/8$$

Example 2. What is the probability of drawing 2 red balls in succession from a bag containing 6 black and 5 red balls?

Solution. The probability of drawing a red ball is $\frac{5}{5+6} = \frac{5}{11}$. We may then propose the solution $\frac{5}{11} \times \frac{5}{11} = \frac{25}{121}$. This is correct if whatever ball is drawn the first time is replaced in the bag before the second draw. In this way the second draw is "independent" of what color ball is drawn on the first draw. But if the ball is not replaced, the second draw is not an "independent event" as stated in Theorem I, for the number of red and black balls will depend on the color of the first draw. If a red ball has been drawn, there remain 6 black and 4 red balls, and the probability of drawing a red ball is $\frac{4}{6+4} = \frac{2}{5}$. Then the probability of drawing two red balls in succession, if the first ball drawn is not replaced, is $\frac{5}{11} \times \frac{2}{5} = \frac{2}{11}$.

Example 3. An employment agency has 100 names listed. Twelve are typists, 7 are bookkeepers, and 4 others are both typists and bookkeepers. If a name is drawn at random, what is the probability that it will be a typist or a bookkeeper?

Solution. The probability that it will be a typist is $\frac{12+4}{100} = \frac{16}{100}$. The probability that it will be a bookkeeper is $\frac{7+4}{100} = \frac{11}{100}$. But the correct answer is not $\frac{16}{100} + \frac{11}{100}$, for these cases are not "mutually exclusive." To make the events mutually exclusive, we must seek the probability that the name selected will be a bookkeeper that is *not* a typist. This is $7/100$ and our correct answer from Theorem II is

$$16/100 + 7/100 = 23/100$$

Example 4. What is the probability of throwing at least one 5 on two throws of a die?

Solution. On one throw the probability is $1/6$. Checking the cases enumerated at the beginning of this section, we see that the solution is $11/36$ and not $1/6 + 1/6 = 1/3$. We see the events are not "mutually exclusive," for one case gives a throw of 5 each time. However, we may use the theorems to solve the problem in this manner: The probability of throwing a 5 on the first throw is $1/6$. If this happens we do not need the second throw. But the probability that we do not get a 5 on the first throw is $5/6$. In this case we try the second throw, and the probability of a 5 is $1/6$. By Theorem I, the probability of a failure on the first throw *and* a success on the second throw is $5/6 \times 1/6 = 5/36$. Then the probability of a 5 in two throws, that is, a success on the first throw *or* a failure followed by a success on the second throw, is $\frac{1}{6} + \frac{5}{36} = \frac{11}{36}$ by Theorem II. This checks with the solution found by counting cases.

EXERCISES

1. What is the probability that a coin tossed three times will fall heads all three times?

2. On a Saturday in May the Wisconsin and Northwestern baseball and track teams are competing against each other. The probability that the Wisconsin baseball team will win its game is $\frac{2}{3}$. The chance that the Wisconsin track team will win its meet is $\frac{1}{4}$. What is the probability that both Wisconsin teams will win?

3. One box contains five white and three black balls, and a second box contains seven white and five black balls. At random a person selects one box and draws one ball. What is the probability that it will be drawn from the first box and be white?

4. Now suppose all the balls are dumped into one box and one ball is drawn at random. What is the probability that it is white? Compare with Prob. 3.

5. In Prob. 4, what is the probability of drawing two white balls in succession if the first ball drawn is not replaced?

6. What is the probability of throwing an even number with a die if we have two tries?

??????????? PROBLEM JUST FOR FUN ???????????

A grocer sells a pound of sugar to two customers, but his balance scale has arms which are not quite the same length. The first time he puts the weight in one pan and the sugar in the other; the second time he reverses the procedure. Does he gain or lose?

?? ?????????????? JUST FOR FUN ?????????????????

15. Mathematical expectation

An important use of the theory of probability is the determination of the mathematical value of a person's expectation. If a person wagers that a certain event will happen, *the mathematical value of his expectation* is defined as the product of the probability that an event occurs and the value of the prize the person receives if he wins.

If a person pays an amount to take part in a game of chance, and if this amount is more than the value of his expectation, he has made a bad deal. If this person continues to gamble and to pay more than his mathematical expectation, he will end up in the red on Skid Row.

Example. A person pays 20 cents to draw a card from a well-shuffled deck of cards. He is to receive $2 is he draws an ace. Is he paying too much for this chance?

Solution. The probability of drawing an ace is $\frac{4}{52}$ and his expectation is $\frac{4}{52} \times 2 = \frac{2}{13}$ of a dollar, or approximately 16 cents. This person pays too much for the chance to play.

EXERCISES

1. A person is to receive $5 if he tosses two coins and they both come up heads. What is the value of his expectation?

2. A person pays $1.25 for the privilege of drawing three balls from a box known to contain five white and four black balls and is to receive $10 if he draws three black balls. Does he pay too much for this privilege?

3. In a lottery, 1,000 tickets are sold for 10 cents each. A prize worth $25 is to be paid to the person holding the lucky number. Do these lottery tickets cost too much?

4. A fancy bedspread valued at $50 is to be raffled off at a church bazaar. If 250 chances at 25 cents per chance are sold, is this price too high?

5. A person is to receive 10 cents if he throws a total of 8 using 2 dice. What should he pay to play?

??????????? PROBLEM JUST FOR FUN ???????????

A carnival spieler shows his audience three cards. One card is red on both sides; one blue on both sides; and one red on one side and blue on the other. He has one of his audience shuffle the cards and place one on the table in such a way that no one knows what color is on the bottom side. The top side is red. The spieler says: "Obviously this is not the blue-blue card. Then it is either the red-red card or the red-blue card. I will bet even money that it is the red-red card." Is this a fair bet?

???????????????? JUST FOR FUN ????????????????

CHAPTER

18

Introduction to Statistics

(Figures Don't Lie but Liars Do Figure)

Battalions of figures are like battalions of men, not always as strong as is supposed. M. SAGE.

1. Empirical probability

In Chap. 17, we found the probability of an event by determining the exact number of ways the particular event could happen or fail to happen. But the mathematician is also interested in determining the probability of an event in problems for which he cannot enumerate the number of ways the event could happen or fail. For this type of problem the probability must be determined by an actual examination of particular cases.

For example, a firm which is manufacturing men's shirts would like to know the probability that a potential customer wears a collar size of 16, in order to know how many shirts of this collar size to make. The way this probability can be determined is to find experimentally the collar size of the shirts worn by a large number of men who are selected at random from potential consumers so as not to favor a special class. If b men out of N men in a group wear a 16 collar size, the probability that another man selected at random from this group would wear a 16 collar is b/N.

Probabilities which are determined by an actual examination of the particular cases are called *empirical.*

The insurance companies base many of their calculations upon empirical probability. The data are contained in mortality tables which are based upon case records. This table applies to large groups of people and furnishes no surety to an individual person.

Table 39 is based upon 1,000,000 people observed from their first birthday until death. From the table, we see that 971,804 live to the age of ten. Then the empirical probability that a person age one will live to age ten is

$$\frac{971{,}804}{1{,}000{,}000} = 0.972 = 97.2\%$$

TABLE 39

At age	Number surviving	At age	Number surviving
1	1,000,000	60	677,771
10	971,804	70	454,548
20	951,483	75	315,982
25	939,197	80	181,765
30	924,609	85	78,221
35	906,554	90	21,577
40	883,342	95	3,011
50	810,900	99	125

The empirical probability that a person age one will live to be twenty-five is

$$\frac{939{,}197}{1{,}000{,}000} = 0.939 = 93.9\%$$

The empirical probability that a person age twenty-five will live to be thirty-five is

$$\frac{906{,}554}{939{,}179} = 0.965 = 96.5\%$$

EXERCISES

1. What is the probability that a person age forty will not live to age sixty?

2. What is the probability that a person age eighty will live another 10 years?

3. Of 7,820 men attending a certain university, 5,432 were under 6 feet in height. What is the probability that a man chosen at random from this group will be 6 feet or taller?

4. In a certain community there were 8,932 children under five years of age. If 6,280 were girls, what is the probability that a child chosen at random from this group will be a boy? A girl?

??????????? PROBLEM JUST FOR FUN ???????????

Find the numbers which are represented by asterisks in the following problem in division:

```
            * * 8 * *
      * * | * * * * * * * *
            * * *
            -----
                  * *
                  * *
                  ---
                    * * *
                    * * *
                    -----
```

??????????????? JUST FOR FUN ???????????????

5. In a certain community there are 4,806 people forty years of age. According to Table 39, what is the probable number of people who will live to reach fifty, sixty, seventy, and ninety, if the people in this community are typical of the group in the table?

2. The field of statistics

The determination of empirical probability must be made by an examination of a number of cases which have been selected at random from a large group and which are considered representative of the larger group. It is assumed that an empirical probability will approach a true and unknown probability as the number of observed cases increases.

We find that we must work with a collection of data which may contain many items. The general problems of accumulating, summarizing, and interpreting such data are included in the *field of statistics.* The bounds of mathematical statistics are not sharply defined, but we will regard the field as including all the mathematics applied to the analysis of quantitative data obtained from observation.

This branch of mathematics is of interest because of the numerous and varied applications of statistics. We are bombarded daily with statistical information on the radio and in newspapers and magazines. Statistics may be encountered in articles on economics, education, politics, social, biological, and physical science, business, etc.

3. The two basic problems of mathematical statistics

A statistician who has been given a set of measurements obtained by observation is usually asked (*a*) to summarize, analyze and interpret this data; or (*b*) to draw conclusions about the whole *population* or *universe* from which the set of measurements was obtained.

In case (*a*), the data may or may not include the whole population, but in case (*b*), the available data is usually a small fraction of the population. In either case, the observed data must have been collected accurately if the statistical worker is to be able to give a valid report. In the second case, it is essential that the relatively few observations that the statistician uses be a *random sample* of the universe under consideration. We say that an object is selected randomly from a population whenever each object in the population has an equal chance of being selected. A set of such selections is called a *random sample.* It is not an easy task to ensure that a sample be truly a random sample, although various means have been devised to accomplish this.

Many tools and techniques have been developed for summarizing, analyzing, and interpreting data obtained from observations. There are also a large number of techniques for drawing conclusions about a population on the basis of the information given by a random sample. We shall study a few of the more common techniques and fundamental ideas of both phases of statistics.

The data with which the statistician works must be accurately and legitimately obtained. The statistician must be extremely careful in all computations that he makes. Actually, this computation is only arithmetical in nature, but it is often so involved and lengthy that mechanical computers and automatic calculating machines are used.

We must keep in mind that even if the data are faultlessly collected and the computations are errorless, the conclusions and interpretations drawn from this data may be incorrect and distorted. Sometimes this happens because the statistical worker is ill-informed, and sometimes because he presents a misleading report of his work. The latter case gives rise to the common statement that "a statistician can make the figures show whatever he pleases." One objective of our study will be to observe how one can be led to fallacious conclusions concerning the measurements under study.

One study of graduates of Princeton University showed an average of 1.8 children per graduate. A similar study of graduates of Wellesley College showed 1.3 children per graduate. One careless observer concluded from these figures that men had more children than women!

4. Types of problems

Let us look at some examples of the two broad problems of mathematical statistics named in Sec. 3 and the questions we might be called upon to answer. We shall assume that we know some of the fundamentals of mathematical statistics.

Example 1. In their first 18 games, the 1949–1950 Purdue basketball players who played in 12 or more of the 18 games attempted the number of free throws shown in Table 40 (data taken from the *Purdue Exponent*, Feb. 15, 1950).

TABLE 40

Williams	67	Westall	24
Axness	96	Greiner	21
Butchko	143	Banks	23
Horn	26	Price	4
Brewster	37	Butterfield	27

Question. What can one say about this squad *as a group* concerning the number of free throws attempted?

Example 2. Thirty students in a mathematics class made the test grades shown in Table 41.

TABLE 41

78	63	92	48	80	74
96	85	71	90	87	82
58	67	58	70	49	72
34	75	74	76	86	67
77	83	62	52	60	57

Question. How can these data be summarized, and what can be said about the class as a whole?

Example 3. A random sample of 200 voters in Tippecanoe County showed that 55% of them were Democratic.

Question. Does this fact disprove the statement that "Tippecanoe County is predominantly Republican"?

Example 4. The average grade point index of a random sample of 50 fraternity members was 3.84 and was 3.96 for a random sample of 40 independent students.

Question. Do these figures show that the independent students do better in their academic work than the organized students?

5. Average—the measure of central tendency

Usually the first step in the analysis of a set of observations is to find a single number which is more or less representative of all the observations. This single number is called an *average, or measure of central tendency.* There are a number of different kinds of average, but we shall consider just three of them.

Let us look at the data in Table 40. If we add the 10 observations given in the table and divide the result by 10, we obtain 46.8, which is the *arithmetic mean* average, or simply the *mean* of the 10 figures. Likewise, we find that the *mean* grade for the grades given in Table 41 is 70.8.

It is conventional to assign some letters, say, x, to the data. We indicate the first figure by x_1, the second by x_2, etc. Each observation is designated by x_i, where $i = 1, 2, 3, 4, \ldots$. Then we use $\bar{x}$ to represent the arithmetic mean of all the data represented by the letter x_i. In using the arithmetic mean we have each time to write the sum of the terms x_i. This becomes tiresome, so we shorten the task by using the symbol Σ to represent the sum of terms following, or

$$\sum_{i=1}^{N} x_i = x_1 + x_2 + x_3 + x_4 + \cdots + x_N$$

The symbol Σ is the Greek letter for S and thus suggests "sum." We read the symbol above as "sum of the x_i's from $i = 1$ to N."

Example 1. If $x_i = i$, then

$$\sum_{i=1}^{5} x_i = x_1 + x_2 + x_3 + x_4 + x_5$$
$$= 1 + 2 + 3 + 4 + 5 = 15$$

Example 2. If $x_i = i^2$

$$\sum_{i=1}^{4} x_i = x_1 + x_2 + x_3 + x_4$$
$$= 1 + 4 + 9 + 16 = 30$$

Then the *arithmetic mean*, or *mean*, is given by

$$\bar{x} = \frac{1}{N}\sum_{i=1}^{N} x_i = \frac{x_1 + x_2 + x_3 + \cdots + x_N}{N} \tag{1}$$

For the data in Table 40,

$$\bar{x} = \frac{1}{10}\sum_{i=1}^{10} x_i = \frac{468}{10} = 46.8 \text{ free-throw attempts}$$

The arithmetic mean is the most commonly used average. However, if we used the arithmetic mean of 46.8 to represent the free-throw attempts made by each member of the squad, we should be misled by its value. In this example, this average does not represent the individual members of the squad very well, because the one extreme value of 143 in the data raised the value of the mean average out of proportion. We observe that there are only four men on the squad who attempted more than 30 free throws.

Whenever we wish to avoid the undue influence of extreme values in the set of observations, we use the *median* average, or simply the *median*, to represent the set. To find the median of a set of numbers, we arrange the numbers in order from the smallest to the largest, and the median is the middle number in the array. When there are an even number of observations, by convention, we take the median as being halfway between the two middle values. For the values in Table 40 we have 143, 96, 67, 37, 27, 26, 24, 23, 21, 4, and the median is 26.5. Notice that this is more representative of the whole set of x's.

Sometimes we use a third measure of central tendency, which is called the *mode*. The mode of a set of observations is simply that value which occurs most frequently. Sometimes a set of observations does not have a mode, and sometimes it has more than one mode. For the data in Table 40 there is no mode.

Often the mode is more useful than either the mean or the median. For example, a collar manufacturer may find it more useful to know that more men wear 15 collar size than any other collar size than to know that the mean collar size is 15.2865.

EXERCISES

1. Find the value of $\sum_{i=1}^{N} x_i$,

a. When $x_i = i$ and $N = 8$
b. When $x_i = i^3$ and $N = 4$
c. When $x_i = i - 1$ and $N = 7$
d. When $x_i = i^2 - i$ and $N = 5$

2. Find the value of the arithmetic mean

$$\bar{x} = \frac{1}{N} \sum_{i=1}^{N} x_i$$

a. When $x_i = i$ and $N = 10$
b. When $x_i = i^2$ and $N = 5$
c. When $x_i = i + 10$ and $N = 8$
d. When $x_i = 4$ and $N = 10$

3. Do you see that the median is free from the influence of extreme values in the data? Explain.

4. Find the median for the set of grades given in Table 41 (page 181).

5. Does the median found in Prob. 4 give a better representation of the data in Table 41 than the mean? Explain.

6. In a recent "Letter to the Editor" in a newspaper, a telephone-company worker complained that although the company asserted that the "average" pay of its employees was $90 per week, he got only $72 per week and was the highest paid man in his department. What are the possibilities for accounting for this apparent discrepancy?

7. Take a group of 10 coins and toss the group 25 times. After each toss count the number of heads. Prepare a table showing the number of times you obtained 0, 1, 2, 3, . . . 9, and 10 heads. Find the mode for your data.

8. Count the number of words in each line of page 175 of this book. Arrange your data to show the number of lines having 1, 2, 3, . . . words. Find mean, mode, and median for your data. Which average best describes the data?*

* Footnote on page 184.

??????????? PROBLEM JUST FOR FUN ???????????

An army officer decided to arrange his men to form a solid square. He found that he had 27 men left over. When the officer increased the number of men on a side by 1, he found that 30 additional men were needed to complete the square. How many men did the officer have?

???????????????? JUST FOR FUN ????????????????

6. Variability of data—standard deviation

Usually it is not enough to give only the average value of a set of observations.

Let us consider another basketball squad of 10 men that had attempted the number of free throws shown in Table 42.

TABLE 42

A	73	F	25
B	55	G	63
C	32	H	69
D	28	I	51
E	29	J	43

The mean of this set is 46.8, which is the same as the mean for the data in Table 40 for the Purdue squad. But when we compare these two basketball squads, we find a striking difference between them when we notice how scattered, or variable, the two sets of data are. The range of free-throw attempts for the Purdue squad was 4 to 143 and for the other squad 25 to 73. This is the simplest way of showing the variability of the data. Whenever we use an average to summarize a set of data, we should also give the extent to which the values in the set of data vary among themselves. In fact, variability is the essence of statistics. If there were no variability, there would be nothing to study about the data, because the knowledge of the one item would then tell the entire story.

The variability or dispersion in a set of observations is usually measured by the *standard deviation*. The standard deviation is a measure of the average of the amounts that the individual numbers deviate from the mean of all the observations. If x_i represents one observation, and the mean $\bar{x}$, calculated by equation (1) of Sec. 5, is the mean of a set of N observations, then the deviation of the observation x_i from the mean

* Notice that the instruction for gathering these data is not precise. To make it precise we must agree on what a word is. Is a numeral such as 1.8 counted? Is a hyphenated word such as "ill-informed" counted as one word or two? Where is a word which is divided between two lines counted? One of the fundamental requirements of good statistics is that it be made perfectly clear how the data are to be gathered.

is $x_i - \bar{x}$. In order to find the average of all the deviations, we cannot add them and divide by N, because we should always get zero for an answer no matter how variable the data might be. Explain why this is so.

Since some of the deviations will be plus and some minus, we shall square each of the deviations and obtain the average of the squares of the deviation. This number is called the mean square average, or *variance* of the data. The measure of variability that is most often used is the square root of the variance and is called the root mean square (rms), average deviation, or *standard deviation* of the data.

$$\sigma_x = \text{standard deviation of the } x\text{'s} = \sqrt{\frac{1}{N}\sum_{i=1}^{N}(x_i - \bar{x})^2}. \qquad (2)$$

In general, the average along with the standard deviation will summarize the information contained in a small set of observations. In a later section we shall discuss further the use of the standard deviation.

For the data in Table 40, the mean is 46.8. Calculating the variance and standard deviation, we get the results shown in Table 43.

TABLE 43

Player	x_i	$x_i - \bar{x}$	$(x_i - \bar{x})^2$
Williams	67	20.2	408.04
Axness	96	49.2	2,420.64
Butchko	143	96.2	9,254.44
Horn	26	−20.8	432.64
Brewster	37	− 9.8	96.04
Westall	24	−22.8	519.84
Greiner	21	−25.8	665.64
Banks	23	−23.8	566.44
Price	4	−42.8	1,831.84
Butterfield	27	−19.8	392.04

$$\sum_{i=1}^{10}(x_i - \bar{x})^2 = 16{,}587.60$$

$$\text{Variance} = \sigma^2_x = 1{,}658.76$$

$$\text{Standard deviation} = \sigma_x = \sqrt{1658.76} = 40.73$$

EXERCISES

1. Calculate the standard deviation for the data in Table 42.
2. What conclusions can you draw from the data in Tables 40 and 42?
3. Calculate the standard deviation for the data in Table 41 (page 181).

4. Calculate the standard deviation for the data in Prob. 7, page 183.

5. If each coin used is just as likely to fall heads as tails, it can be shown that the mean number of heads of a large number of tosses of 10 coins will be 5 and that the standard deviation will be $\frac{1}{2}\sqrt{10}$. Compare your mean and standard deviation in Prob. 4 with these theoretical results.

??????????? PROBLEM JUST FOR FUN ???????????

A commuter train leaves New York fairly well filled. At the first stop half of the passengers get off and 12 new passengers board the train. At the second stop half the passengers leave the train and 8 people climb aboard. At the third stop again half leave the train and 10 board the train. At the fourth stop half leave the train and 4 board the train. At the fifth stop half leave as before but only 2 new passengers appear. At the sixth and last stop 14 passengers leave the train. How many passengers were on the commuter train when it left New York?

???????????????? JUST FOR FUN ????????????????

CHAPTER

19

Frequencies and Distributions

(*Grouping the Data*)

> It is a truth very certain that, when it is not in our power to determine what is true, we ought to follow what is most probable.
>
> René Descartes

1. Types of statistical data

The data with which we are concerned in mathematical statistics are obtained by making (*a*) measurements or (*b*) counts.

Measurements. Scientists need to measure accurately the magnitude of the physical quantities with which they work, for example, the weight and physical dimensions of objects, the strength of an electric current, the distance between two points, the charge on the electron, the mass of the atom, etc. Many of us would be inclined to make a single measurement and to accept this value as being the correct value. For careful scientific work, however, a number of independent measurements are made under the same conditions, and an average of these measurements is taken as the correct value. Any attempt to measure the magnitude of a quantity is subject to error. The error is the difference between the unknown real or correct value and the measured value. But we have no way of knowing what the correct value is, and no one measurement is exactly correct except by chance. The chance errors in measurement are such that some of the measurements are too large and some of them are too small. If we have many measurements, the positive and negative errors will tend to balance each other. In contrast to chance errors, we have errors which persist and are always in the same direction. For example, if a grocer's scales are out of adjustment and read 1 pound when 15 ounces is placed on the pan, the error in any number of weighings will always be in the same direction. If a clock runs too fast we will not get a correct measurement of time, since the errors will all be in the same direction. Such errors are called persistent error, constant error, or biased error. Biased error can sometimes be discovered and eliminated, but random error can never be eliminated, although its effect may be reduced by taking a large number of observations or measurements.

Counts. Other data may be obtained by counting, and these data seem to be different from those obtained by measurement. If we say that there are 25 students in a mathematics class, the figure 25 is supposed to be absolutely exact and not an approximation. But in practice this distinction is more apparent than real, for there are many probable causes of error in a count, and when the numbers involved are large, the counts are only approximations. If a city decides to determine its population by an actual count, the count will give only an approximation of the population, because the population will be different at different times of the day, and some people will not be counted at all while others may be counted twice.

The statistical data which have been collected are classified as either (*a*) discrete or (*b*) continuous.

Distributions of data in which only certain values are possible are called *discrete.* For example, if we were listing the number of rooms in the houses in a certain district, we would get 5-room houses or 4-room houses, but there would be no house with 4.6 rooms. If the data listed the number of bets made at the $2, $5, $10, and $20 windows at a horse race, no bet of $7.50 could be listed.

In contrast to discrete distributions, we may have *continuous distributions,* in which any intermediate value may occur. For example, heights of women do not necessarily fall at 61, 62, or 63 inches or any other particular value. It is possible that a woman be 62.67 inches in height or any other possible value between the tallest and the shortest heights.

With discrete data there is a bunching of values at particular points because no intermediate values can occur. Sometimes we get a similar bunching for continuous data. For example, the U.S. Census Bureau has found that when asked to give his age, a person usually gives whole numbers of years, and that there is a tendency to give ages in multiples of 5 and 10. That is, a person says he is 50 years of age even though he may be 51, 52, 53, or 54 years old. Or even 70!

2. Accuracy of measurements and calculations

If we are required to summarize a set of observations, we should estimate the probable accuracy of the data, whether they have come from measurements or from counts. It may well happen that the observations themselves are stated with spurious accuracy. For example, suppose we are given data which claim to represent the waist measurement of various individuals. We should not be surprised if the numbers were, say, 29 inches, 30.5 inches, 32.75 inches, etc. But if the numbers were given as 29.7128 inches, 30.4157 inches, 33.0182 inches, etc., we should very likely question if it was possible to obtain such apparently accurate measurements. Or if the data claim that a certain city had yearly populations of 43,516, 45,782, 49,103, etc., we might doubt whether these counts could have been taken this accurately.

Assuming that the observed data do possess their claimed accuracy, the person who summarizes the data may give his results with spurious accuracy. For example, if we are told that family incomes for 158 families are $1,800, $2,500, $2,800, $3,600, $2,900, $4,200, etc., the arithmetic mean of these incomes might turn out to be $4,151.898. It is apparent from the original data that these incomes have been given to the nearest $100 and that a reported average of $4,151.898 gives a false impression of the accuracy of the observations. In this case, we could prevent such a situation by giving the average as $4,150, or even $4,200. Although there are no hard and fast rules for rounding off numbers, we should realize that results computed from data are limited by the accuracy of the individual items included in the data.

EXERCISES

Discuss the possibilities for spurious accuracy in the following statements concerning observed data.

1. The population of the United States in 1940 was 132,322,408.

2. The average height of 63 students is 66.312581 inches.

3. The indebtedness of the United States government on Mar. 29, 1950, was $255,745,196,000.

4. A newspaper report says that "the exact center of United States population in 1940 was on top of a fence post in a southern Indiana county."

5. In 1808 Alexander Wilson said that he saw a great flight of 2,230,272,000 pigeons pass over Kentucky in 4 hours.

??????????? PROBLEM JUST FOR FUN ???????????

When Barnacle Bill and his pals leave ship to go ashore, it is low tide and they climb down 12 rungs of the ship's ladder to reach the small boat. When they come back about 6 hours later, it is high tide. If the water level has risen 9 feet and the rungs of the ladder are 18 inches apart, how many rungs do Bill and his pals have to climb to get aboard?

???????????????? JUST FOR FUN ????????????????

3. Arrangement and presentation of data—frequency distribution

Whenever there are a large number of observations to be considered, the statistical worker reduces the bulkiness of the data by classifying them into a *frequency table,* or *frequency distribution.* The data are separated into groups or *classes* which are usually represented by their *class marks.* A *class mark* is the mid-point of the class or group, and it is assumed that all the values in a class are either at the class mark or evenly distributed throughout the class. A count or tally is made to determine the number of observations in each class.

We shall use the data in Table 41 (page 181) to illustrate the procedure. Let us take 10 as the *class interval* and take as a class those grades which start with the same digits. The first and last elements in the classes are 30 and 39, 40 and 49, 50 and 59, etc. The class marks are 35, 45, 55, etc. Table 44 gives the frequency with which the grades fall within the limits of each class.

TABLE 44

Class limits	*Class mark*	*Frequency tally*	*Frequency*
30–39	35	1	1
40–49	45	11	2
50–59	55	1111	4
60–69	65	~~1111~~	5
70–79	75	~~1111~~ 1111	9
80–89	85	~~1111~~ 1	6
90–99	95	111	3

It is apparent that if we group the data into too few classes, that is, make the class width too large, we gain simplicity but lose detail and information. There is a danger of using too few or too many classes. When we use a few classes, the number of cases in each class is enough so that the erratic variations tend to disappear and the pattern of the distribution becomes plainer. Of course, we can go too far and choose too few classes so that no pattern at all is evident. If the class widths are too small, we do not have any distribution at all, but we have only "lined up" the numbers in an array.

A statistician wants the number of classes to be large enough so that all the items in a class may reasonably be treated as equal without too much error, and so that the general pattern of the distribution is not obscured.

If the data are discrete, class marks should be permissible observed values. If we were to make a frequency distribution of the number of theater tickets which sell for 15, 40, 50, and 60 cents, we would not select 32.5 cents as a class mark, because no ticket was sold at this price. If the data are continuous, the value of the class marks depends on whether the class limits are regarded as rounded-off values or as not rounded off. For example, suppose the data concerned the ages of a population. If age twenty represents any age between 19.5 and 20.5, the class limits might be taken as 19.5–24.5, 24.5–29.5, etc., and the class marks would be 22, 27, etc. But if twenty represents the age as of the last birthday, then the actual class limits are 20–24.9, 25–29.9, etc., and the class marks are 22.5, 27.5, etc. The 24.9 means that the class includes all numbers less than 25, but not 25 itself.

4. Relative and cumulative frequency distributions

It is sometimes useful to know the relative and cumulative frequencies of the distribution. The *relative frequency* corresponding to a particular class mark is its frequency divided by the total number of figures in the data. The relative frequency of a test grade between 70 and 79 in Table 44 is $9/30 = 0.3$. Often the relative frequency is expressed in per cent. The *cumulative frequency* of a particular value is the sum of all measurements less than or equal to the given value. The cumulative frequency corresponding to a test grade between 70 and 79 in Table 44 is $1 + 2 + 4 + 5 + 9 = 21$. We may add the relative frequencies to get the *cumulative relative frequency*, which is the cumulative frequency of a particular value divided by the total number of counts. The cumulative relative frequency of the range 70 to 79 is $21/30 = 0.7$. Cumulative relative frequencies must be used if one is to compare two cumulative-frequency curves which are based on different numbers of items.

We shall add these new types of frequencies to the data in Table 44 to get Tables 45 and 46.

TABLE 45

Class limits	*Class mark*	*Frequency*	*Relative frequency*
30–39	35	1	0.03
40–49	45	2	0.07
50–59	55	4	0.13
60–69	65	5	0.17
70–79	75	9	0.30
80–89	85	6	0.20
90–99	95	3	0.10
		30	1.00

TABLE 46

Upper limit	*Cumulative frequency*	*Relative cumulative frequency*
39.5	1	0.03
49.5	3	0.10
59.5	7	0.23
69.5	12	0.40
79.5	21	0.70
89.5	27	0.90
99.5	30	1.00

5. Graphical representation of frequency distributions

The frequency tables are often presented in graphical form, because a graph gives a better visual picture of the distribution than a table. Bar charts, pie charts, etc., are used to show the fluctuations in the original data. Statisticians use the histogram or the frequency polygon to graph a frequency table. The *histogram* is a bar graph with the bars centered over the class marks and with heights equal to the class frequencies. The total of each bar is proportional to the number of observations falling in this class. A *frequency polygon* is a broken-line graph connecting the points whose coordinates are class marks and class frequencies. The frequency polygon is always drawn down to the axis at the class mark of the first empty class. The relative frequency is shown by an appropriate vertical scale on the right side of the figure. Figure 82 is a histogram with a frequency polygon superimposed as a broken dotted line for the data in Table 44.

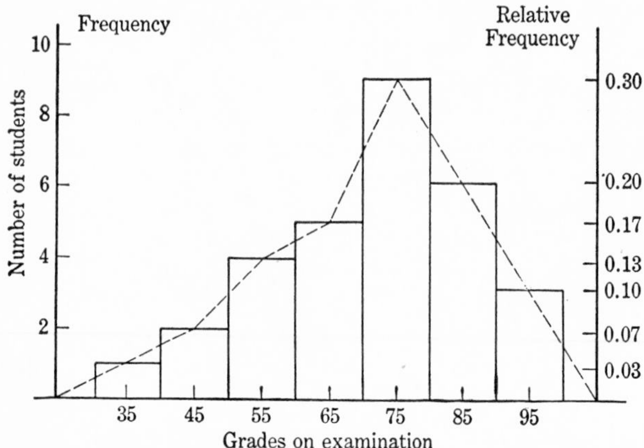

Fig. 82

The histogram is often used for popular presentation of a frequency distribution because it is more striking and causes the individual classes to stand out more clearly. If we need to compare two frequency distributions, the frequency polygons are more effective.

The data in Table 46 are plotted by constructing ordinates at the upper limit of the class boundary. The height of the ordinate is equal to the cumulative frequency. The tops of these ordinates are joined by straight lines. The relative cumulative frequency is shown by an appropriate vertical scale on the right side of the figure. The graph of the cumulative frequency of a distribution is called an *ogive*. Figure 83 is the *ogive* for the data in Table 46.

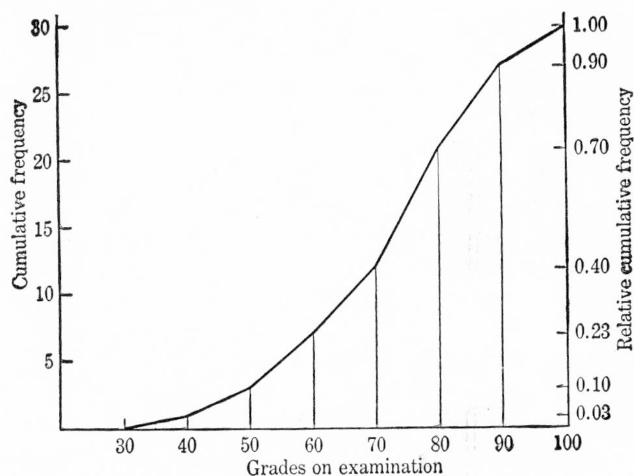

Fig. 83

EXERCISES

1. Make a frequency table for the data in Prob. 8 (page 183).

2. Make a histogram and a frequency polygon for the frequency table in Prob. 1 above.

??????????? PROBLEM JUST FOR FUN ???????????

Prove that the following enrollment data are inconsistent:

1000 total enrollment in college
525 freshmen
312 male students
470 married students
42 male freshmen
147 married freshmen
86 married male students
25 married male freshmen

??????????????? JUST FOR FUN ???????????????

3. Plot the ogive for the cumulative frequency of the data in the frequency table in Prob. 1 above.

4. A class of students tossed eight coins 240 times and obtained the results shown in Table 47. Take the class limits to be $-0.5, 0.5, 1.5, 2.5, \ldots, 7.5, 8.5$. Draw the relative-frequency histogram and relative-cumulative-frequency ogive for this distribution.

TABLE 47

No. of heads in a toss	*No. of times occurring*
0	2
1	11
2	32
3	45
4	65
5	53
6	26
7	5
8	1

5. The data in Table 48 represent 100 measurements of the distance in degrees between the first and last stars in the handle of the big dipper. (These were made by Professor Green at the Haverford College Observatory.) Note that the smallest measurement is 10.82 and the largest is 12.43. The total range, then, is 1.61. Choose class intervals of 10.695–10.895, 10.895–11.095, etc. Make a frequency table for this data. Then construct a histogram and an ogive.

TABLE 48

10.90	11.46	12.06	11.82	12.38
11.30	11.48	11.05	12.19	11.51
10.86	11.90	12.08	11.49	11.31
11.72	11.87	11.10	12.24	11.51
11.74	11.87	11.15	11.12	11.11
11.74	11.48	10.86	11.06	11.68
12.03	10.93	10.89	11.79	11.30
12.28	11.16	11.55	11.91	11.23
11.42	11.60	11.20	11.10	12.22
11.57	12.34	12.24	11.77	11.76
11.71	11.57	11.13	11.43	11.55
11.53	11.48	11.29	11.44	11.34
11.86	11.60	12.04	11.45	11.35
11.80	11.46	11.40	12.30	11.75
11.29	11.85	11.94	11.38	11.52
11.84	12.31	11.77	11.15	12.03
10.82	12.04	12.43	12.00	11.19
10.96	12.24	11.22	11.88	11.66
10.98	11.44	12.09	11.18	12.30
11.78	11.57	11.10	11.93	11.39

6. Averages for grouped data

When working with unclassified data, we found it necessary to give both an average for the data and a measure of the variability of the data.

We should learn also how to give an average for a frequency distribution and a measure of the extent of its variability.

How shall we find an average—mean, mode, or median—for a set of observations which have been grouped into a frequency distribution? The *mode* is defined as that class mark which has the greatest frequency. The mode can be found by noting which class mark is under the highest point on the frequency polygon. For example, from the frequency polygon in Fig. 82 (page 192), we find that 75 is the mode of the data in Table 44. The frequency distribution need not have a mode, or it may have several.

The *median* is defined as that value of the variable which has a relative cumulative frequency of 0.50 or a cumulative frequency of $N/2$.

We can find the median from the *ogive* by locating the point 0.50 on the relative-cumulative-frequency axis, moving parallel to the horizontal axis until we reach a point Q on the ogive, and then moving down to the axis to locate the point x which is the value of the median. The median for the data graphed in Fig. 83 is about 74, and the method of obtaining this value is illustrated in Fig. 84.

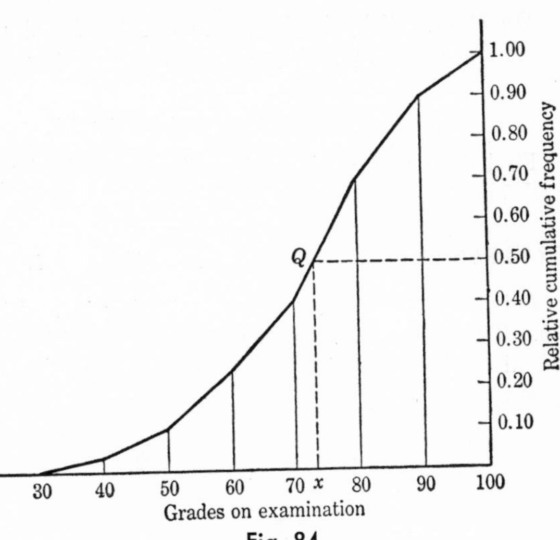

Fig. 84

In order to find the mean from a frequency table, we assume that each class mark x_i ($i = 1, 2, 3, \ldots, k$, where k is the number of classes) represents all the measurements which fall in its class. In order to get the sum of all the observations in a class, we multiply the class mark x_i by the frequency f_i of the class. The mean $\bar{x}$ is the sum of these products $x_i f_i$ ($i = 1, 2, 3, \ldots k$) divided by the total number of observations N.

$$\bar{x} = \frac{1}{N} \sum_{i=1}^{k} x_i f_i \tag{1}$$

where k is the number of classes, and N is given by

$$N = \sum_{i=1}^{k} f_i \tag{2}$$

For the data in Table 44,

$$N = \sum_{i=1}^{7} f_i = 1 + 2 + 4 + 5 + 9 + 6 + 3 = 30$$

$$\sum_{i=1}^{7} x_i f_i = (35)(1) + (45)(2) + (55)(4) + (65)(5) + (75)(9) + (85)(6) + (95)(3) = 2{,}140$$

and

$$\bar{x} = \frac{1}{N}\sum_{i=1}^{k} x_i f_i = \frac{1}{30}\sum_{i=1}^{7} x_i f_i = \frac{2{,}140}{30} = 71.3$$

Question. Why is the mean of 71.3 for the data in Table 44 different from the mean of 70.8 for the same data in Table 41 (page 181)?

EXERCISE

Find the mean, mode, and median from the frequency tables in Probs. 1, 4, and 5 on pages 193-194.

??????????? PROBLEM JUST FOR FUN ???????????

A tribe of Indians use finger reckoning to multiply numbers between 5 and 10. They extend the number of fingers equal to the excess of one number over 5 and do the same with the other number on the other hand. The sum of the

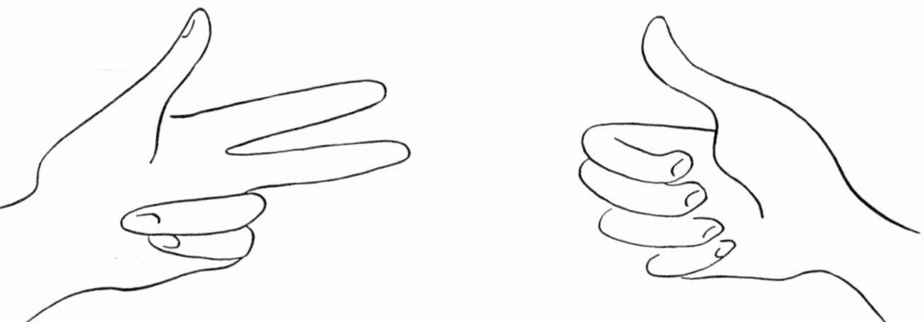

extended fingers gives the first figure of the product, and the product of the unextended fingers gives the second figure. For example, if we wish to multiply 8 times 6 we extend three fingers on one hand and one on the other. These are the excess over 5 of 8 and 6. Then $3 + 1 = 4$ is the sum of the extended fingers, and $2 \times 4 = 8$ is the product of the unextended fingers. We get 4 and 8, or 48, the product of 8 times 6. Can you explain why this Indian finger method is correct?

???????????????? JUST FOR FUN ????????????????

7. Variability of frequency distributions

We shall use the standard deviation to measure the spread, or variability, in a frequency distribution. We must remember that the x's are class marks and that each class mark represents f_i figures. The square of the standard deviation is given by

$$\sigma_x^2 = \frac{(x_1 - \bar{x})^2 f_1 + (x_2 - \bar{x})^2 f_2 + \cdots}{f_1 + f_2 + f_3 + \cdots} = \frac{\sum_{i=1}^{k} (x_i - \bar{x})^2 f_i}{\sum_{i=1}^{k} f_i}$$

The standard deviation σ_x is easily found by extracting the square root of σ_x^2.

Let us calculate σ_x for the data in Table 44. We have found that $\bar{x} = 71.3$ for this data.

TABLE 49

Class marks	*Frequency* f_i	$(x_i - \bar{x})$	$(x_i - \bar{x})^2$	$(x_i - \bar{x})^2 f_i$
35	1	−36.3	1,317.69	1,317.69
45	2	−26.3	691.69	1,383.38
55	4	−16.3	265.69	1,062.76
65	5	− 6.3	39.69	198.45
75	9	3.7	13.69	123.21
85	6	13.7	189.69	1,138.14
95	3	23.7	561.69	1,685.07

$$\sum_{i=1}^{7} f_i = 30 \quad \text{and} \quad \sum_{i=1}^{7} (x_i - \bar{x})^2 f_i = 6{,}908.70$$

$$\sigma_x^2 = \frac{6{,}908.70}{30} = 230.29$$

$$\sigma_x = \sqrt{230.29} = 15.2$$

EXERCISES

1. Find the standard deviation for the frequency distributions in Probs. 1, 4, and 5 on pages 193 194.

2. John measured the length of a field 10 times by pacing. His 10 measurements had a mean of 320 feet, with a standard deviation of 8 feet. George did the same thing and also got a mean length of 320 feet, but the standard deviation of his 10 measurements was 2 feet. Comment.

??????????? PROBLEM JUST FOR FUN ???????????

Which will cost more, a dozen dozen balls at half a dozen dimes a dozen or half a dozen dozen balls at a dozen dimes a half dozen?

??????????????? JUST FOR FUN ???????????????

CHAPTER

20

The Normal Curve and Sampling

(A Question of Distribution)

The most important questions of life are, for the most part, really only problems of probability.
LAPLACE

1. Common shapes of frequency curves

A frequency polygon can assume almost any shape, but statisticians have found from experience that the frequency polygons of most distributions fall into one of a small number of types. The most common of the shapes is found to be humpbacked or bell-shaped, with the larger frequencies occurring near the center and the smaller frequencies occurring at the extreme values of the distributions. Often this mound-shaped distribution is symmetrical about its maximum frequency, that is, the right-hand portion of the frequency polygon is a mirror image of the left-hand portion (see Fig. 85). But sometimes the high point on the frequency polygon is not halfway between the extreme values, and the polygon is said to be skewed. In this case, the frequencies decrease more rapidly on one side of the value of the maximum frequency than on the other side. The two frequency polygons in Fig. 86 are skewed.

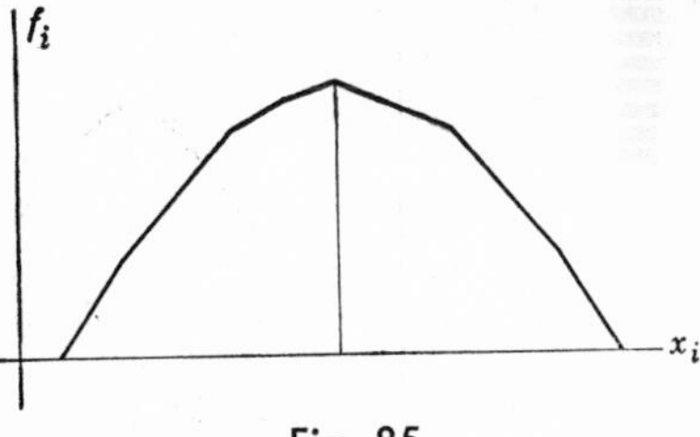

Fig. 85

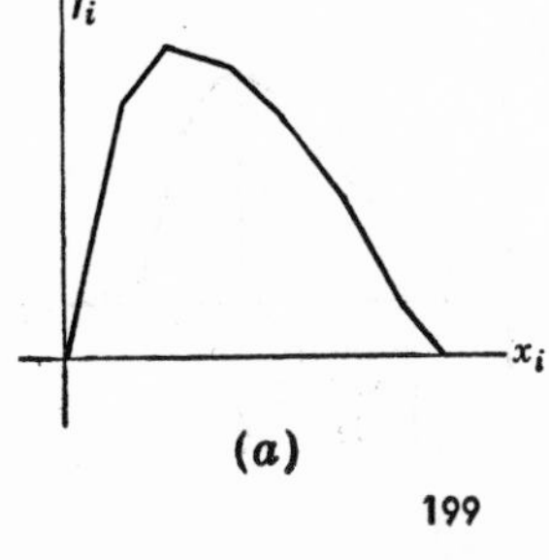

(*a*)

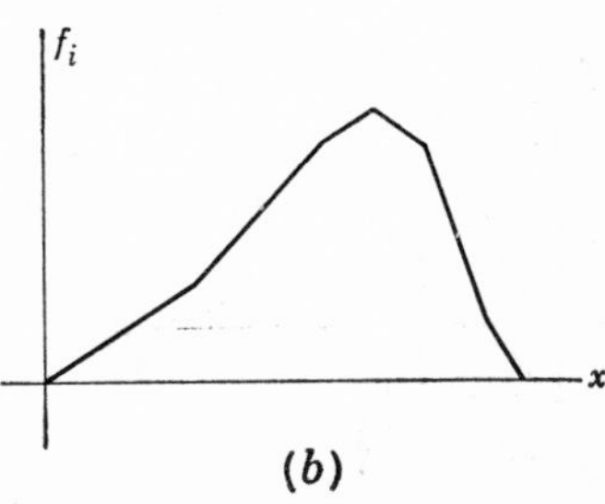

(*b*)

Fig. 86

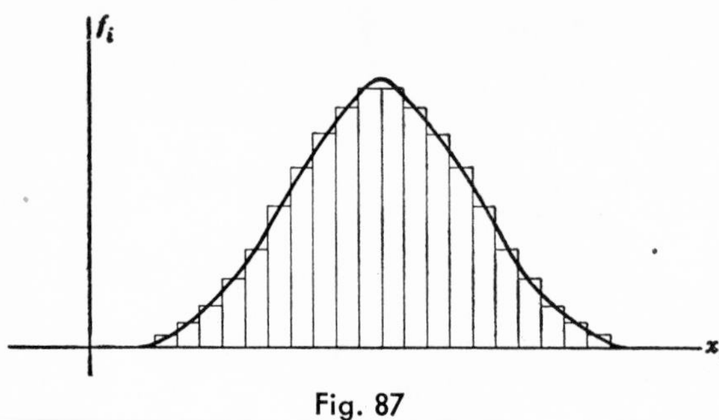

Fig. 87

If we have a frequency distribution for a large number of measurements or counts arranged so that there is a large number of classes, each of small class width, the bases of the rectangles in the histogram will be small, and the rectangles will rise in such tiny steps that the frequency polygon is almost a smooth curve (Fig. 87).

If we increase the number of classes in the frequency distribution, the frequency polygon and the smooth curve are very close together. We will assume that the area under the smooth curve is the same as the total area of the histogram.

In the work that follows, we shall draw frequency polygons as smooth curves.

If a mound-shaped distribution is of the symmetrical type, the mean, mode, and median fall together. If the distribution is skewed, the mode lies under the highest point of the frequency polygon, and the median and the mean lie in that order toward the longer branch of the polygon. The positions of the mean, median, and mode are shown in Fig. 88. The mean falls farthest from the mode because it is affected the most by the extreme values.

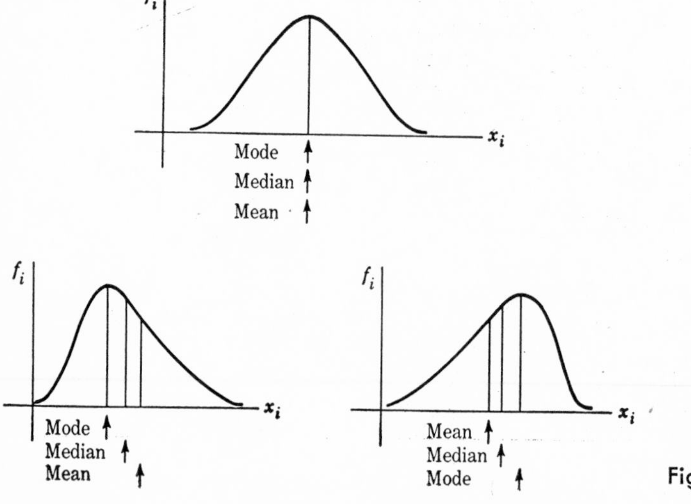

Fig. 88

The differences between the values for the mode, median, and mean are an indication of the symmetry of the distribution. When there is a marked skewness—that is, the mode, median, and mean differ greatly in value—the mean is not a good representative of the data, and the median or mode will give the better indication of the central tendency of the distribution.

EXERCISES

1. Look over the frequency polygons that you have made and determine which of them were symmetrical and which skewed.

2. Erect vertical lines at the points of the mode, median, and mean on each of the frequency polygons that you have made.

3. In symmetrical or moderately skewed bell-shaped distributions having to do with a rather large number of cases, the standard deviation of the distribution is roughly about one-sixth of the distance between the lowest and the highest class mark. This fact is useful in estimating the value of σ before it is actually computed. See how good this approximation is for the values of the standard deviations you found in Prob. 1 on page 197.

??????????? PROBLEM JUST FOR FUN ???????????

Joe, an inveterate gambler, said to his friend, Jim, "I'll bet you half the money that I have in my pocket against an equal sum on the toss of a coin—heads I win, tails I lose." Jim took the bet. The coin was tossed and the money paid. Joe repeated this offer again and again, always betting one-half the money then in his possession. After a number of bets Joe found that he had won just as many times as he had lost. Now, did Joe gain or lose on these bets?

???????????????? JUST FOR FUN ????????????????

2. The normal frequency curve

While the plotted frequency polygon of data may sometimes have more than one mode and may be skewed, it has been observed that more often data plot into frequency polygons which have a single hump and which are symmetrical about the mean. This is particularly true of data resulting from measurements in the physical, social, or biological sciences. These distributions have the form of a certain mathematical curve. Hence this curve has been extensively used in studying distributions. This curve has been named the *normal curve*, and a distribution which follows this form is

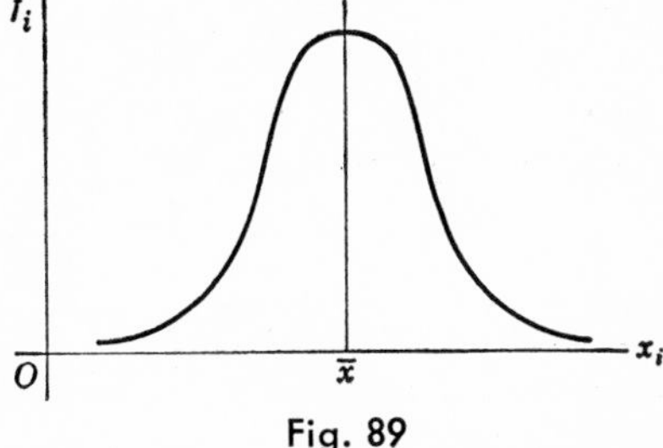

Fig. 89

called a *normal distribution.* In Fig. 89 we show a normal distribution in which the frequency polygon has been plotted with such short class intervals that the polygon resembles a smooth curve.

3. The equation of the normal curve

Let us plot the graph for the curve

$$y = e^{-t^2/2}$$

TABLE 50

t	0	$\pm .5$	$\pm .7$	$\pm .9$	± 1	± 1.5	± 2	± 3
y	1	.88	.78	.67	.61	.32	.14	.01

We obtain a curve (Fig. 90) which is very similar to the shape of the distribution plotted in Fig. 89, and statisticians have used this curve to represent the idealized distribution of data.

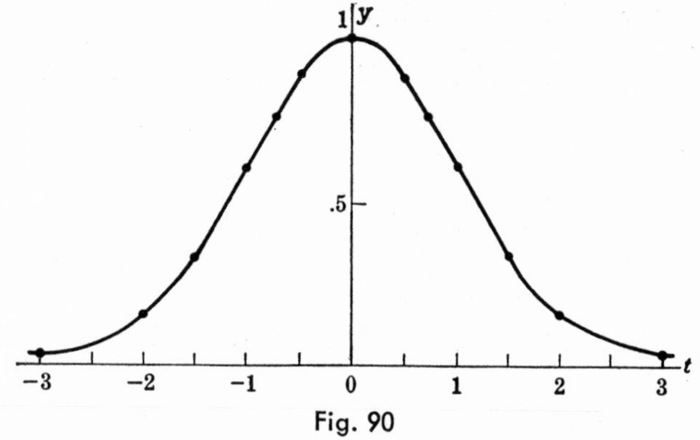

Fig. 90

However, we must modify our equation to make it fit the practical distributions. The normal distribution centers about its mean $\bar{x}$, while the curve we have just plotted is symmetrical about the y axis. To change the symmetry to the proper line, we will replace t by $(x - \bar{x})/\sigma_x$. The factor σ_x is introduced so that the width of the hump will change with the variability of the distribution. If σ_x is small, the hump in the curve will be steep and narrow; while if σ_x is large, the hump will be broad and flat. Our equation now becomes

$$y = e^{-(x-\bar{x})^2/2\sigma_x^2}$$

If we plot this curve for $\bar{x} = 0$ and $\sigma_x = 1$, we get the graph of Fig. 90. Other values σ_x will make the hump steeper or flatter but will not change the general shape.

We notice that the curve flattens out very near the x axis but never touches it, no matter how far out we plot it. The curve and the x axis bound an area which extends to infinity in both directions. While it extends to infinity it becomes narrow so rapidly that the area turns out to be finite. Mathematicians have computed the area and found it to be $\sqrt{2\pi}\,\sigma_x$. The applications we shall make of the normal curve have to do with questions of probability. Portions of the area will represent probabilities, which we remember are always fractions from 0 to 1, and thus it will be desirable for the total area to equal 1, which is the largest probability number. We can do this by introducing a factor of $\sqrt{2\pi}\,\sigma_x$ in the height of the curve. With this final modification we take as the equation of the *normal curve*

$$y = \frac{1}{\sqrt{2\pi}\,\sigma_x} e^{-\frac{1}{2}[(x-\bar{x})/\sigma_x]^2} \tag{1}$$

In this equation, if $(x - \bar{x})/\sigma_x$ is replaced by t and $\sigma_x = 1$, the normal curve is said to be in standard form. So the *standard normal curve* has the equation

$$y = \frac{1}{\sqrt{2\pi}} e^{-t^2/2} \tag{2}$$

To find areas under the normal curve of equation (1) would require different tables for all possible values of $\bar{x}$ and σ_x, while only one table is required for the standard curve of equation (2). A frequency distribution is said to be *standardized* when the variable x is changed to the variable $t = (x - \bar{x})/\sigma_x$. Notice that t tells us how many standard deviations a given x is from its mean $\bar{x}$. If x is one standard deviation σ_x away from its mean $\bar{x}$, then the corresponding t is $+1$ or -1 according as x is larger or smaller than $\bar{x}$. For $t = 2$, $x - \bar{x} = 2\sigma_x$, and x is two standard deviations $(2\sigma_x)$ above its mean. This means that a distance $x - \bar{x} = 2\sigma_x$ on the x axis of Fig. 89 corresponds to a distance of 2 units on the t axis of Fig. 90.

4. A property of the normal curve

When we were working with histograms we may have noticed that

$$\frac{\text{Area of one rectangle}}{\text{Total area of histogram}} = \frac{\text{class frequency times class width}}{\text{total number of cases times class width}} = \frac{\text{number of cases in the one class}}{\text{total number of cases}}$$

From our definition of probability, this last ratio is the probability that an x chosen at random from the distribution will be in the particular class represented by the one rectangle. In general, the probability for a random chosen x to lie between two limits x_1 and x_2 will be equal to the sum of the rectangles between x_1 and x_2 divided by the total area of the histogram. Now we may think of the graph of equation (1) as a histogram with extremely narrow rectangles. Then the probability that an x chosen at random will lie between two values x_1 and x_2 is simply the area under the curve between these two limits divided by the total area. Here we see the advantage of introducing the factor $\sqrt{2\pi}\,\sigma_x$ into the equation to make the total area 1. With this total area 1, we do not need to divide, and the area under the curve between x_1 and x_2 equals exactly the probability that the random x occurs between x_1 and x_2. As we have already discussed, it is more convenient to use the standard normal curve, changing x_1 to $t_1 = (x_1 - \bar{x})/\sigma_x$ and x_2 to $t_2 = (x_2 - \bar{x})/\sigma_x$. Then our table of areas under the standard normal curve given in the next section will give us the probability for t to lie between t_1 and t_2, which is the same as the probability for x to lie between x_1 and x_2. Figure 91 illustrates what we have just said.

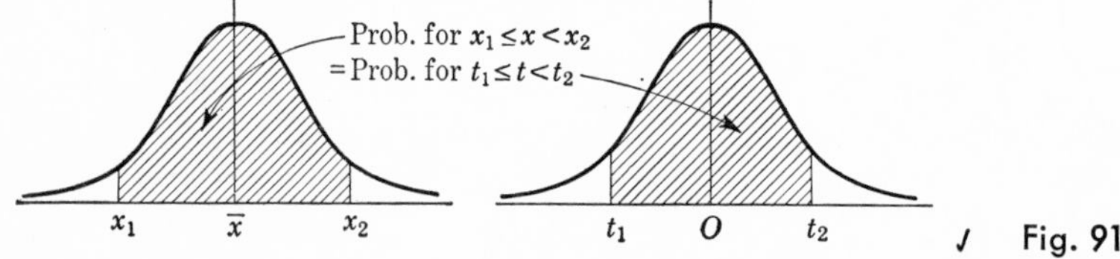

Fig. 91

5. The probability that an x differs from $\bar{x}$ by less than $t\sigma_x$

Suppose a problem requires that we determine the probability that an x in a normal distribution *differs* from $\bar{x}$ *by less* than $1\frac{1}{2}$ standard deviations. Then $t = (x - \bar{x})/\sigma_x = 1.5$. When we use the word *differ*, we imply that the difference may be either to the left or to the right of the mean. The probability that x *differs* from $\bar{x}$ *by less* than $1.5\sigma_x$ will be the area under the standard normal curve lying less than 1.5 units from $t = 0$. This area is shown as the shaded area in Fig. 92.

In the work that follows, we will find it necessary to determine the probability that a value x, in a normal distribution, differs from the mean value $\bar{x}$ in either direction by less than a specified number of standard deviations. We must find how large t needs to be in order that x lie as far from $\bar{x}$ as the given number of σ_x's. Then we may use Table 51 to find the required probability. From

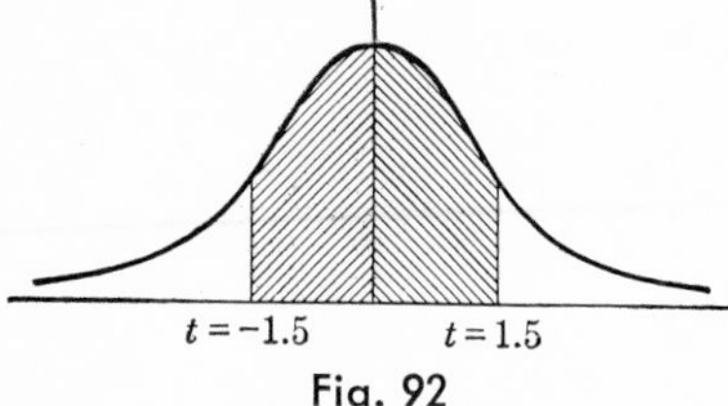

Fig. 92

the table, we find that for $t = 1.5$ the required probability for t to differ from $t = 0$ by less than 1.5 is 0.866. This says that 86.6% of all the x's in a normal distribution are less than 1.5 standard deviations from the mean, and hence 86.6/2, or 43.3%, of all the x's are greater than the mean and less than $t = 1.5$. Thus each of the shaded areas in Fig. 92 has an area of 0.433 and is 43.3% of the entire area under the curve.

TABLE 51. Probability of x Differing from $\bar{x}$ by Less than t times σ_x
(Area under standard normal curve from $-t$ to $+t$.)

t	*Probability*	*t*	*Probability*	*t*	*Probability*
0.0	0.000	1.3	0.807	2.5	0.988
0.1	0.080	1.4	0.838	2.58	0.990
0.2	0.159	1.5	0.866	2.6	0.991
0.3	0.236	1.6	0.891	2.7	0.993
0.4	0.311	1.7	0.911	2.8	0.995
0.5	0.383	1.8	0.928	2.9	0.996
0.6	0.451	1.9	0.943	3.0	0.997
0.7	0.516	1.96	0.950	3.1	0.998
0.8	0.576	2.0	0.955	3.2	0.9986
0.9	0.632	2.1	0.964	3.3	0.9990
1.0	0.683	2.2	0.972	3.4	0.9993
1.1	0.729	2.3	0.979	3.5	0.9995
1.2	0.770	2.4	0.984	4.0	0.9999

Example 1. It is found that the test grades on a certain test follow a normal curve. If grades of A and F are to be given to the students who are more than 1.6 standard deviations from the mean, what proportion of the students receive grades of B, C and D?

Solution. The dividing line for the F and A grades is at

$$t = \frac{(x - \bar{x})}{\sigma_x} = -1.6 \qquad \text{and} \qquad t = \frac{(x - \bar{x})}{\sigma_x} = 1.6$$

respectively. From the table, we find that the proportion of the area lying less than $t = 1.6$ units on either side of the mean is 0.891. Hence 89.1% of the grades will be B's, C's and D's, and 10.9% of the grades will be A's and F's.

Example 2. The semester grades given by a certain department in a university follow a normal curve. If 83.8% of the grades were B's, C's, or D's, how many standard deviations from the mean were the grades of the students who got A's or F's?

Solution. Here we must use Table 51 in reverse. Since 83.8% of the grades were B's, C's, or D's, the center area in Fig. 93 has an area of 0.838. We look at the entries in Table 51 and see that an area of

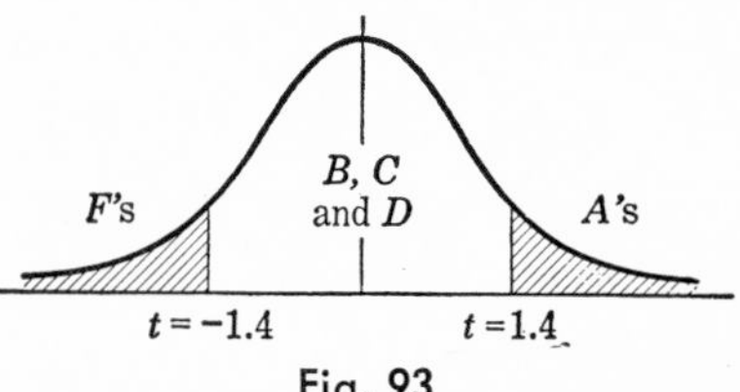

Fig. 93

0.838 under the curve lies between $t = 1.4$ and $t = -1.4$. Then the x for any grade of A or F is 1.4 or more standard deviations σ_x from the mean of the grades.

Example 3. It is known that the lengths of telephone calls form a distribution which is approximately normal, with mean 8 minutes and standard deviation 2½ minutes. What is the probability that a telephone call will last more than 15 minutes?

Solution. We have $\bar{x} = 8$ minutes, $\sigma_x = 2.5$ minutes, $x = 15$ minutes. Then

$$t = \frac{x - \bar{x}}{\sigma_x} = \frac{15 - 8}{2.5} = 2.8$$

From Table 51 we see that the area under the curve from $t = -2.8$ to $t = +2.8$ is 0.995, or that the chance that a randomly chosen t will lie between these limits is 99.5%. Then ½ of 1% of all calls will lie outside these limits, which are $x = 15$ and $x = 1$. The value $x = 1$ corresponds to $t = -2.8$. Since these two "outside" areas are equal, we see that about ¼ of 1% of all calls, or 1 out of 400, are longer than 15 minutes.

Example 4. Within what limits do we find 50% of all telephone calls?

Solution. Given $\bar{x} = 8$ minutes and $\sigma_x = 2.5$ minutes, we need to know within what values of x will be found 50% or 0.500 of the area under the normal curve. Consulting Table 51, we see that this corresponds to t about 0.67. Then

$$x_2 = \bar{x} + t\sigma_x = 8 + (0.67)(2.5) = 9.7 \text{ minutes}$$
$$x_1 = x - t\sigma_x = 8 - (0.67)(2.5) = 6.3 \text{ minutes}$$

We see that 50% of all telephone calls last between 6.3 and 9.7 minutes.

EXERCISES

In each of the following problems assume that a normal distribution represents the frequencies of the x's.

1. What proportion of the x's are greater than the mean $\bar{x}$?

2. What proportion of the x's are less than two standard deviations away from $\bar{x}$? More than two standard deviations from $\bar{x}$?

·**3.** What is the probability for an x to lie within $1.8\sigma_x$'s from $\bar{x}$?

4. What is the probability for an x to be *less* than $\bar{x}$ by more than $\frac{1}{2}\sigma_x$? What is the probability for x to deviate from $\bar{x}$ by more than $\frac{1}{2}\sigma_x$? To deviate from $\bar{x}$ by less than $\frac{1}{2}\sigma_x$?

5. A normal distribution of 500 weights has $\bar{x} = 145$ pounds and $\sigma_x = 4$ pounds.

a. What proportion of these weights are within 6 pounds of 145 pounds? How *many* of the weights are within this range?

b. If a weight is selected at random, what is the probability that it is more than 12 pounds away from 145 pounds?

c. What is the probability for a weight to lie between 140 pounds and 150 pounds?

d. What range of weights will include the middle 50% of the cases?

e. What weight is exceeded by only 10% of all the cases?

6. A group of tobacco farms in 1926 had mean income $905 with standard deviation $1,409. What proportion of the farms lost money, if the incomes followed a normal distribution?

??????????? PROBLEM JUST FOR FUN ???????????

Three men raced up a staircase, and the finish of the race is shown in the sketch. Allen, who is leading, went up three risers at a time; Jones, the second

man, went up four risers at a time; and Smith, who is last, went up five risers at a time. Of course, Allen wins the race; but what is the smallest number of risers, counting the top landing as a riser, in the staircase? (The entire staircase is not shown.)

??????????????? JUST FOR FUN ???????????????

6. Problems involving sampling

We find ourselves frequently desiring to make statements about averages: the average grade of a class of students on a botany test, the average salary of department-store clerks, the average weight of football players, the average life of an automobile tire. If the number of objects involved is small, this is a simple computation. For example, if we wished to know the average weight of the players on the Georgia Tech football line, it would not require too much time to write down the weight of each man and compute the mean. But if we should wish to know the average weight of all the college football linesmen in the United States, the problem is of quite a different magnitude. There are more than one thousand teams, and even if we took the time and expense of writing to all of them, we should probably not get replies from all. And even if we received replies from every one of them, we should have such a mass of figures that it would require many hours to compute the mean.

Common sense would lead us to sampling. We should collect the weights of linesmen from a group of colleges, being careful to include both large and small colleges. If we chose the colleges to be reasonably representative of the entire group, we should reason that the mean figure obtained is quite satisfactorily near to the mean of the entire group. As indicated above, the mean of the entire group would require too much work to compute or might be impossible to compute (if some colleges did not reply to letters).

If a tire manufacturer wishes to state precisely the average life of his tires, he can do so only if he tests every single tire he produces. Obviously he will not do this, for he would have no tires left to sell and would go bankrupt. So he would choose a sample which was small compared to his total output and expect that the average of this sample would be very near to his true but unknown average. But how many tires should he test? One? Ten? One hundred? And having made his test, how near can he expect his test average to be to his true but unknown average? These are important problems in sampling.

Suppose the tire manufacturer chooses a random sample of 100 tires and tests them. He finds the mean life for these tires to be 29,500 miles and their standard deviation to be 2,200 miles. Should he claim that 29,500 miles is the mean life of all his tires? Obviously not, for another sample of 100 tires may give a different mean just by chance variation. We realize that the manufacturer can never be certain of the true mean of his entire production and must be satisfied with an estimate of this mean. The estimate will be made by the method of *confidence intervals.* To establish a confidence-interval estimate of the true mean is to claim that the true mean is somewhere in the range from $\bar{x} - d$ to $\bar{x} + d$ where $\bar{x}$ is the sample mean. That is, we estimate that the true mean is somewhere near the sample mean. Our problem is to determine the value of d. If d is relatively large, we can be fairly certain that the true mean lies in this interval; and as d is made smaller, we are less confident that the estimate is an accurate one. We can never be absolutely sure that the true mean lies in this interval unless d is taken so large as to make the estimate of no value. For example, the tire manufacturer might be quite certain that the mean life of his entire production is somewhere in the interval 0 to 59,000 miles, but this estimate is so broad as to have little value. In this case the d was taken to be 29,500 miles. On the other hand, if the true mean life is estimated to be in the interval 29,500 miles $\pm$ 5 miles, the manufacturer will probably have very little confidence that this is a true estimate. Before an estimate is made, a *confidence level* must be arbitrarily decided upon. The confidence level is simply the degree of assurance that the estimate of the true mean is accurate. Most estimates are made with 90, 95, or 99% confidence in practical situations. In our problems we shall use one or another of these three confidence levels. Having decided upon a confidence level, the question remains as to how to determine the value of d in any given problem. Before we can arrive at an answer to this question, we must study the behavior of sample means as they vary under random sampling.

7. Chance variation in sample means

The problem is to estimate the mean of a population of x values. These x values might be tire lives, test grades, girls' weights, etc., and the *population* consists of all such values under consideration. If we were able or willing to observe each and every x in the population, there would be no sampling problem, and the population mean could be computed precisely. But if sampling is to be used, we can only estimate the population mean with a specified degree of confidence, as has been explained above. The tire manufacturer would certainly not test every tire produced, since he would have no tires left to sell—an unpleasant thought for the stockholders in his company We shall use the symbol $\tilde{x}$ to represent the unknown population mean, and the symbol $\bar{x}$ will stand for the mean of our sample Now there will be a standard deviation for all the x's in the population, as well as a standard deviation for the relatively few x's in the sample. We shall use σ_x for the standard deviation of the population and s_x for the standard deviation of our sample. Usually we have no more knowledge about the value of σ_x than we do about $\tilde{x}$. As we shall see, our estimate of $\tilde{x}$ will require that we have a value for σ_x. It can be shown that if the sample has a sizable number of cases, say, over 20 or 30, we may take s_x to be the same as σ_x. This replacement will bring about no appreciable difference in the desired estimate of $\tilde{x}$. For example, the tire manufacturer does not know σ_x, the standard deviation of all his tires, but he may use $s_x = 2{,}200$ miles in place of the unknown σ_x, since the sample was fairly large, namely, 100 tires.

To admit that different samples will give different $\bar{x}$'s just by chance alone is to admit the existence of a frequency distribution of the sample means. If all possible samples, each having the same number of cases, are drawn from a population of x's, the sample $\bar{x}$'s could be tallied into a frequency table just as we have done before with other statistical data. This distribution of sample means would have its own mean and standard deviation, as does any frequency distribution. The histogram or frequency polygon could be plotted in order to observe the shape of the distribution of means. Fortunately we do not have to do this for the populations we study, because mathematicians have proved that the distribution of all possible sample means, each having n cases, drawn from a large population of x's, will have the following properties:

1. The distribution will be normal, or very nearly so, even if the original population does not have a normal distribution.

2. The mean of all the sample means will be the population mean $\tilde{x}$.

3. The standard deviation of the distribution of sample means will be the standard deviation of the population divided by the square root of n, that is,

$$\sigma_{\bar{x}} = \frac{\sigma_x}{\sqrt{n}}$$

Figure 94(a) and (b) illustrates what we have just said.

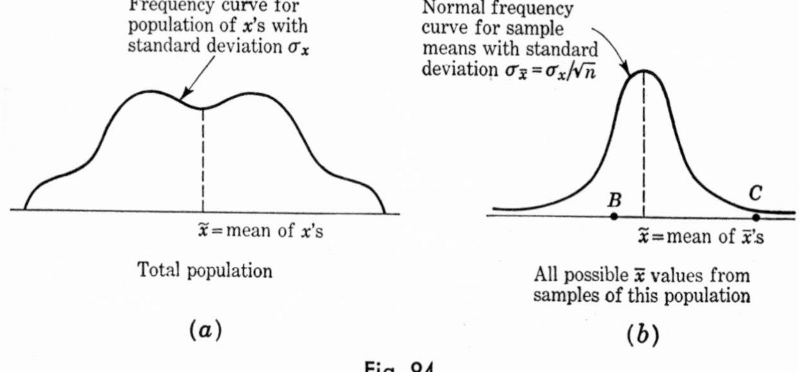

(a) (b)

Fig. 94

In order to illustrate our previous discussion, we shall relate the following actual experiment: A class of students drew 360 samples of 10 counters

TABLE 52

$\bar{x}$ = *mean of a sample of 10 counters*	*Number of samples having this mean*
0–0.5	2
0.5–1.0	9
1.0–1.5	47
1.5–2.0	122
2.0–2.5	134
2.5–3.0	38
3.0–3.5	7
3.5–4.0	1

each from a bag. The x's were numbers stamped on the counters. The mean of all the x's in the counter population was $\tilde{x} = 2.00$, and their standard deviation was $\sigma_x = 1.715$. When the 360 sample means were computed and tallied, the distribution of means obtained by the students was as shown in Table 52. The mean of this distribution of $\bar{x}$'s is 1.98, and its standard deviation $\sigma_{\bar{x}}$ is 0.52.

Question. According to the previous theory, what would have been the mean and standard deviation in this experiment if *all possible* samples of 10 counters had been drawn?

8. Estimating the population mean from a sample mean

Now, in a practical situation we have drawn only one sample and have only one mean. Figure 94*b* shows how all possible means will behave under chance variation, but we have no way of knowing whether our sample mean is at a point like B or at a point like C, or at any other point along the $\bar{x}$ scale. A mean such as B is below the true mean and relatively near $\tilde{x}$, while a mean like C is considerably above $\tilde{x}$. As we have said, we shall estimate the location of $\tilde{x}$ by going out a distance d on either side of $\bar{x}$ and then claim that $\tilde{x}$ is in this interval. It should be clear that, if our claim is to be correct, the distance d will depend upon the width of the hump in Fig. 94*b*. That is, d depends on the size of $\sigma_{\bar{x}}$. If $\sigma_{\bar{x}}$ is small, the distance d does not need to be very large in order to ensure that $\tilde{x}$ is between $\bar{x} - d$ and $\bar{x} + d$. If $\sigma_{\bar{x}}$ is large, the sample means are more scattered and a larger d will be necessary for an accurate estimate of $\tilde{x}$. The size of $\sigma_{\bar{x}}$ measures the reliability of the mean, or the extent to which $\bar{x}$ is expected to be in error from $\tilde{x}$ just by chance variation. When we observe the formula for $\sigma_{\bar{x}}$ we see that the mean of the sample becomes more reliable as the number of cases in the sample is increased. For example, if the tire manufacturer had selected a sample of 25 tires, $\sigma_{\bar{x}} = \sigma_x/5$ instead of $\sigma_{\bar{x}} = \sigma_x/10$. That is, a sample of 100 gives twice the reliability that is given by a sample of 25 tires. Now, even if $\sigma_{\bar{x}}$ is relatively small, there can still be sample means as far away from $\tilde{x}$ as the point C in Fig. 95. And although we take d large enough so that the intervals $A \pm d$ and $B \pm d$ do include $\tilde{x}$, i.e., give a correct claim as to the location of $\tilde{x}$, the same d is not large enough to make correct the claim that $\tilde{x}$ is in the interval $C \pm d$. But remember that we are willing to run a specified risk of making an inaccurate claim. Let us agree that we need to be only 90% confident that our claim about $\tilde{x}$ is true; that is, we would expect only 9 of 10 such claims to be correct. This means that we shall take d large enough that the claim would be correct for 90% of all possible sample means. But our normal-curve-area

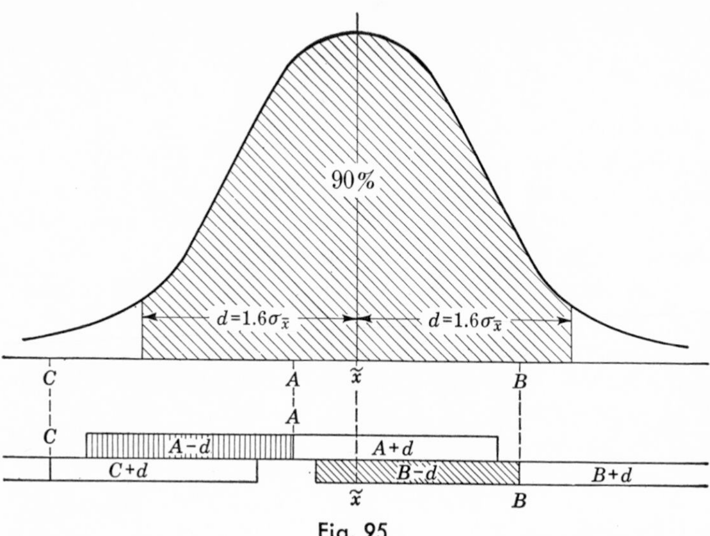

Fig. 95

table tells us that 90% of all the cases in a normal distribution are no more than 1.6 standard deviations from the mean of the distribution. Since the standard deviation of the normal curve in Fig. 95 is $\sigma_{\bar{x}}$, then 90% of all sample means are within $1.6\sigma_{\bar{x}}$ of $\tilde{x}$. So if we make the claim that $\tilde{x}$ is in the interval from $\bar{x} - 1.6\sigma_{\bar{x}}$ to $\bar{x} + 1.6\sigma_{\bar{x}}$, we can be 90% certain that our claim is correct. This is because only 10% of all possible sample means are like C, which is farther away from $\tilde{x}$ than $1.6\sigma_{\bar{x}}$.

Thus we have found how to determine the value of d for a given confidence level. Returning to the tire problem, suppose the manufacturer wants a 90% confidence interval for the true mean life of all his tires. From Table 51 we find that d will have to be 1.6 standard deviations. So $d = 1.6\sigma_{\bar{x}} = 1.6\sigma_x/\sqrt{100} = 1.6(2{,}200/10) = 350$ miles approximately. Then the manufacturer may have 90% confidence in the estimate that $\tilde{x}$ is between 29,150 and 29,850 miles.

Example 1. Suppose the tire manufacturer desires more confidence in his statement, say 95%. We know that 100% is impossible unless the range is so large as to be of no value. We look at Table 51 and find that when $t = 1.96$, 95% of the sample means are within the range $\pm t\sigma_{\bar{x}}$ of the true mean $\tilde{x}$. Then

$$d = t\sigma_{\bar{x}} = t\frac{\sigma_x}{\sqrt{n}} = t\frac{s_x}{\sqrt{n}} = 1.96\frac{2{,}200}{\sqrt{100}} = 430 \text{ miles approximately}$$

Then we may state that the average life of the tires lies between 29,070 and 29,930 miles with 95% confidence, or only 1 chance in 20 of being wrong.

Example 2. If our tire manufacturer wants 99% confidence, we find from Table 51 that $t = 2.58$ and $d = 2.58 \cdot \frac{2200}{\sqrt{100}} = 570$ miles approximately.

Example 3. What is the average number of hours of study per week of a college student? Suppose a random sample of 50 students shows a mean of 20.6 hours and a standard deviation of 2.2 hours. Suppose we desire 95% confidence. Then $t = 1.96$, and

$$d = t\frac{s_x}{\sqrt{n}} = 1.96 \times \frac{2.2}{\sqrt{50}} = 0.6 \text{ hour}$$

We may state that the true mean $\tilde{x}$ lies between 20 and 21.2 hours with only 1 chance in 20 of being wrong.

9. An experiment in sampling

Place the numbers 0 to 10 on 200 counters in accordance with the frequencies given in Table 53. The mean of this total counter population is obviously $\tilde{x} = 5.0$. Have each member of the class select a random sample of 16 counters. This is to be done with replacement, that is, a counter is drawn and its number recorded, then it is replaced and the counters mixed before the next counter is drawn. Each student is to compute $\bar{x}$ and s_x for his sample and from this compute his estimate of $\tilde{x}$ with confidence interval at the 90% level. Find the percentage of students whose intervals contain the true population mean $\tilde{x} = 5.0$, and compare this with the percentage expected by the theory of sampling, which is 90%. Use the same samples to compute 95 and 99% confidence intervals, comparing the results obtained in the class with the theory of sampling.

TABLE 53

Mark printed on counter $= x$	0	1	2	3	4	5	6	7	8	9	10
Number of counters with this mark x	1	3	10	23	39	48	39	23	10	3	1

For this population, the true standard deviation $\sigma_x = 1.715$. Use this figure in place of the standard deviation s_x of the sample in computing the 90, 95, and 99% confidence intervals. To what extent does this change the results?

EXERCISES

1. Suppose we are given a sample and are asked to locate the true mean of the entire population. What sacrifice is made as a higher and higher degree of confidence in our answer is required?

2. We can obtain more accurate information about the location of the true mean by increasing the size of our sample. Suppose the tire manufacturer had used 200 tires in the test which gave $\bar{x} = 29{,}500$ miles and $s_x = 2{,}200$. Compute d for 90% confidence. Do you think this increased accuracy would justify the doubled expense of the testing?

3. Compute d for 90% confidence if the tire manufacturer had used only 10 tires in the test.

4. In a certain town, a random sample of 25 families showed a mean yearly income of $4,200, with a standard deviation of $400. Make a 90% confidence statement about the location of the mean yearly income of all the families in this town.

5. In a breeding experiment, the average height of a certain type of cornstalk was theoretically 60 inches. A random sample of 25 stalks had a mean height of 62 inches with standard deviation 6 inches. Decide whether the theory of a height of 60 inches should be revised.

6. Suppose it is found from a random sample of 400 students that the average semester expense of going to college is $480, with a standard deviation of $75. You would like to be able to say that the average semester expense of the entire student body is no more than D dollars and be quite certain that the number D is quoted correctly. What will you give as a value for D?

??????????? PROBLEM JUST FOR FUN ???????????

A man draws a gallon of water from his auto radiator and replaces it with alcohol. During the month ½ quart of alcohol evaporates. He then drains out 6 quarts of the mixture and puts in 6½ quarts of alcohol, which again fills the radiator to capacity. If it then tests 50% alcohol, what is the capacity of the radiator?

???????????????? JUST FOR FUN ????????????????

CHAPTER

21

Glimpses of Modern Mathematics—Introduction

(*Something Old, Something New*)

> If a time could arrive when all was known, when there could not be a new investigation or experiment, our keenest pleasure would be at an end. We may therefore feel happy in the thought of how much is still unknown.
>
> A. G. V. Harcourt

1. Mathematics a living science

Most of the mathematics which we have studied dates far back into history. Plane geometry existed in almost its present form at the time of Euclid, 300 years before Christ. The arithmetic and algebra we have studied dates back into the dawn of history and reached their modern form before the discovery of America. There was a book on trigonometry as early as the thirteenth century, and some of the facts of the subject were known to the early Babylonian astronomers. In the sixteenth century, trigonometric tables were calculated to ten decimals.

All this gives us the feeling that mathematics is very ancient, and this is quite true. But what is not so well known is that mathematics is also quite new. Most of us have read of great recent discoveries in chemistry and nuclear physics, but we are not aware that great discoveries have been made in mathematics also in the past century and many of them during our own lifetime. For example, a book on the theory of lattices was published recently in this country. Essentially everything in this book was discovered in the 20 years previous to its publication. Volumes have been written on a branch of geometry called topology. Topology was born in our grandfathers' time, and most of it has been discovered since 1900. We shall take a brief look at it later in this book.

There remains much to be discovered even today in this mathematics, which is so old and yet so new. Each new discovery seems to raise new problems to be solved and new theorems to be proved. No true science is ever finished.

We shall devote the next three chapters of this book to brief glimpses into these modern phases of mathematics. This will not be a complete view, since many phases of modern mathematics involve understanding parts of mathematics which we have not studied. Without certain parts of modern mathematics, the development of new designs for higher speeds and more efficiency in aircraft would be impossible. But we cannot discuss these parts of modern mathematics, because to understand them would require a knowledge of analytic geometry, calculus, ordinary and partial differential equations, and perhaps several other branches of mathematics and physics.

There are, however, some phases of modern mathematics which we can discuss and understand without so much preliminary machinery. We shall look briefly at the theory of numbers and topology. Some of the theory of numbers is very old, and parts of it are recent discoveries. Topology, as we remarked earlier, is almost entirely of the twentieth century. We shall not only see some recent mathematics but shall also mention some problems in mathematics which have not been solved as yet.

2. Of what use is this?

Michael Faraday, one of the great pioneers in the field of electricity, was giving a lecture demonstration before the Royal Society in London. He was showing that a tiny current of electricity was produced in a coil of wire when a magnet was suddenly brought near the coil. The experiment was not very impressive, and no doubt many in the audience agreed with the lady who asked, "But, Professor Faraday, even if the effect you explained is obtained, what is the use of it?" Then came the famous reply, "Madam, will you tell me the use of a newborn child?"

This "newborn child" of Faraday, this seemingly unimportant discovery, grew into the mighty adult of present-day industry and life. Without this unimpressive discovery of Faraday there would be no electric motors, no electromagnets or many other machines of industry. This useless child of Faraday led to electric lights, vacuum cleaners, mechanical refrigerators, etc., in our homes.

We may find ourselves mentally asking this same question about some of these discoveries in mathematics which we shall discuss, and the answer is often the same as Faraday's. In some cases we know their value in other parts of mathematics, in modern physical theories, and in industrial applications. In many cases we know of no application for the work at the present time. But no discovery of the facts of nature is ever useless. Somewhere, sometime, often years in the future, it fits in as one step in man's understanding of this world we live in. If the discovery is new and interesting, we need not worry about its usefulness.

CHAPTER

22

The Basis of Our Number System

(How Much Is 6 and 5?)

God created the natural numbers; everything else is man's handiwork.

LEOPOLD KRONECKER

1. What is a number?

At the center of all mathematics is the concept of number. But what is number? What do we mean when we write $\frac{1}{2} + \frac{1}{4} = \frac{3}{4}$, $2 \cdot 4 = 8$, $\sqrt{3} \cdot \sqrt{3} = 3$? We learn the rules of the game and can solve problems with numbers, but how many of us have ever thought about "What is a number?" In order to examine this question, let us turn to the simplest of all numbers, the whole numbers, or integers, or natural numbers, 1, 2, 3, 4, 5, ...

The integers were created in order to count various collections of things, and they have no physical being. The number 7 applies whether it is seven eggs, seven cars, seven words, or seven ideas. In fact, the number 7 may be defined as that quality which these four groups of objects, as well as other similar-sized groups, have in common. The number 7 answers the question, "How many?" but gives us no information on size, shape, or nature. We use it so commonly and with such certainty that most of us are immediately shocked that anyone should even ask, "But what do you mean by the number 7?" To children, numbers are always connected with definite objects, such as fingers or beads. But clearly, the number 7 is not tied up with fingers or beads but has a meaning independent of these.

Also, it is clear that there is nothing magic in the form of 7. While it might confuse us at first, we could soon learn to compute if 7 were replaced by ∃ or ∧ or some other symbol. Once we become accustomed to it, we could add and subtract and multiply just as rapidly as before. So 7 is just a symbol which we all understand and which has only this importance.

2. The roman system

Roman numerals, the number system of the Latin language, are used today for numbering clock faces, for marking books (particularly the pages of prefaces, the chapters, and the volumes of a series), for dates on monuments and public buildings, and for numerous less important things. In the beginning it was not a letter system, although it is now written with the capital letters of the Latin alphabet. The Roman numerals consist of seven symbols as follows (note that there is no zero):

I = 1
V = 5
X = 10
L = 50
C = 100
D = 500
M = 1,000

Numbers are written from left to right and are made thus: an M is written down for every separate thousand; then 500 is taken, and D is written for it; next, as many hundreds are taken as possible, and a C is written for each; 50 is then taken, and L is written for it; as many tens as possible are next taken, and X is written for each; 5 is then taken, and V is written for it; and finally, I is put down as many times as there are units left over. Thus 3,500 is written as MMMD (and means 1,000 plus 1,000 plus 1,000 plus 500); and 1,550 is written as MDL; and 1,883 as MDCCCLXXXIII.

At a later date, subtraction by changing the position of the symbols came into use. Instead of writing IIII, the I is placed before the V and we have IV, which means 1 subtracted from 5. Thus 9 is written as IX instead of VIIII, 40 as XL instead of XXXX, 90 as XC, 900 as CM. Thus 1,949 would be written as MCMXLIX, and 1,950 is written as MCML.

Addition is not too difficult, and we might do a problem like this:

```
CXXXVII
CXX  III
─────────────
CCXXXXXVIIIII
    L     V   = CCLX
```

Remember to think entirely in Roman symbols—it is cheating to translate into Arabic figures, do the problem, and translate back.

Multiplication is more complicated, and we may consider multiplying XVI by XII as follows:

```
XVI
XII
----------
XXXXXXXXXX
VVVVVVVVVV
IIIIIIIIII
XVI   XVI
----------
CLX
XXXII
----------
CLXXXXII
----------
CXCII
```

We are not sure this is exactly the way the Roman schoolboy did this problem, but we can see that his problem was not as easy as ours, and we can appreciate the difficulty involved in using large numbers. Also, the very contemplation of the problem of dividing MMCCLIX by XVI is enough to produce cold shivers. This Roman symbolism, which is a good example of an additive number system, is cumbersome, and, as we pass to larger numbers, new symbols must be added at each stage to keep the figures within even reasonable bounds. Imagine the difficulty of expressing some of the numbers of astronomy or atomic physics in this system! At this point, we can begin to understand why all computing in Roman times was done by a few specially trained persons.

EXERCISES

Solve the following problems in addition and multiplication. Remember: Translating into Arabic symbols is against the law!

1. XXVIII + XVI
2. CLXXXI + LVII
3. CCXXVII + XXXII
4. MCXXXI + CLIX
5. VI · VII
6. XIII · VI
7. XXVI · XV
8. XXII · XVI
9. XVI · XIV
10. XLI · XIX

??????????? PROBLEM JUST FOR FUN ???????????

A cylindrical glass is 4 inches high and 6 inches in circumference. On the inside of the glass, 1 inch from the top, is a drop of honey, and on the opposite side of the vessel, 1 inch from the bottom on the outside, is a fly. How far must the fly walk to reach the honey?

???????????????? JUST FOR FUN ????????????????

3. Positional notation

Having floundered through these problems in Roman notation, we begin to appreciate the simplicity of our modern notation. The invention of positional notation was one of the great inventions of all time. Its discovery is attributed to the Babylonians, and it was developed by the Hindus. It was introduced into medieval Europe by the Italian merchants, who had learned it in their travels to the East. For the first time, computation was no longer entirely in the hands of trained specialists. Now any school child could do problems in multiplication and division which had been mysteries to all but these specialists, and the time was cut from minutes to seconds.

Positional notation derives its name and its great simplicity from the fact that we use only 10 symbols, 0, 1, 2, 3, 4, 5, 6, 7, 8, and 9 and may denote any number by the position in which they appear. Thus 354 means something quite different from 543. In the symbol 543, we mean 5 hundreds, 4 tens, and 3 units. We may express larger numbers with the same 10 symbols by using more positions:

$$\begin{aligned} 3{,}642 &= 3 \cdot 1{,}000 + 6 \cdot 100 + 4 \cdot 10 + 2 \\ &= 3 \cdot 10^3 + 6 \cdot 10^2 + 4 \cdot 10 + 2 \end{aligned}$$

We see that any number from 1,000 to 9,999 may be expressed by

$$abcd = a10^3 + b10^2 + c10 + d$$

where a, b, c, and d are chosen from the 10 original number symbols, 0, 1, 2, 3, 4, 5, 6, 7, 8, and 9. Similarly, any number from 100 to 999 may be expressed by

$$abc = a10^2 + b10 + c$$

and any number from 10,000 to 99,999 may be expressed by

$$abcde = a10^4 + b10^3 + c10^2 + d10 + e$$

Thus the expressing of any number is equivalent to writing an expression such as

$$a10^3 + b10^2 + c10 + d$$

in powers of 10. But why 10? Why not 6 or 8 or 12 instead of 10? The earliest form of counting was done on the fingers. Primitive savages and small children still use them for this purpose. As we have 10 fingers, it was inevitable that man developed a number system based on 10. Had man four fingers on each hand, it is almost certain that our present number system would be based on 8.

4. Number system based on eight

Let us consider what arithmetic would be under a number system based on 8. We would use only the eight symbols 0, 1, 2, 3, 4, 5, 6, and 7. Eight would appear as 10, 9 as 11, and 10 as 12 in this arithmetic.

We may see how the smaller numbers appear in the scale of 8 in Table 54.

TABLE 54

Scale of 10	1	2	3	4	5	6	7	8	9	10	11	12	13	14	15	16	17	18	19	20
Scale of 8	1	2	3	4	5	6	7	10	11	12	13	14	15	16	17	20	21	22	23	24
Scale of 10	21	22	23	24	25	26	27	28	29	30	31	32	33	34	35					
Scale of 8	25	26	27	30	31	32	33	34	35	36	37	40	41	42	43					

We see that $28 = 3 \cdot 8 + 4$ and so appears as 34 in the scale of 8. Similarly, $35 = 4 \cdot 8 + 3$ and appears as 43.

To express any number x in this system, we must determine the letters a, b, c, and d in the equation

$$x = a8^3 + b8^2 + c8 + d$$

just as we did before with the equation

$$x = a10^3 + b10^2 + c10 + d$$

Thus the number commonly written as 99 becomes 143 in the system based on 8, since

$$99 = 1 \cdot 8^2 + 4 \cdot 8 + 3$$

This may seem complicated and queer to us at first, but our system would seem just as queer to a man from Mars where each man had four fingers on a hand.

In an arithmetic based on 8, the rules are the same, but the child would learn a different set of addition and multiplication tables. Just as our children parrot "5 times 4 is 20," the children of the four-fingered race would parrot "5 times 4 is 24" since

$$20 = 2 \cdot 8 + 4$$

Let us try a few simple problems in this four-fingered arithmetic. But first let us write down the addition and multiplication tables which the four-fingered child has memorized just as we memorize our multiplication tables.

Addition

	1	2	3	4	5	6	7
1	2	3	4	5	6	7	10
2		4	5	6	7	10	11
3			6	7	10	11	12
4				10	11	12	13
5					12	13	14
6						14	15
7							16

Multiplication

	1	2	3	4	5	6	7
1	1	2	3	4	5	6	7
2		4	6	10	12	14	16
3			11	14	17	22	25
4				20	24	30	34
5					31	36	43
6						44	52
7							61

Now let us try a few problems:

Example 1.

Scale of 8	*Scale of* 10
25	21
+46	+38
13	59
6	
73	

Check

$$73 \text{ (scale of 8)} = 7 \cdot 8 + 3 = 59 \text{ (scale of 10)}$$

Example 2.

64	52
+56	+46
12	98
13	
142	

Check

$$142 \text{ (scale of 8)} = 1 \cdot 8^2 + 4 \cdot 8 + 2 = 98 \text{ (scale of 10)}$$

Example 3.

24	20
×13	×11
14	20
6	20
24	220
334	

Check

$$334 \text{ (scale of 8)} = 3 \cdot 8^2 + 3 \cdot 8 + 4 = 220 \text{ (scale of 10)}$$

Example 4.

```
  45        37
 ×63       ×51
 ---       ---
  17        37
 14        35
 36       15
30        ----
----      1887
3537
```

Check

$$3537 \text{ (scale of 8)} = 3 \cdot 8^3 + 5 \cdot 8^2 + 3 \cdot 8 + 7 = 1{,}887 \text{ (scale of 10)}$$

EXERCISES

The numbers in these problems are given in four-fingered arithmetic. Do these problems using the scale of 8 addition and multiplication tables, and then check your work by translating into the scale of 10 and solving.

1. 24 + 32
2. 34 + 26
3. 57 + 64
4. 347 + 234
5. 23 × 6
6. 35 × 5
7. 34 × 24
8. 56 × 63

??????????? PROBLEM JUST FOR FUN ???????????

The following is a problem in addition in which each letter represents a number and two different letters cannot be the same number.

```
 S E N D
 M O R E
---------
M O N E Y
```

Can you figure out what numbers the letters represent?

???????????????? JUST FOR FUN ????????????????

5. Other number systems

Having tried our hand at four-fingered arithmetic, we may ask whether systems other than 10 have ever been used or have any value as possibilities. There has been some argument in favor of a number system based on 12. The points in favor of such a system are its ease in division and handling of fractions. In the scale of 10, only the fractions $\frac{1}{2}$, $\frac{1}{5}$, and $\frac{1}{10}$ have simple equivalents 0.5, 0.2, 0.1. On the other hand, the scale of 12 would give this same simplicity to $\frac{1}{2}$, $\frac{1}{3}$, $\frac{1}{4}$, $\frac{1}{6}$, $\frac{1}{12}$. To change to a scale of 12 would require the introduction of two new symbols for 10 and 11 and the learning of different tables of addition and multiplication.

There are some vestiges of number systems based on 12 in the history of civilization. There is evidence that the Mayans of Central America had such a system. Also, both the English and German languages have special words for 11 and 12 but revert to words based on 10 at 13, 14, etc. This is exactly what we should expect to find in a number system based on 12.

6. The dyadic system

If the number system has a large base, we have too many symbols for the digits and too complicated a multiplication table. It might seem desirable, then, to change to the dyadic system, or scale of 2. This uses exactly two symbols, 0 and 1, and has the following simple tables:

Addition

	0	1
0	0	1
1	1	10

Multiplication

	0	1
0	0	0
1	0	1

This would appear to be a paradise for the grade-school child, with only two symbols and almost no multiplication table to learn. However, even relatively small numbers become formidable in the dyadic system. Thus 87 becomes 1010111, since

$$87 = 1 \cdot 2^6 + 0 \cdot 2^5 + 1 \cdot 2^4 + 0 \cdot 2^3 + 1 \cdot 2^2 + 1 \cdot 2 + 1$$

Multiplication is very simple in the dyadic system, since we need remember only that $1 \times 1 = 1$ and $1 + 1 = 10$. As an example, let us multiply 7 and 11, which are 111 and 1011.

$$\begin{array}{r} 1011 \\ \underline{111} \\ 1011 \\ 1011 \\ \underline{1011} \\ 1001101 \end{array} = 2^6 + 2^3 + 2^2 + 1$$

This gives us 77, as it should.

While individual numbers have complicated representations, the dyadic system has many advantages. It is used in the high-speed electronic computing machines and many other places in mathematics.

7. How much is 6 and 5?

Now we return to the title of this chapter, "How much is 6 and 5?" There is only one answer, "11," if the symbols 6 and 5 have their usual meaning. But how do we write 11? Before studying this chapter, we could have answered easily and confidently, "11." But now we have learned to be more cautious, and we ask, "In what number base?" Six plus five equals 11 in base 10, 13 in base 8, 1011 in a dyadic system, and whatever the single symbol for 11 is if the base is 12.

EXERCISES

1. Express 127 in the base of 8.
2. Express 1,425 in the base of 12.
3. Express 12 in the base of 2, 3, 4, and 5.
4. Express 147 in a dyadic-base number system.
5. Express 125 in a dyadic-base number system.
6. Using the dyadic base, add the numbers 1011, 1101, 110, and 1110. Check by translating to base 10.
7. Using the dyadic base, add the numbers 11111, 1001, 101, 11010. Check by translating to base 10.
8. Multiply in dyadic base the numbers 1101 and 101. Check by translating to base 10.
9. Multiply in dyadic base the numbers 1011 and 1001. Check by translating to base 10.
10. Construct the addition and multiplication table for base 5. Use this to multiply the numbers 123 and 43 in base 5. Check the result by translation to base 10.

??????????? PROBLEM JUST FOR FUN ???????????

Consider the following equations:

$$3x + y = 5$$
$$x = 2 - (1/3)y$$

Substituting the value of x from the second equation into the first, we obtain

$$6 - y + y = 5$$

or

$$6 = 5$$

What is wrong?

???????????????? JUST FOR FUN ????????????????

CHAPTER

23

The Theory of Numbers

(*Building Blocks of Arithmetic*)

Mathematics is the queen of sciences and the theory of numbers is the queen of mathematics. K. F. GAUSS

1. Some parlor tricks

Since the very earliest days of history, man has been fascinated by the whole numbers and their properties. The numbers have always been associated with superstition and mysticism. Although man's superstition has waned, 3 is still thought to be a lucky number, and 13 is considered unlucky by so many people that most hotels and office buildings omit the thirteenth floor. The interest in integers and their properties is just as alive today as it was centuries ago.

The properties of integers form the basis of many parlor tricks. One very puzzling trick is based on the property that any three-digit number repeated gives a six-digit number which is divisible by 7, 11, and 13. Thus on successive division of the six-digit number by these three numbers, the final quotient is the original three-digit number. For example, choose the number 436 and form the number 436,436. Dividing successively by 7, 11, and 13, we have $436{,}436 \div 7 = 62{,}348$; $62{,}348 \div 11 = 5{,}668$; $5{,}668 \div 13 = 436$!!! To use this as a mystifying trick, we ask a person to choose a three-digit number and repeat it to give the six-digit number. We ask a second person to divide it by 7. Have a third and a fourth person divide the result by 11 and 13. Then we astonish the first person by handing him the result, which will be his original number. But we will be the ones astonished unless our friends can divide without mistakes!!!

A much simpler trick is as follows: Think of any number. Add 2. Double the result. Add 6. Divide by 2. Subtract the original number. The result is always 5. Why?

2. The prime numbers

Of foremost interest among the integers are the primes. A whole number greater than 1 is called *prime* if it is divisible only by itself and 1. The smallest prime numbers are 2, 3, 5, 7, 11, 13, 17, etc. The number 1 might be considered prime, but this is not the custom. To do so would force us to state an exception to many of the theorems of prime numbers. For this reason 2 is considered the smallest prime. Information about primes is important, because they are the building blocks of all numbers, and the question of whether a number is prime or not enters into many statements in the theory of numbers.

How many primes are there? More than 2,000 years ago, Euclid, who is most famous for his book on plane geometry, proved that the number of primes is infinite. His proof is so elegant and clear that we shall repeat it here.

First, let us consider the two primes 2 and 3 and form the number $2 \cdot 3 + 1 = 7$. Observe that 7 is not divisible by 2 or 3, for each such division leaves the remainder 1. Thus 7 is a prime, or has a prime factor different from 2 and 3. So we have proved the existence of three primes. Similarly we may show that $2 \cdot 3 \cdot 7 + 1$ is not divisible by 2, 3, or 7 and thus must either be a prime or have as a factor a fourth prime. Euclid's proof follows this line of reasoning and is an elegant example of a *reductio ad absurdum* argument.

Euclid reasons: Suppose the total number of primes is n, and we denote them by $p_1, p_2, p_3, \ldots, p_n$. Now form the integer

$$p_1 \cdot p_2 \cdot p_1 \ldots p_n + 1 = N.$$

The number N is not divisible by any of the n primes, since such a division clearly leaves the remainder 1. Then N is either itself a prime or has a prime factor different from any of the n primes, giving a total of $n + 1$ primes. Thus the original assumption that the number of primes is finite leads to a contradiction.

Euclid's elegant proof shows that the sequence of all integers 1, 2, 3, 4, 5, 6, 7, 8, . . . , contains infinitely many primes. But we may also show that other sequences such as 3, 7, 11, 15, 19, . . . , or 5, 7, 11, 17, . . . , contain infinitely many primes. In fact, Dirichlet (1805–1859) proved that every sequence of the form, a, $a + b$, $a + 2b$, $a + 3b$, . . . , contains infinitely many primes if a and b have no common factor. However, his proof, unlike that of Euclid, is extremely difficult and complicated.

Now that we know what primes are and that they are scattered among all the numbers, no matter how large, we naturally ask for a formula which will give all the primes. Many such formulas have been given, but someone has always found that each formula gave at least one number which was not a prime. To date, no one has ever found a formula which always yields a prime.

Fermat (1601–1665) made the famous conjecture that $2^{2^n} + 1$ was always a prime. However, Euler (1707–1783) discovered that for $n = 5$ the number given is not prime, for $4,294,967,297 = 641 \times 6,700,417$.

Another famous formula is $n^2 - n + 41$. This gives a prime number for every $n < 41$. However, for $n = 41$, it gives 41^2, which is certainly not a prime. Incidentally, this formula gives a fine lesson in the danger of drawing conclusions from experiments. Suppose we are asked to test the assertion that "$n^2 - n + 41$ is always a prime." Every try for $n < 41$ will give success. After ten or twenty such trials, we may be willing to grant the truth of the assertion. Beware of such conclusions!

3. Some unsolved problems about prime numbers

Despite the immense amount of knowledge about primes, there are other simple questions, like the formula for primes, whose answer is not known as yet. There remains much to do in mathematics. No one today knows the answer to any of the following simple questions:

1. Given a prime P, what is the next larger prime?

2. Are there an infinite number of pairs of primes differing by 2? Examples are 5 and 7, 11 and 13, 17 and 19, 29 and 31.

3. Given a number N, how many primes are less than N? Or what is the formula for the number of primes between two numbers M and N?

There is, however, a remarkable theorem about the distribution of primes. Gauss (1777–1855) conjectured that the number of primes less than n is approximately $n/\log n$, where this is the Napierian or natural logarithm to the base $e = 2.718 \ldots$. The proof of Gauss's conjecture was attempted by many mathematicians, but it was nearly 100 years later, in 1896, that Hadamard and de la Vallée Poussin completed the proof, using the most complicated tools of analysis. More precisely, the theorem states that the ratio of P_n, the number of primes less than n, and $n/\log n$ approaches 1 as n becomes large. We may see this for a few values, since P_n is known by counting primes:

$n = 1,000$	ratio is 1.16
$n = 1,000,000$	ratio is 1.08
$n = 1,000,000,000$	ratio is 1.05

4. Is every even number, except 2, the sum of two primes? $4 = 2 + 2$, $6 = 3 + 3$, $8 = 5 + 3$, $10 = 5 + 5$, $12 = 7 + 5$. The famous Goldbach (1690–1764) conjecture affirmed this.

No one had ever solved this problem, but in 1931 the Russian Schnirelman proved that every integer is the sum of at most 300,000 primes. While 300,000 is so large that it may seem ludicrous to call this a partial solution, Schnirelman's success led others to attempt the problem, and Vinogradoff later proved that all large integers may be expressed as the sum of at most 4 primes. Vinogradoff's proof is of the *reductio ad absurdum* type, so we do not know how large "large integers" are and cannot test the ones below this. What he really proved is that the assumption that the number of integers requiring more than 4 primes is infinite leads to a contradiction.

EXERCISES

1. What are the prime numbers given by the formula $2^{2^n} + 1$ for $n = 0, 1, 2, 3$?

2. Compute the prime numbers given by the formula $n^2 - n + 41$ for $n = 1, 2, 3, 4, 5, 6, 7, 8, 9, 10$.

3. Write down all the prime numbers less than 75.

4. How many pairs that differ by 2 are found among the primes less than 75?

5. Express each of the even numbers from 40 to 50 as the sum of two primes.

6. Show that every odd prime number can be represented as the difference of two perfect squares in one and only one way. Find this representation for 13, 17, and 23.

7. Show that there are no positive integers x and y such that $y^2 = 2x^2$. From this it follows that $\sqrt{2}$ is not a rational number, i.e., the quotient of two integers.

??????????? PROBLEM JUST FOR FUN ???????????

A three-figure number is peculiar. It ends with 4. If the 4 is moved to the front, the new number is as much greater than 400 as the original number was less than 400. What is the number?

???????????????? JUST FOR FUN ????????????????

4. The Perfect numbers

An intriguing group of integers are those which have been named the *perfect numbers.* These are the integers which are exactly equal to the sum of all their divisors except themselves. The smallest perfect number is 6, for the divisors of 6 are 1, 2, 3, and 6, and $6 = 1 + 2 + 3$. Some numbers, such as 10, have divisors that add to less than themselves, $5 + 2 + 1 = 8$, and some numbers, like 12, are "too perfect," for $6 + 4 + 3 + 2 + 1 = 16$.

On the surface one sees no connection between prime numbers and perfect numbers. Yet, as in many cases in number theory, there is a very close connection. A theorem states that if $2^n - 1$ is a prime number, then $2^{n-1}(2^n - 1)$ is a perfect number.

Notice that every perfect number given by this formula is an even number, since a power of 2 is one factor. Then what are the odd numbers which are perfect? To date the mathematicians have not found the answer to this question. No odd perfect number has been found, and it is not known whether one exists.

EXERCISES

1. Test the numbers up to 40 to see which ones are perfect.

2. Using the formula given above, find four perfect numbers and verify that they are perfect.

??????????? PROBLEM JUST FOR FUN ???????????

Find a group of two or more consecutive numbers which add up to 100. Can you show that there are exactly two different solutions?

???????????????? JUST FOR FUN ????????????????

5. Pythagorean numbers

A second group of interesting numbers are the integers which satisfy the equation $x^2 + y^2 = z^2$. These triples are called *Pythagorean* or *right-triangle numbers,* since it is possible to construct a right triangle with x and y as legs and z as hypotenuse. Thus, if we find all the solutions of $x^2 + y^2 = z^2$ in whole numbers, we have found all the right triangles that we can construct with whole numbers as sides.

In fact, this gives all the shapes of right triangles which have rational numbers as sides. For each right triangle with rational numbers as sides is similar to one with whole numbers as sides. Suppose $\frac{a}{b}, \frac{c}{d}, \frac{e}{f}$ are the sides of a right triangle, where the six letters represent integers. We may write these three sides as $\frac{adf}{bdf}, \frac{cbf}{dbf}, \frac{ebd}{fbd}$. Then the triangle with the whole numbers adf, cbf, ebd as sides is similar to the original triangle. Thus we see that a knowledge of the solutions of $x^2 + y^2 = z^2$ in whole numbers gives us the knowledge of every type of right triangle possible which does not involve a square root in the length of any side.

One triple, 3, 4, 5, of Pythagorean numbers is well known, for $3^2 + 4^2 = 5^2$. This immediately leads us to a whole series of triples—6, 8, 10; 9, 12, 15; 12, 16, 20; etc., which satisfy the equation $x^2 + y^2 = z^2$. We see that whenever a, b, c is Pythagorean, then ka, kb, kc is Pythagorean for any integer k. If $a^2 + b^2 = c^2$, then

$$\begin{aligned}(ka)^2 + (kb)^2 &= k^2a^2 + k^2b^2\\ &= k^2(a^2 + b^2)\\ &= k^2c^2\\ &= (kc)^2\end{aligned}$$

Thus each solution of $x^2 + y^2 = z^2$ leads to a whole infinity of solutions. These are not particularly interesting, for all the triangles formed are similar, differing only in size.

We shall be interested in *primitive* Pythagorean triples, that is, solutions of $x^2 + y^2 = z^2$ such that x, y, and z have no common factor except 1. We see that 3, 4, 5 is a primitive solution, but 6, 8, 10 is not a primitive solution. Two primitive solutions yield triangles which are not similar. For example, 3, 4, 5 and 5, 12, 13 are Pythagorean triples of numbers, and the right triangles produced are quite different in shape.

The problem of finding primitive Pythagorean numbers has been completely studied, and it has been proved that x, y, z will be a triple of primitive Pythagorean numbers if

$$\begin{aligned}x &= 2mn\\ y &= m^2 - n^2\\ z &= m^2 + n^2\end{aligned}$$

where m and n are any two positive integers such that (a) one integer is even and one integer is odd; (b) the two integers have no common factor except 1; and (c) $m > n$.* Since $m = 2$, $n = 1$ satisfy these conditions, we should expect the resulting x, y, z to be Pythagorean. Substituting into the equations above, we obtain $x = 4$, $y = 3$, $z = 5$, which we already knew is Pythagorean.

EXERCISES

1. Show that $m = 3$, $n = 2$ yields the Pythagorean numbers 5, 12, 13.

2. Find four other sets of primitive Pythagorean numbers by using other small values of m and n. Check to prove that the numbers are Pythagorean.

3. If $x = 2mn$, $y = m^2 - n^2$, $z = m^2 + n^2$, prove that $x^2 + y^2 = z^2$.

??????????? PROBLEM JUST FOR FUN ???????????

Two ferryboats leave opposite sides of the Hudson River at the same time. They pass each other at a point 700 feet from one shore. Each boat remains at the dock 10 minutes and returns. On the return trip they pass each other at a point 400 feet from the opposite shore. How wide is the Hudson at this point?

???????????????? JUST FOR FUN ????????????????

* For proof of this statement see Carmichael, "Theory of Numbers," p. 85, John Wiley & Sons, Inc., New York, 1914.

6. Fermat's last theorem

Having made a complete study of the solutions of $x^2 + y^2 = z^2$, we naturally want to know about the integral solutions of $x^3 + y^3 = z^3$, of $x^4 + y^4 = z^4$, and in general of $x^n + y^n = z^n$ for $n > 2$.

This problem derives its name as the last of the theorems left unsolved by Pierre de Fermat (1601–1665). Fermat owned a copy of Bachet's "Diophantus," and as he read, it was his habit to make marginal notes, frequently stating results but not their proof. After his death in 1665 this book was found, and various mathematicians supplied the proofs which Fermat did not write down. In time, proofs were devised for all these notes except the one in which Fermat wrote: "On the other hand, it is impossible to separate a cube into two cubes, or a biquadrate into two biquadrates, or generally any power except a square into two powers with the same exponent. I have discovered a truly marvelous proof of this which, however, the margin is not large enough to contain." Thus, Fermat wrote that he had a proof that it was impossible to solve $x^n + y^n = z^n$ in integers for all $n > 2$. It seems very doubtful that Fermat really had a proof, for no one has been able to give a complete proof up to the present time.

In 1908, a bequest of 100,000 marks was made to the Royal Academy of Göttingen to establish a prize for a correct proof of Fermat's last theorem. Since this had a value of about $24,000, interest in the problem was greatly stimulated. Hundreds of solutions poured in, but errors in reasoning were found in all of them. Even some famous mathematicians have thought they had a solution, only to find an error. The inflation following World War I wiped out the monetary value of this prize, but interest in the problem continues. No solution exists today, but some new advance of knowledge may yield a solution tomorrow, next year, next decade, or next century. Who knows?

While no complete solution of Fermat's last theorem is known, many partial solutions are known. Fermat left a proof for $n = 4$, and Euler (1707–1783) proved the theorem for $n = 3$. Dirichlet (1805–1859) proved it for $n = 5$ and $n = 14$. Lamé (1795–1870) proved it for $n = 7$. Kummer (1810–1893) gave a proof which covered all cases except certain ones. The missing cases are all above 100 and are rare among the smaller numbers. Among others, the American mathematicians L. E. Dickson (1874–) and H. S. Vandiver (1882–) have made significant advances on the theorem. The solution is now known to be impossible for all values of $n < 619$ and for most values of n to 10,000. In the case where x, y, z, and n are *relatively prime*, that is, no two have a common factor, D. H. and Emma Lehmer proved in 1941 that the solution is impossible for $n < 253, 747, 889$!!

7. Waring's theorem

Every integer may be expressed as the sum of perfect squares, since we may write $1^2 + 1^2 + 1^2 + \cdots$ and thus construct any integer n. But the real question is the minimum number of perfect squares necessary to represent any number. Thus,

$$13 = 1 + 1 + 1 + 1 + 1 + 1 + 1 + 1 + 1 + 1 + 1 + 1 + 1$$

but $13 = 9 + 4$ also, so we need only two squares in this case.

EXERCISE

Express each integer less than 100 in as few squares as possible. What is the largest number needed? The general result that every integer may be expressed by not more than this number of squares was stated by Fermat.

How many cubes are needed to express any integer? Edward Waring (1734–1798) stated without proof that at most nine cubes are needed. This was proved by Wieferich in 1909. Waring also stated that at most 19 fourth powers are needed. Wieferich proved that it could be done with not more than 37, and better results have been found more recently.

EXERCISES

1. Express each integer less than 50 in as few cubes as possible. What is the maximum number needed?

2. Express each integer less than 50 in as few fourth powers as possible. What is the maximum number needed?

??????????? PROBLEM JUST FOR FUN ???????????

"Goodbye, my little darlings," said the Sultan of Nabob to his harem. "I'm off to market and won't be back until next week. And girls," said the Sultan, opening two identical boxes of bonbons and chocolates, "I want you to watch your figures. So I am rationing you to 7 bonbons and 11 chocolates apiece."

On his return the Sultan counted the remaining bonbons and chocolates and blew his top. "Somebody has been cheating," he yelled. "There are only 49 bonbons and 17 chocolates left."

"Relax your blood pressure, big boy," replied his favorite wife. "My sister, Grace, paid me a visit, and we gave her the same share."

How many wives did the Sultan have?

???????????????? JUST FOR FUN ????????????????

CHAPTER

24

Topology

(*The World Made of Rubber*)

[Geometry] that held acquaintance with the stars,
And wedded soul to soul in purest bond
Of reason, undisturbed by space or time.

WORDSWORTH

1. What is topology?

Topology is the branch of geometry which deals with properties which are not affected by changes in size and shape. We may understand its nature if we think of a very elastic rubber sheet on which some geometrical figures have been drawn. We are allowed to stretch and bend the sheet but must not cut or tear it. Distance has no meaning in topology, for two points an inch apart may easily be made 2 inches apart by stretching the sheet. Angle size is meaningless, for by careful stretching we may change an angle of 15° on the sheet to 45°. Even straight lines have no place in topology, for the straight line AB A———B may be changed into any one of the shapes shown in Fig. 96 by proper stretching of the sheet. Perhaps it is not so easy to see how the third one is obtained, but it can be done.

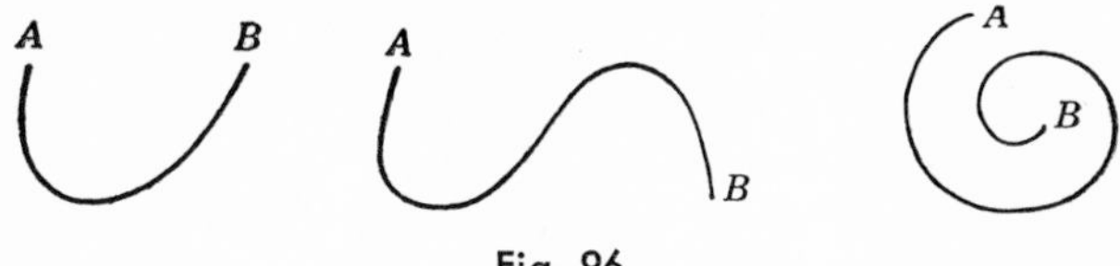

Fig. 96

So many of the properties of geometry become meaningless in this rubber world of topology that it may seem that nothing remains. But notice that no matter how we stretch or bend, the path from A to B remains a path from A to B which does not cross itself. It may become very crooked, much worse than the three pictures above, but it remains a path from A to B. Thus a path from A to B belongs to the language of topology, and the topologist calls it the *arc* AB.

Now consider a circle on the rubber sheet (Fig. 97). By distorting the sheet it may become an oval (Fig. 98), or something worse (Fig. 99), or even something like Fig. 100. But it remains a path $ABCDA$, which returns to its original point without crossing itself. Since topology ignores changes produced by stretching, all these figures are the same for the topologist, and he calls each of them *a simple closed curve*, or *closed circuit*. It consists of two arcs ABC and ADC which have only the points A and C in common.

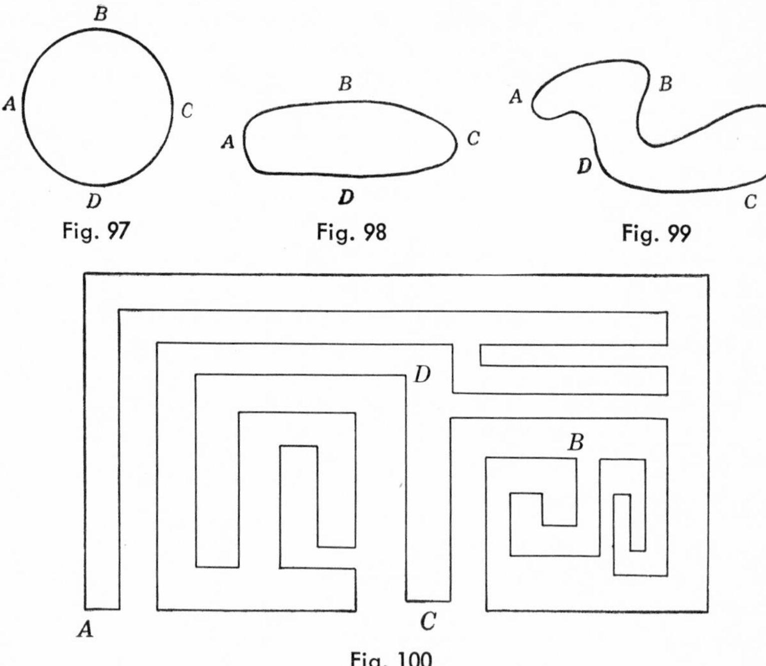

Fig. 97 Fig. 98 Fig. 99

Fig. 100

We notice that no matter how the original circle is distorted by stretching, it always divides the sheet into two parts, the outside and the inside region. This is the Jordan curve theorem, one of the fundamental theorems of topology. This may seem very obvious, but it is not so obvious if we look at Figure 100, where it is only with some difficulty that we are able to distinguish which is "outside" and which is "inside." Actually, this theorem, which states that two paths from A to C which have no other points in common always divide the plane into two regions, is a very difficult theorem to prove, and the first correct proof was given just at the dawn of the twentieth century.

2. A story

But topology is not concerned primarily with proving "obvious" theorems, and we shall begin our brief visit to this fascinating land with a story reprinted with permission from the *Ford Times* (July, 1949):

PAUL BUNYAN *versus* THE CONVEYOR BELT

BY WILLIAM HAZLETT UPSON

One of Paul Bunyan's most brillant successes came about not because of brilliant thinking; but because of Paul's caution and carefulness. This was the famous affair of the conveyor belt.

Paul and his mechanic, Ford Fordsen, had started to work a uranium mine in Colorado. The ore was brought out on an endless belt which ran half a mile going into the mine and another half mile coming out—giving it a total length of one mile. It was four feet wide. It ran on a series of rollers, and was driven by a pulley mounted on the transmission of Paul's big blue truck "Babe." The manufacturers of the belt had made it all in one piece, without any splice or lacing, and they had put a half twist in the return part so that the wear would be the same on both sides.

After several months' operation, the mine gallery had become twice as long, but the amount of material coming out was less. Paul decided he needed a belt twice as long and half as wide. He told Ford Fordsen to take his chain saw and cut the belt in two lengthwise.

"That will give us two belts," said Ford Fordsen. "We'll have to cut them in two crosswise and splice them together. That means I'll have to go to town and buy the materials for two splices."

"No," said Paul. "This belt has a half-twist—which makes it what is known in geometry as a Möbius strip."

"What difference does that make?" asked Ford Fordsen.

"A Möbius strip," said Paul Bunyan, "has only one side, and one edge, and if we cut it in two lengthwise, it will still be in one piece. We'll have one belt twice as long and half as wide."

"How can you cut something in two and have it still one piece?" asked Ford Fordsen.

Paul was modest. He was never opinionated. "Let's try this thing out," he said.

They went into Paul's office. Paul took a strip of gummed paper about two inches wide and a yard long. He laid it on his desk with the gummed side up. He lifted the two ends and brought them together in front of him with the gummed sides down. Then he turned one of the ends over, licked it, slid it under the other end, and stuck the two gummed sides together. He had made himself an endless paper belt with a half-twist in it just like the big belt on the conveyor.

"This," said Paul, "is a Möbius strip. It will perform just the way I said—I hope."

Paul took a pair of scissors, dug the point in the center of the paper and cut the paper strip in two lengthwise. And when he had finished—sure enough—he had one strip twice as long, half as wide, and with a double twist in it.

Ford Fordsen was convinced. He went out and started cutting the big belt in two. And, at this point, a man called Loud Mouth Johnson arrived to see how Paul's enterprise was coming along, and to offer any destructive criticism that might occur to him. Loud Mouth Johnson, being Public Blow-Hard Number One, found plenty to find fault with.

"If you cut that belt in two lengthwise, you will end up with two belts, each the same length as the original belt, but only half as wide."

"No," said Ford Fordsen, "this is a very special belt known as a Möbius strip. If I cut it in two lengthwise, I will end up with one belt twice as long and half as wide."

"Want to bet?" said Loud Mouth Johnson.

"Sure," said Ford Fordsen.

They bet a thousand dollars. And, of course, Ford Fordsen won. Loud Mouth Johnson was so astounded that he slunk off and stayed away for six months. When he finally came back he found Paul Bunyan just starting to cut the belt in two lengthwise for the second time.

"What's the idea?" asked Loud Mouth Johnson.

Paul Bunyan said, "The tunnel has progressed much farther and the material coming out is not as bulky as it was. So I am lengthening the belt again and making it narrower."

"Where is Ford Fordsen?"

Paul Bunyan said, "I have sent him to town to get some materials to splice the belt. When I get through cutting it in two lengthwise I will have two belts of the same length but only half the width of this one. So I will have to do some splicing."

Loud Mouth Johnson could hardly believe his ears. Here was a chance to get his thousand dollars back and show up Paul Bunyan as a boob besides. "Listen," said Loud Mouth Johnson, "when you get through you will have only one belt twice as long and half as wide."

"Want to bet?"

"Sure."

So they bet a thousand dollars and, of course, Loud Mouth Johnson lost again. It wasn't so much that Paul Bunyan was brilliant. It was just that he was methodical. He had tried it out with that strip of gummed paper, and he knew that the second time you slice a Möbius strip you get two pieces—linked together like an old fashioned watch chain.

3. The Möbius band

Take a narrow strip of paper (Fig. 101) and paste or Scotch tape the ends together, but give one end a half twist before joining them together, so that ABC on one end is pasted along ABC at the other end. Now repeat Paul Bunyan's experiments by cutting the strip down the center and then a second time.

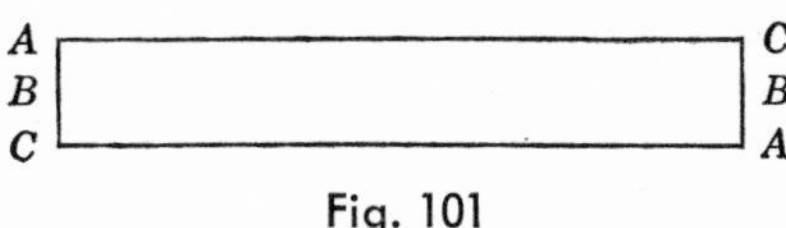

Fig. 101

The original strip which you had before cutting is called a Möbius band, named after A. F. Möbius, who explained its properties in a paper submitted to the Academy of Sciences in 1858. It has some most amazing properties, two of which we have already seen. It has only one side, since a person walking along it will return to a point just underneath his starting point without crossing the edge. If we try to paint the two "sides" of this band each a different color, we shall see that the two "sides" are really one. This is called a *one-sided surface* and is the simplest case of a whole family of such surfaces. We notice also that the "two edges" are really one, and that the edge is a simple closed curve. Truly, in the words of the limerick,

A mathematician confided
That a Möbius band is one-sided
And you'll get quite a laugh
If you cut it in half,
For it stays in one piece when divided.

??????????? PROBLEM JUST FOR FUN ???????????

Can you place 12 pennies on the squares of a 36-square checkerboard so that (*a*) no square has more than one penny and (*b*) no line, horizontal, vertical, or diagonal, has more than two pennies?

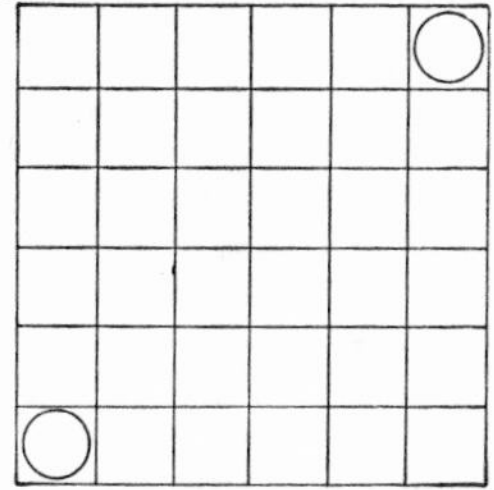

Start by placing one penny at each end of the long diagonal, as shown in the diagram.

???????????????? JUST FOR FUN ????????????????

EXERCISES

1. Instead of cutting the Möbius band in the center, cut it one-third of the distance from the edge. What happens? The smaller of the two pieces is a Möbius band. Why?

2. Make a strip as before, but give one end a full twist instead of a half twist before pasting the ends together. Is the resulting surface one-sided or two-sided? How many edges does it have? What happens if we cut it down the center? What happens if we cut it one-third of the way from the edge?

3. Make another strip, but give one end a twist and a half before pasting. How many sides to the surface? How many edges? What happens when we cut it down the center? At the one-third point?

4. Networks

Many of the elementary problems of topology depend on the properties of networks. A *network*, or *finite graph*, is a collection of points which are called *vertices*, together with a collection of *arcs* or *paths* such that

1. Each arc has two of the vertices as end points.
2. Each vertex is an end point of at least one arc.
3. No two arcs intersect except at an end point of both.
4. The entire configuration is one connected piece.

The simplest network is a single arc and its two vertices. Another simple network is the simple closed curve, which consists of two arcs and two vertices, or we may locate n points on a simple closed curve and consider it as a network of n arcs and n vertices. Examples of more complicated networks are the lines on a checker board and the highway map of the United States. Here the cities are the vertices and the highways between two adjacent cities are the arcs.

Condition (3) does not prevent a situation such as shown in Fig. 102 from occurring in a network. It requires only that the point E be designated as a vertex and that AE, CE, DE, and BE be arcs of the network. It is not permissible to consider the complete paths AB and CD as arcs of the network, since they would intersect at a point which is not a vertex.

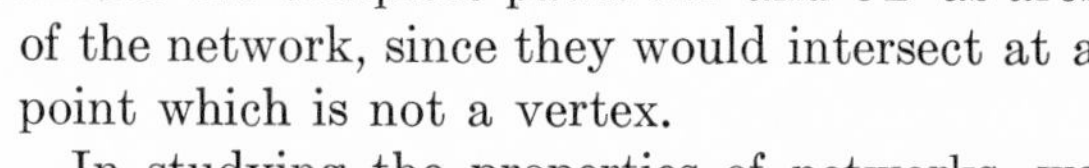

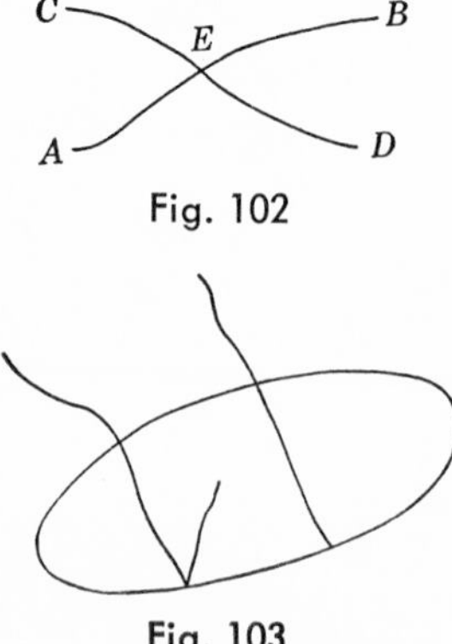

Fig. 102

Fig. 103

In studying the properties of networks, we shall be interested, among other properties, in the question of the number of pieces or *regions* into which the network divides the plane. For example, in Fig. 102 there is only one region, for you can go from any point in the plane to any other point without crossing the network. On the other hand, there are two regions associated with any closed circuit. However, the network in Fig. 103, consisting of seven vertices and nine arcs, has four regions.

5. Euler-Poincaré formula

If, in any network lying in a plane, V denotes the number of vertices, A the number of arcs, and R the number of regions into which the plane is cut by the network, then

$$V - A + R = 2$$

Here we have one of the deepest and most fundamental properties of networks. This relation holds, regardless of how simple or how complicated the network is.

Euler (1707–1783) observed this relation between the vertices, edges, and faces of the polyhedra. Poincaré (1854–1912) developed the extensions of the formula to apply on all types of surfaces.

We shall give a simple proof of this formula depending only on the intuitive use of the Jordan curve theorem. First, notice that the formula is true for the simplest network, a single arc with its two end points as vertices. Here $V = 2$, $A = 1$, $R = 1$ and $2 - 1 + 1 = 2$. Now we shall consider three modifications of any given simple network to produce a more complicated one:

Modification 1. Designate a point on an arc of the network as a vertex, and divide the arc into two arcs. For example, in Fig. 104 we have a network consisting of two vertices and three arcs. The modification indicated changes it into a network which looks the same but consists of three vertices and four arcs. Whatever may have been the values of V, A, and R in the original network, this modification makes them $V + 1$, $A + 1$, R, and we have

$$(V + 1) - (A + 1) + R = V - A + R$$

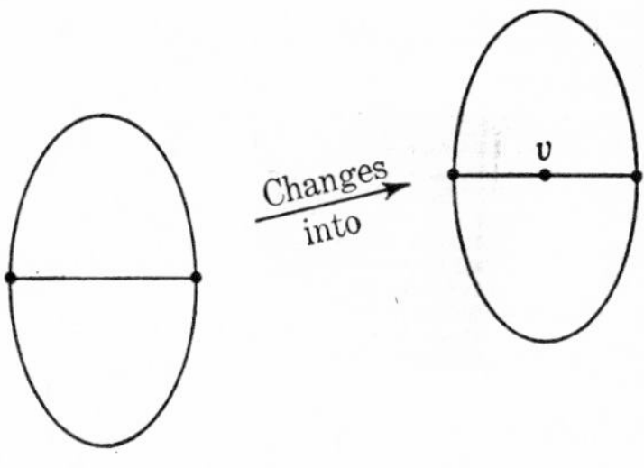

Fig. 104

This means that the value of this relationship between the vertices, arcs, and regions is the same in the original and modified networks.

Modification 2. At a vertex of the network attach an arc which has no other point in common with the original network, as, for example, in Fig. 105. This modification always increases the value of A by 1. It also increases the value of V by 1, namely, the vertex which is the end point of the new arc not on the original network. The quantity R remains unchanged. Since V and A

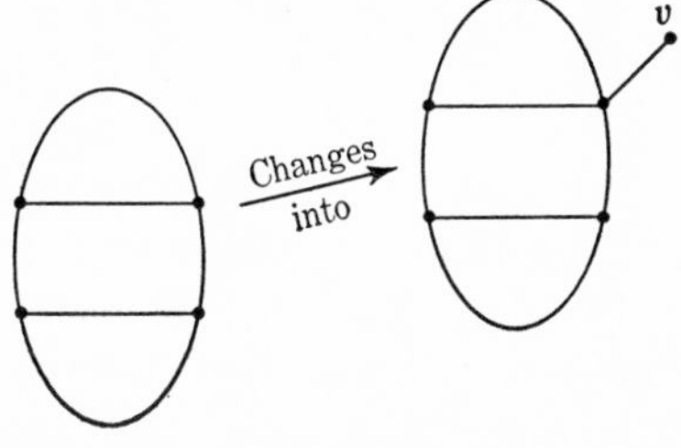

Fig. 105

are both increased by 1, the value of $V - A + R$ is the same in both the original and the modified network.

Modification 3. Join two vertices of the network by a new arc having no other points in common with the network, as, for example, in Fig. 106. This modification increases A by 1, but it also increases R by 1. The quantity V remains unchanged. Then the original and modified network gives the same value of $V - A + R$.

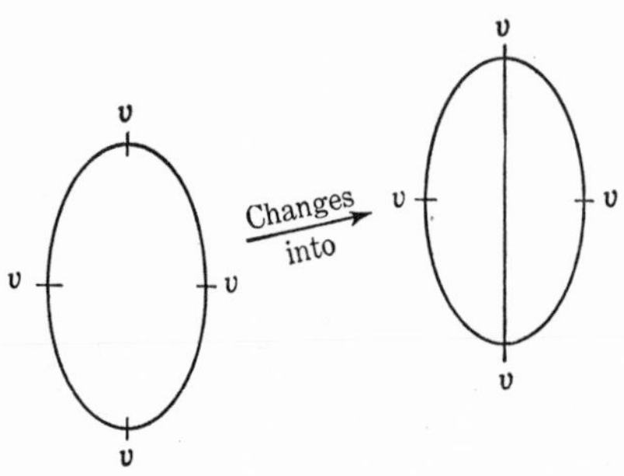

Fig. 106

Now, starting with a single arc, we may build up any network whatever in the plane by using, as needed, the modifications 1, 2 and 3 discussed above. But we have shown that the network consisting of a single arc and its two end points as vertices satisfies the equation $V - A + R = 2$, and no one of the three modifications changes the value of the left-hand side. Thus this relationship is still true for whatever final network is produced.

EXERCISES

1. Compute V, A, and R for the lines of the checkerboard of 9 squares. Verify $V - A + R = 2$.

2. Repeat Prob. 1 for the usual checkerboard of 64 squares.

3. Considering the corners as vertices, the edges as arcs, and the faces as regions, verify $V - A + R = 2$ for the cube.

4. Repeat Prob. 3 for the tetrahedron shown in Fig. 107.

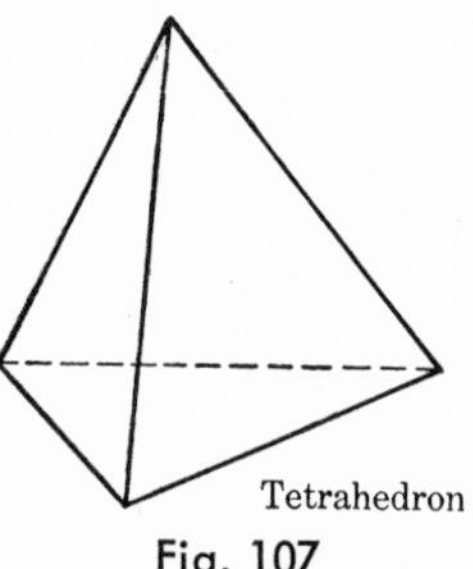

Fig. 107

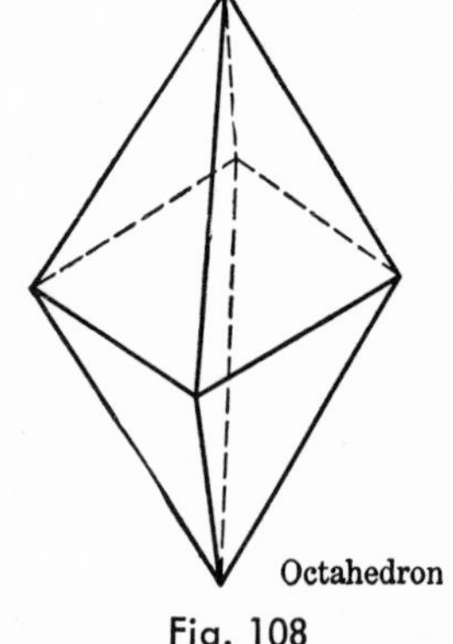

Fig. 108

5. Repeat Prob. 3 for the regular octahedron. An octahedron (Fig. 108) consists of two pyramids with square bases joined along the bases. It consists of eight faces, each of which is an equilateral triangle.

6. Show that any network separating the plane into exactly two parts has the same number of arcs as it does vertices.

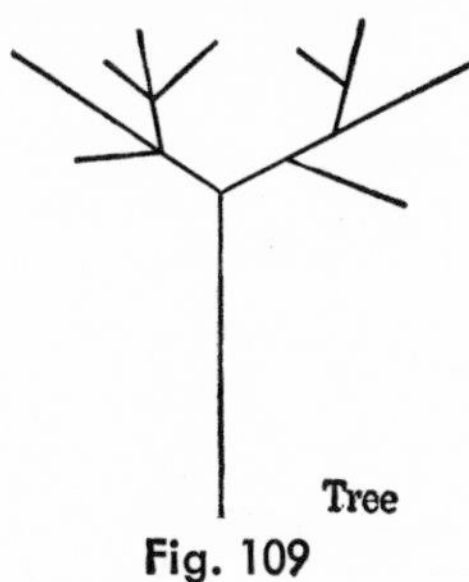

Fig. 109

7. A *tree* is a network which does not contain any simple closed curve. In Fig. 109 we see that such a network may resemble a tree with branches, hence its name. Prove that in any tree the number of vertices is always one more than the number of arcs.

??????????? PROBLEM JUST FOR FUN ???????????

Four schoolboys living in Switzerland start home from school on their skis. They leave the school by the four doors marked A, B, C, and D, and boy A goes to home A, boy B to home B, etc.

How do they ski home without having two tracks cross and without leaving the square shown?

???????????????? JUST FOR FUN ????????????????

6. The seven bridges of Königsberg

At Königsberg in Germany there were once seven bridges arranged as shown in Fig. 110. The problem is to plan a Sunday afternoon stroll so as to cross each bridge exactly once and return to the starting point. Can you plan the Sunday walk?

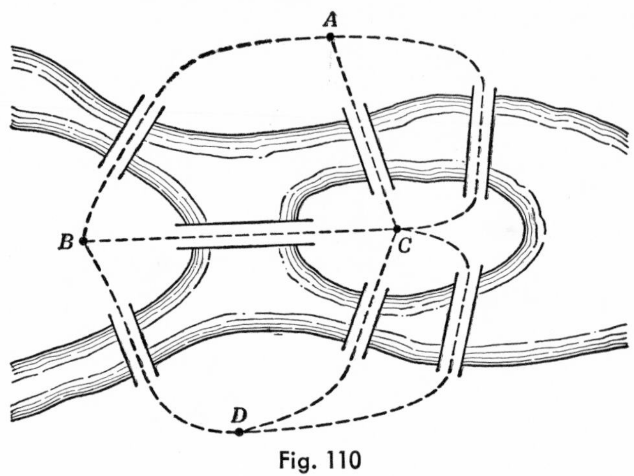

Fig. 110

7. Traversing networks

The Königsberg problem is one example of traversing a network. We say that a network can be walked through or *traversed* if a path exists which starts at a point, covers each arc of the network exactly once, and terminates at the beginning point. This path is permitted to cross itself if needed.

In Fig. 111 we have a network which can be traversed, and one such path is indicated by the numbers, starting with the vertex marked 1 and walking as indicated by the numbers 2, 3, 4, etc. On the other hand, in Fig. 112 we have a network which cannot be traversed, for no matter how we use the three arcs from A to B, our path will terminate at the opposite point from where it started.

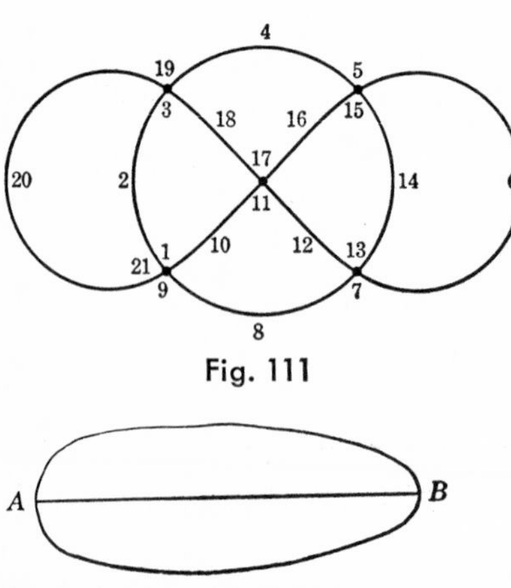

Fig. 111

Fig. 112

Returning to the Königsberg problem, we can convert the figure into a network by labeling the points marked A, B, C, D in Fig. 110 and using the dotted paths as arcs. Then we have a network of four vertices and seven arcs which crosses each bridge exactly once. If this network can be traversed, we have the plan for our Sunday walk. Conversely, the plan for a Sunday walk would give the path for traversing the network. We shall settle this Königsberg bridge problem by means of the principle of the next section.

8. General traversing principle

Statement: A network may be traversed if and only if the order of each vertex is even.

By the *order* of a vertex, we mean the number of different arcs which have that vertex as an end point. In Fig. 111 we saw a network which could be traversed. It has five vertices, and all are of order 4 in agreement with the general traversing principle. In Fig. 112, however, we have a network which cannot be traversed, and we observe that it has two vertices both of odd order in accordance with the general principle.

We shall now prove the general principle in two parts:

1. If a network can be traversed, every vertex is of even order.

This is easily seen, for each time the path approaches a particular vertex along an arc, there must also be an arc along which the path leaves the vertex. As each arc is used just once, the total number of arcs meeting at the vertex is even.

2. If the order of every vertex is even, the network can be traversed.

Select any vertex B as the beginning (Fig. 113). Select any arc meeting at B, say, BC, and proceed along it to the next vertex C. Here select any arc except the ones which have been used and proceed on it to the next vertex. At this vertex choose any arc that has not been used as yet and proceed on it to the next vertex. Continue in this manner. As long as the vertex approached is not B, the total number of arcs at the vertex already used will be odd. Since the order of this vertex is even, we will always have at least one unused arc to lead the path away from this vertex. Thus the path continues through the network until we return to the starting point B. We must return to B at some stage, for the path cannot continue indefinitely (there are only a finite number of

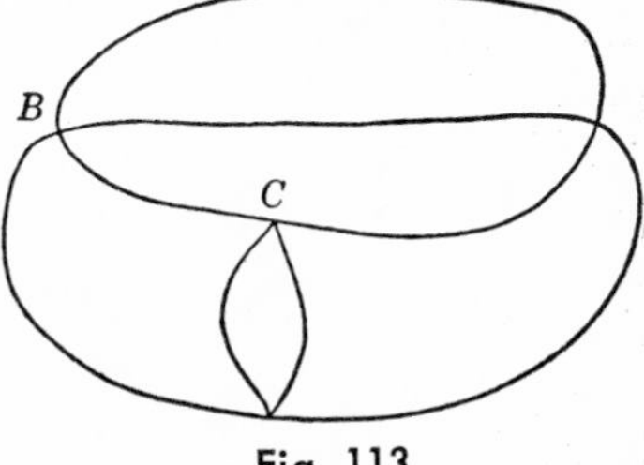

Fig. 113

arcs). We now start the path from B again along an unused arc and continue the previous process. At some stage on a return to B we find no unused arcs available at B. This stops the process.

We have now a path starting and ending at B (it also may pass through B at several intermediate points) and using no arc of the network more than once. If the path uses every arc of the network, it is the desired traversing path.

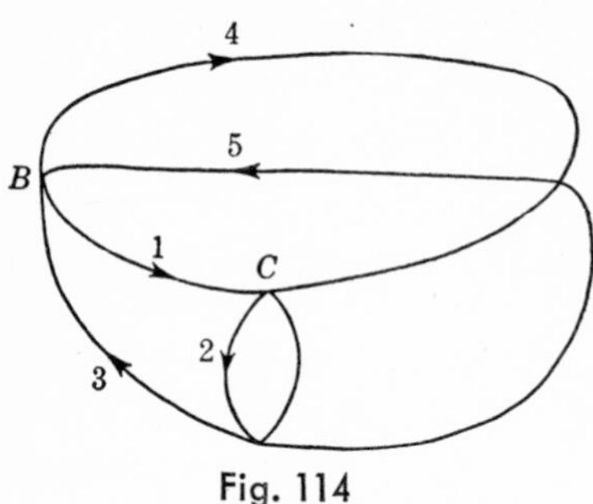

Fig. 114

On the other hand, if there are arcs of the network which do not belong to this path (see Fig. 114), there is an arc which has one of its end points on the path. This follows from the fact that a network is connected. Let C denote such an end point. Since the order of C is even and the path has used an even number of arcs meeting at C, there are at least two arcs at C not used in the path. Choose one of these and proceed along it to the next vertex. Just as before, the total number of arcs used at this vertex will be odd, and we shall have at least one arc available to choose as an exit from the vertex. We can always continue this process unless the vertex approached is C. Furthermore, we must approach C at some stage of this continuing process, since the total number of arcs is finite and the process can continue unless C is approached.

Now we have a path beginning and ending at B, together with a side excursion beginning and ending at C. Let us combine them into a single path by starting at B, proceeding along the original path to C, making the side excursion and returning to C, then continuing on the original path to its ending at B.

This new path begins and ends at B and uses no arc of the network more than once. If every arc is used, it is the desired traversing path. If not, we build a new side excursion and add it to the path. By continuing to increase the path, adding side excursions, we arrive eventually at a path using all the arcs. This completes the proof of the general traversing principle.

9. Walks with different beginning and end

Traversing a network requires the path to begin and end at the same point. What is the situation if we do not require the same beginning and ending? If the number of vertices of *odd* order is *exactly two*, a path exists beginning at one odd vertex and ending at the other and using each arc of the network exactly once. For example, such a path exists in the network of Fig. 112.

On the other hand, if the number of vertices of odd order is neither zero nor two, no path whatever exists which uses each arc exactly once. In the Königsberg bridge network there are four vertices of odd order. Thus no Sunday stroll can be planned at all, even if we allow the walk to end at a different point from its start.

??????????? PROBLEM JUST FOR FUN ???????????

Some years ago a party of five hunters and five native bearers fell into the hands of a hostile tribe of cannibals. After much palavering, the chief agreed that five of the party would be killed and five would be permitted to go unharmed. In order to choose the five to be killed by lot, the chief placed the party of ten in a circle and let the leader of the party, Pat Dimwit, choose a number and point

to the man to start counting. When the count reached the chosen number, that man was to be taken out and killed and the count begun again from that point until a second man was picked for the evening pot, and so on until the five unfortunate ones were chosen.

The white hunters schemed to have the native bearers chosen for death and themselves escape. But poor Pat Dimwit forgot the scheme and started with the wrong man and wrong number. He started his count as shown in the diagram, and all the white hunters were killed.

Can you find (*a*) the number Pat used and (*b*) the number he should have used and where he should have started counting?

???????????????? JUST FOR FUN ????????????????

EXERCISES

1. If one of the Königsberg bridges is closed, can you plan a Sunday walk crossing each open bridge exactly once? Can the stroll end at the same point it began?

2. Where can a new bridge be built so that a Sunday stroll will be possible (not requiring the same point as beginning and end)?

3. Which bridges must be closed if a Sunday walk beginning and ending at the same point is to be possible?

4. Where must new bridges be built if a Sunday walk with the same beginning and end point is to be possible?

5. Plan a walk through the five-room house shown in Fig. 115 so as to pass through each door exactly once. Is such a walk possible? Why?

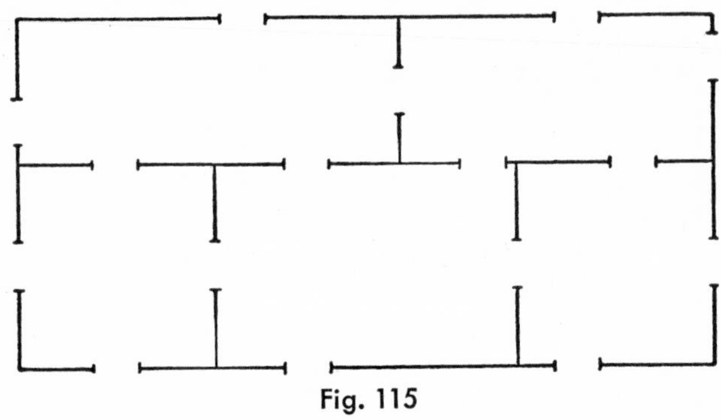

Fig. 115

10. Euler-Poincaré formula for surfaces

We proved the Euler-Poincaré formula for networks lying in the plane. However, it is easy to see that it also applies to networks drawn on the surface of a sphere. Select one region into which the network divides the surface of the sphere and cut a small hole in this region. Now, imagining the sphere to be made of very elastic rubber, we may flatten out the sphere with a hole in it until it becomes a circular flat piece with the edge of the hole as its outer edge. The network on the sphere becomes a network in the plane with the same number of vertices, arcs, and regions. The region on the sphere containing the hole becomes the outside region of the network in the plane. Then

$$V - A + R = 2$$

This formula also holds for the edges of any polyhedron, for if we think of the polyhedron surface as rubber, we may deform it into a sphere, and the edges of the polyhedron become a network on the sphere.

Figure 116 shows the surface known as a torus. It resembles an automobile inner tube. On it draw a network consisting of two circles, C_1 and C_2, one going around the torus in each direction as shown in the figure. In this network we have $V = 3$, $A = 4$, $R = 1$, and substituting in the Euler-Poincaré formula (page 241), we get

$$V - A + R = 3 - 4 + 1 = 0$$

instead of 2 as formerly.

But we notice a fundamental difference between the sphere and the torus. In the sphere, every cut which is a simple closed curve or closed circuit divides the spherical surface into two parts (Fig. 117). On the inner tube, some circuit cuts divide the surface but some do not. Each of the circuits C_1 and C_2 shown in Fig. 116 fails to divide the surface into two parts. But any two nonintersecting circuits divide the torus surface. On the other hand, the more complicated surface shown in Fig. 118 contains two circuit cuts that do not intersect, and still the surface is in one piece.

This property of the number of circuits necessary to divide the surface is called the *genus of the surface*. The surface is said to have *genus p* if there are p nonintersecting circuits on the surface which leave the surface in one piece but each $p + 1$ such cuts divide the surface. Thus the sphere is of genus 0, the torus of genus 1, and the surface in Fig. 118 of genus 2. A torus may be deformed into the sphere with one handle shown in

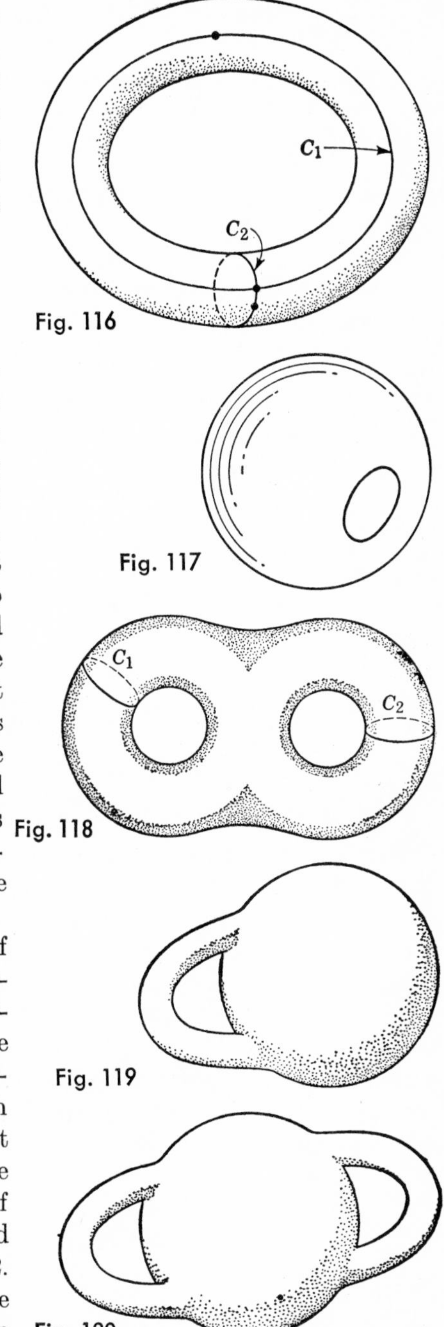

Fig. 116

Fig. 117

Fig. 118

Fig. 119

Fig. 120

Fig. 119. Also, the surface of genus 2 of Fig. 118 may be deformed into a sphere with two handles, as shown in Fig. 120. Thus we may consider each such two-sided surface as a sphere with p handles, and the number of handles is the same as the genus.

For such a two-sided surface, the Euler-Poincaré formula becomes

$$V - A + R = 2 - 2p$$

where p is the genus. This formula applies only to networks that cut the surface into regions that can be deformed into flat disks. The proof of this generalized formula is not too difficult, but it is long, and we shall not give it here.

??????????? PROBLEM JUST FOR FUN ???????????

In the olden days pilgrims on their way to visit holy shrines spent their nights at wayside inns at short distances apart, for travel was slow in those days. They liked to while away their long winter evenings by proposing puzzles to one another.

A devout parson told of his parish, through which ran a small stream which joined the sea some hundred miles to the south. He showed a map of a part of his parish and propounded his puzzler.

"Here, my worthy pilgrims, is a strange riddle. Behold how at the branching of the river is an island. Upon this island doth stand my own poor parsonage, and ye may all see the whereabouts of the village church. Mark ye, also, that there be eight bridges and no more over the river in my parish.

On my way to church it is my wont to visit sundry of my flock, and in the doing thereof I do pass over every one of the eight bridges once and no more. Can any of ye find the path, after this manner from the house to the church, without going out of the parish? Nay, nay, my friends, I do never cross the river in any boat, neither by swimming nor wading, nor do I go underground like a mole, nor fly in the air as doth the eagle; but only pass over by the bridges."

Can you find the parson's path? At first it seems impossible, but the conditions stated provide a loophole.

???????????????? JUST FOR FUN ????????????????

EXERCISES

1. Compute V, A, and R for the network on the torus consisting of four circuits, two going around the torus each way. Verify that $V - A + R = 0$.

2. If the network on the torus consists of only one circuit going around the torus, we have $V = 2$, $A = 2$, $R = 1$ and $V - A + R = 2 - 2 + 1 = 1$. Why?

3. Compute V, A, and R for the network shown in Fig. 121, and verify the generalized Euler-Poincaré formula in this case.

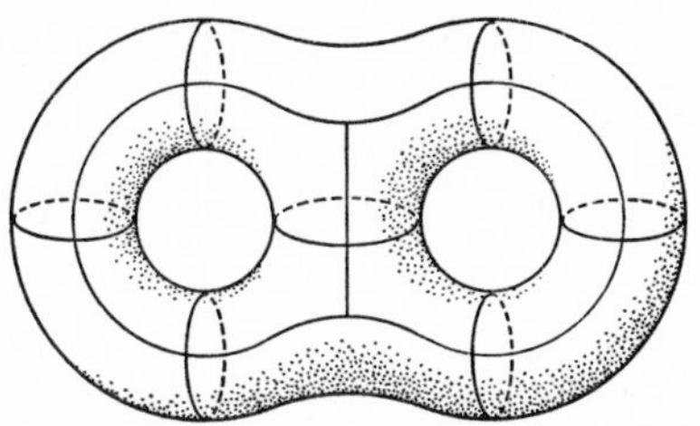

Fig. 121

11. One-sided surfaces

In the preceding section we discussed the two-sided surfaces without edges. Earlier, in the Möbius band, we saw a surface with only one side, but it had an edge. There are surfaces without edges, which have only one side, but they require some imagination to visualize. The simplest one can be visualized by imagining a Möbius band and a circular piece of rubber sewed together along their edges. This is called the *projective plane*. If we try to accomplish this sewing physically, we shall find ourselves in trouble. The physical sewing can be carried out actually in four-dimensional space, but that is another story.

The next simplest one-sided surface can be visualized by imagining two Möbius bands sewn together along their edges. It is called a *Klein bottle* (Fig. 122). This sewing may be done physically in four-dimensional space. In three-dimensional space we can only do it in our mind.

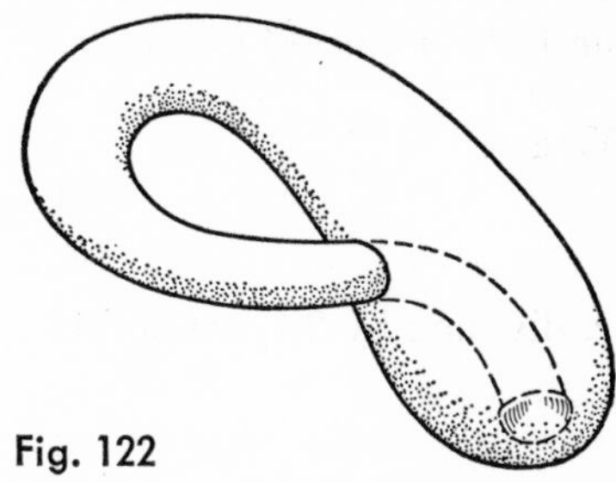

Fig. 122

Thus there exist a whole series of two-sided surfaces and correspondingly a whole series of one-sided surfaces, of which we have examined a few of the simpler ones.

12. Regular polyhedra

A polyhedron is called regular if all its faces are congruent regular polygons, the same number of faces meet at each vertex, and all the dihedral angles are the same. Five regular polyhedrons are known: tetrahedron (Fig. 107), cube, octahedron (Fig. 108), dodecahedron (Fig. 123), and icosahedron (Fig. 124).

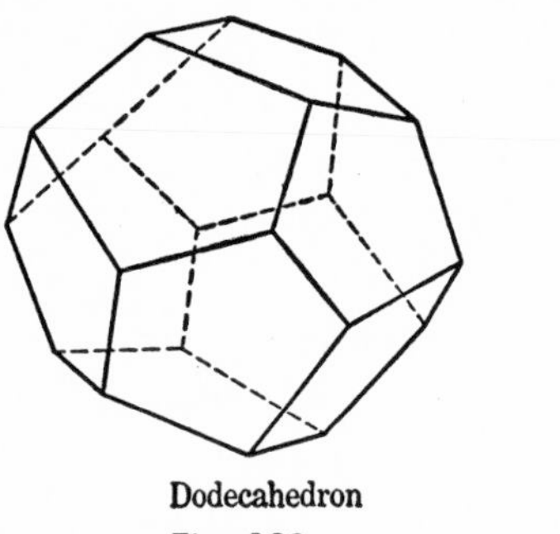

Dodecahedron
Fig. 123

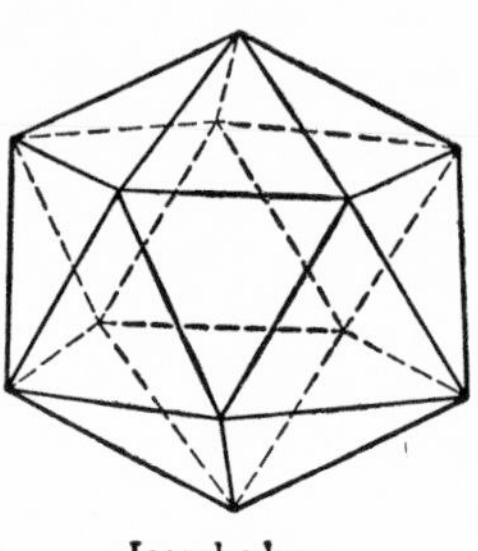

Icosahedron
Fig. 124

The size of face angles and the dihedral angles are not topological properties. Even ignoring these properties, we can prove by topology that there are no more regular polyhedrons to be found. We shall prove that there are only five networks in which each region has the same number of sides and every vertex has the same order.

If each region has n sides, then nR counts all arcs. But each arc bounds two regions, so it has been counted twice, once from each side. Thus in a regular polyhedron

$$nR = 2A$$

Also, if every vertex is of order k, then kV counts all the arcs. But each one has been counted twice, once from each end, so in a regular polyhedron

$$kV = 2A$$

Now we substitute the values of R and V from the last two relations into the Euler-Poincaré formula

$$V - A + R = 2$$

We get

$$\frac{2A}{k} - A + \frac{2A}{n} = 2$$

or, dividing by $2A$, we obtain

$$\frac{1}{k} + \frac{1}{n} = \frac{1}{A} + \frac{1}{2}$$

Now $n \geqq 3$, since the faces are at least triangles. Also, $k \geqq 3$, since there are at least three faces at each vertex. But one of n or k must be 3, for if both k and n are 4 or larger, the left-hand side of the last equation above would be $\leqq \frac{1}{2}$, and no value of A could make the equation true.

If $n = 3$, the above equation becomes

$$\frac{1}{k} - \frac{1}{6} = \frac{1}{A}$$

and k may be 3, 4, or 5. It is not possible to have $k \geqq 6$, for this would make A negative or infinite.

Similarly, if $k = 3$, the equation becomes

$$\frac{1}{n} - \frac{1}{6} = \frac{1}{A}$$

and $n = 3, 4$, or 5 are the only possible values.

All together we have just five solutions, as $n = 3$ and $k = 3$ occurs in each case:

$n = 3$	$k = 3$	$A = 6$	$R = 4$	tetrahedron
$n = 3$	$k = 4$	$A = 12$	$R = 8$	octahedron
$n = 3$	$k = 5$	$A = 30$	$R = 20$	icosahedron
$n = 4$	$k = 3$	$A = 12$	$R = 6$	cube
$n = 5$	$k = 3$	$A = 30$	$R = 12$	dodecahedron

Thus we have proved by topology that there do not exist more than five regular polyhedra.

13. Coloring maps

Father Mapper handed his son two maps to color (Figs. 125 and 126). The son studied the maps a moment and said, "I can color one of them, but I do not have enough colors to color the other." This was found to be correct.

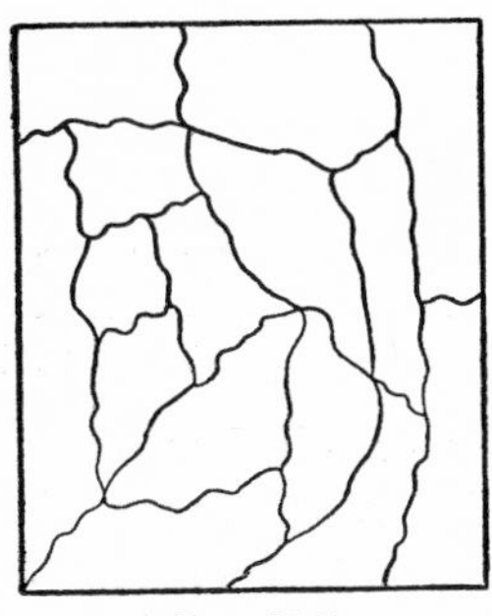

Fig. 125

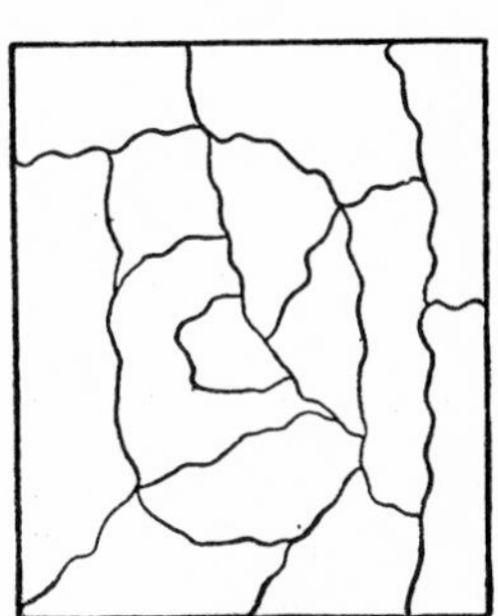

Fig. 126

How many colors did the son have, and which map did he find impossible to color? Of course, we always color a map so that two regions meeting along an arc are colored two different colors.

14. The four-color problem

The puzzle above leads us to the more general question: How many colors must a printer keep in stock in order to be able to print every possible map that may be brought to him? Or, we may say, how many colors are required to color all possible networks so that whenever two regions meet along an arc, they are colored differently. Regions which meet only at a vertex may be colored the same, since this creates no difficulty. Fig. 127 shows a map which requires four colors, for every region meets all the remaining three. But no one has ever discovered a network or a map requiring more than four colors. In 1890 Heawood proved that every network in the plane can be colored in five colors. But no one to this day has proved it can be done in four colors or found a network requiring five. However, if a map needing five colors exists, it must be fairly complicated, for in 1946 DeBacker proved that any such map must have at least 35 regions.

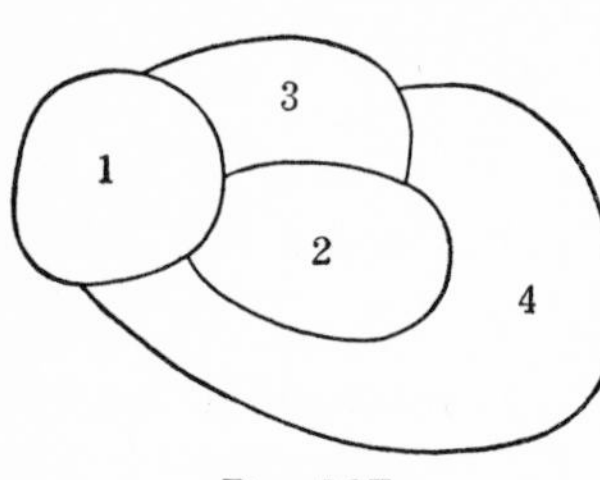

Fig. 127

The four-color problem is unsolved for maps on the simplest of all surfaces, the plane or the sphere. It might be guessed, then, that there is little hope of solving the color problem on the more complicated surfaces. On the contrary, the problem is completely solved for all the other well-known surfaces such as the torus, the surface of genus 2, the Möbius strip, the Klein bottle, etc. The number of colors needed varies with the surfaces. But in each case the problem is completely solved, for we can prove that every map can be colored in q colors and can exhibit a map requiring exactly q colors. For the two-sided surfaces of genus p, we know the number of colors q in all cases below genus 8 except the sphere (Table 55).

TABLE 55

p	0	1	2	3	4	5	6	7	8
q	4(?)	7	8	9	10	11	12	12	13(?)

The torus is the surface of genus 1, and we see in Table 55 that every possible map on the torus can be colored in seven colors. Also, we can exhibit a map of seven regions on the torus in which each region touches all the other six, so we could not color this map in less than seven colors.

Hence the color problem is completely solved for the torus. Also, for the surface of genus 2 shown in Fig. 118 (page 249), the color problem is completely solved and the number is eight. But for the simplest of all surfaces, the sphere or plane, the problem has never been solved.

EXERCISES

1. Draw a map on the torus consisting of five countries, all of which touch the four others.

2. Draw a map on the torus in which there are six countries all touching one another.

3. Draw a map on the Möbius strip of five regions, all touching one another. What does this tell us about the number of colors on a Möbius strip?

4. Draw a map on the surface of Fig. 118 p. 249 consisting of six countries, all of which touch one another.

5. Draw a map on the surface of Fig. 118 of seven countries, all of which touch one another.

6. The color number for the Möbius strip is six and for the torus is seven, that is, we can prove that every map on the surface can be colored in this number of colors. Can you draw maps to prove that these numbers are as small as possible? This means a map of six regions on the Möbius strip, each region touching all others along an arc, and similarly one of seven regions on the torus.

??????????? PROBLEM JUST FOR FUN ???????????

The job of a heating-tunnel inspector is to walk through and examine each day all the heating tunnels joining the 12 buildings shown in the diagram.

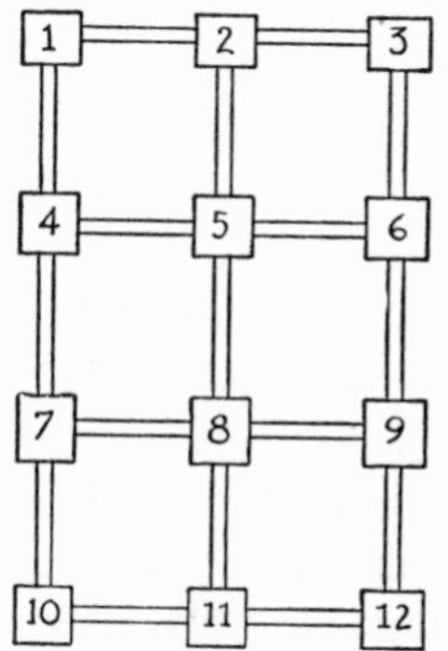

To complete his job he finds he must walk through some tunnels twice, but naturally he wishes to avoid unnecessary walking. Each tunnel is 1 mile long, and he discovers a route which completes his job by walking 19 miles.

Can you find where he should start and how he should walk to go through all the tunnels in 19 miles?

??????????????? JUST FOR FUN ???????????????

CHAPTER

25

Logic—The Art of Reasoning (*How to Influence People and Lose Friends*)

> Formal thought, consciously recognized as such, is the means of all exact knowledge; and a correct understanding of the main formal sciences, Logic and Mathematics, is the proper and only safe foundation for a scientific education. ARTHUR LEFEVRE

1. Reasoning

Aristotle first remarked that the distinct trait which distinguishes human beings from other mammals is the ability to reason. Some recent experiments by psychologists have shown that a number of animals have limited reasoning power. On the other hand, our observations of some human beings make us wonder whether they reason at all. While Aristotle's remark may not be entirely correct, we will agree that human beings do consider various bits of information and draw conclusions from them, and that human beings are exhibiting their best mental talents when this reasoning is being carefully and accurately done. *Logic* is the study of the laws of reasoning and the principles of valid reasoning.

Mathematics is impossible without logic, for we must use correct arguments if we are to solve problems, prove theorems, etc. But logic enters into life in many other ways. In writing and speaking we must state precisely what we mean or we shall be misunderstood. Most arguments and disagreements result from inaccurate statements or the inaccurate use of words. And, correctly or not, all the people about us are continually drawing conclusions from statements and observations. A study of the principles of valid reasoning, that is, of logic, will assist us in understanding this process in which all of us take part.

However, we must not conclude that correct reasoning is always desirable or will best accomplish the desired purpose. An appeal to sentiment or emotion may fall flat if subjected to cold logical analysis. A speech that will win an election may not be logical at all. An opponent of a senator from North Carolina obtained the menu from the Washington hotel where the senator lived and used it as a campaign issue. He made speeches all over the state pointing to the "elegant vittles" the senator was eating compared to the simple fare of the voters. It had little logic, but it changed many votes. Often a politician will win more votes by arousing emotions than by a logical analysis of the issues. But such tactics will fail when the voters are intelligent and logical.

Advertisers are interested in selling their product, not in logic. Often advertising is based on illogical inferences. One example is the picture we often see of a beautiful girl or a distinguished man using the product. How does this sell the product? As readers, we are supposed to reason: It is desirable to be beautiful or distinguished. The picture shows the beautiful or distinguished one using this product. Therefore it is desirable that we use this product. Clearly, this is dubious reasoning, but evidently enough people arrive at the above conclusion so that this is good advertising.

In a great many simple cases we can recognize valid or invalid reasoning without logical principles. But in the more complicated cases, a study of logic or logical principles is of great assistance.

2. Statements

Before we can examine arguments for their validity, we must have a clear understanding of statements—what they mean and what they do not mean. Let us take as an example the simple statement: Not all students pass their courses. Now consider the following statements:

a. Some students fail their courses.
b. If one is a student, one must expect to fail.
c. No student passes all his courses.
d. The teacher will always fail some students.
e. The class in which all students pass does not exist.
f. Among all students will be found some who fail courses.
g. Some students pass their courses.

These statements sound rather similar, and the careless person may feel that they all state the same thing. We must think very carefully to locate the ones which state precisely the same thing. But we must first be certain of the meaning of our words. Does "fail" mean the same as "not pass"? It does if these are the only two alternatives in our grading system. But if *condition* or *incomplete* exist in our grading system, then "not pass" is not the same as "fail." So two students from different colleges may draw quite different meanings from the same statement. To discuss these statements we will assume that "fail" and "not pass" mean the same.

In examining statements, it has been found desirable to use circle diagrams. We let the points inside one circle represent the class of all students, and we let the points inside a second circle represent "persons who pass their courses" (Fig. 128). Now our original statement may be restated: Not all students belong to the class of persons who pass their courses. This tells us that some points of the *student* circle are outside the other circle, and we indicate this by placing a T for true in this portion. Now, do some students belong to the class of persons who pass their courses? We may consider this as obvious, but if we examine our original statement, we see that it does not say so. Thus this is not answered by the statement, and we indicate this by placing the question mark in that portion. We might also question whether any part of the circle "persons who pass their courses" is outside the "student" circle. This is a matter of definition of the word "student" and is not pertinent to the examination of the statements.

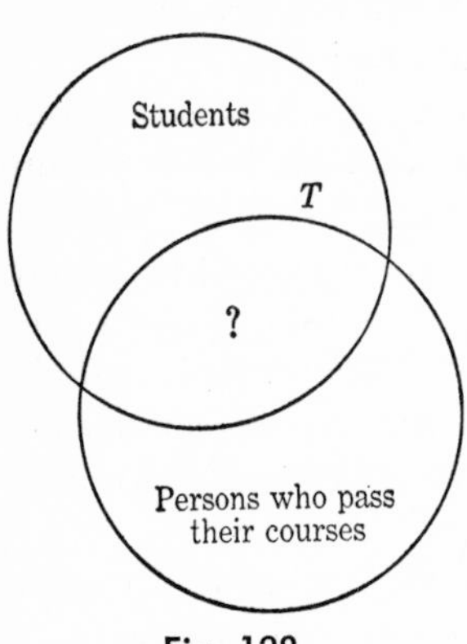

Fig. 128

Now, if we examine the various statements we see that a and f are equivalent to the original statement. Statements b, c, and g are not equivalent. Whether d and e are equivalent depends on what we mean by "all the students." If our original statement refers to all the students under one teacher, then d is equivalent; otherwise not. Similarly e is equivalent only if we refer to students of one class in the original statement.

Let us consider the four statements:

Some good people are not happy.

Some unhappy people are good.

Some unhappy people are not wicked.

Some good people are unhappy.

These four statements are all equivalent, but we may be uncertain of this as we get mixed up with the nots and somes. For instance, "some happy people are not good" and "some unhappy people are not good" sound very much like the other four but are not equivalent statements. The diagram will help us in this difficulty, and we draw the first statement (Fig. 129). The second statement says that some points outside the "happy" circle are inside the "good" circle, and this agrees with the diagram. Similarly, we see that the third and fourth statements are equivalent.

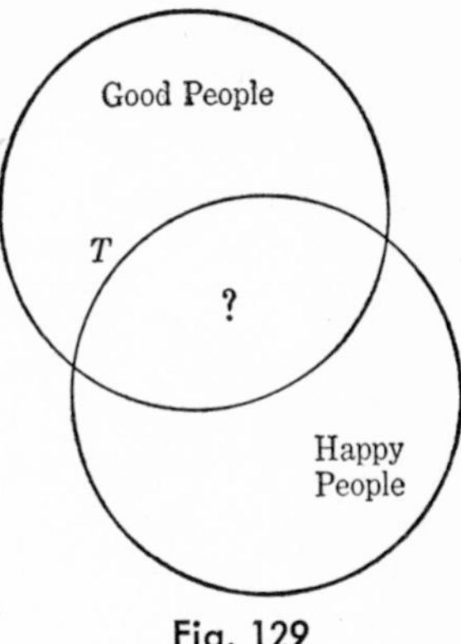

Fig. 129

EXERCISES

1. Assuming that the first statement in each set is correct, decide which of the remaining ones are equivalent and which are true, false, and doubtful.

a. All Yankees are Americans.
Some Americans are not Yankees.
No non-American is a Yankee.
No Yankee is not an American.

b. No cat is a vegetarian.
Some cats are not vegetarians.
Either it is a cat or it is a vegetarian.
All cats are nonvegetarians.

c. It never rains in the desert.
If we are in the desert, it is not raining.
We are not in the desert, so it must rain sometime.
Where it is raining is not desert.

d. If we lose this game, I'll eat my hat.
Unless the game is not lost, I'll not eat my hat.
Either the game is won or I eat my hat.
Unless I eat my hat, the game is won.

e. While poverty exists, the world is not perfect.
Either the world is perfect or poverty exists.
I know the world is not perfect, therefore poverty exists.
Unless poverty does not exist, the world cannot be perfect.

2. What statement can you know is true if each of the following statements is false?

a. No man lives a century.
b. Some students are dishonest.
c. All Cretans are liars.
d. Every even number is divisible by 4.

e. Some people are not happy.
f. The stories were either dull or dirty.
g. If it rains, we must go home.

3. Four milers on the track team all propose marriage to Susie just before the Big Ten meet. She makes the following promises:

a. To Bob: Only if you win will I marry you.
b. To John: If I do not marry you, you will not have won.
c. To Sam: Either you win, or I will not marry you.
d. To Bill: Unless you do not win, I will not marry you.

Consider the possibility that each one may win, and state in each case what Susie must, may, and may not do, if she is to keep all her promises.

4. A football coach has four fullbacks. The following statements are true:

a. Either he does not use Murphy or he does not win the game.
b. Only if he does not use Brown does he win the game.
c. Only if he does not use Smith does he not win the game.
d. Unless he does not use Jones, he does not win the game.

Which fullback should he use and why to be sure of winning?

??????????? PROBLEM JUST FOR FUN ???????????

A set of balls, some of which are white and some yellow, are all spotted with one or more of the colors green, blue, and red. All the balls with red spots have blue spots also. All the white balls with blue spots and all the yellow balls which do not have both red and green spots are removed. Describe the balls which remain.

???????????????? JUST FOR FUN ????????????????

3. Hidden implications

There is a very old proverb which goes, Say what you mean and mean what you say. Failure to observe this maxim is the cause of much confusion between people, some of which is accidental and some deliberate. Much malicious gossip has its origin in statements, innocent in themselves, which have double meanings or can be twisted into other interpretations. In other words, the hearer understands something different from what the speaker said.

If we are to study logic, or the art of thinking and reasoning correctly, we must learn to phrase our statements so that they express our meaning precisely. And we must learn to be on guard for statements with hidden implications. Sometimes these statements are made deliberately, and we must be wary of the trap. There is the case of the student who had not started his term theme and who was asked by his instructor how the theme was coming. He replied, "I have not finished it yet!" The student spoke the truth, and yet the instructor probably drew an incorrect conclusion.

An anecdote from the day of sailing vessels will further illustrate our point of hidden implications. One day the captain wrote in the ship's log, "The mate was drunk today." The mate protested long and ardently but had little to reply to the captain's insistent comment, "It's the truth, isn't it?" Some days later it was the mate's turn to keep the log for the day, and he wrote in it, "The captain was sober today." To the angry captain he replied calmly, "It's the truth, isn't it?"

EXERCISES

Discuss the following statements for hidden implications.

1. Have you stopped beating your wife?

2. Well, there is no reason why he should lie.

3. All pigs are created equal, but some pigs are more equal than others. (*Orwell*, "The Animal Farm.")

4. More male drivers are involved in traffic accidents than women drivers.

5. If you are feeling bad, use Mrs. Springer's Tonic; you'll never feel better.

6. Those who called him a wit were half right.

7. John Hancock, the signer of the Declaration of Independence was a graduate of Harvard College.

8. Dr. Smith, I never heard you give a better lecture.

4. Argument

The meat of logic is the combining of several statements into a valid argument, or the drawing of a valid conclusion from several given statements. The original statements are called *premises* (or in mathematics, *hypotheses*), and the resulting statement the *conclusion*. The process of passing from the premises to the conclusion is called *deduction*.

Sometimes this process is very simple, and sometimes it is not. If we admit all men are liars and all liars are evil, then we conclude easily that all men are evil. We see this also from Fig. 130, where the points representing men are entirely within the circle of points representing liars, and both these circles are entirely within the "evil" circle. In this simple case, the diagram seems unnecessary; but in more involved arguments, diagrams are frequently helpful.

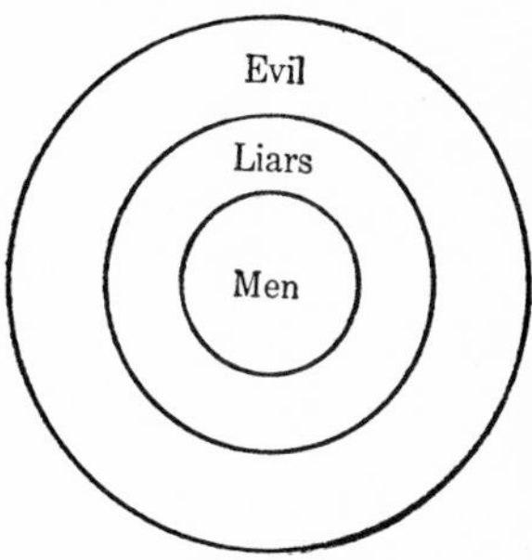

Fig. 130

The direct argument is the simplest type of deduction or proof. But sometimes this is not available, and we are forced to the indirect proof. This usually takes the form of a set of statements, one of which must be true. We show that all except a particular one must be false. Thus, by this indirect way, we prove the truth of the statement. A prosecuting attorney is using this method when he argues before a jury that one of three men must have committed the murder, and two of the men have proved their presence elsewhere at the time of the murder.

The indirect argument is valid, but we must be certain that all possible alternatives have been listed and examined. If we are sitting on the jury mentioned, we must be very certain that the prosecuting attorney has proved his point that one of three men must have committed the murder. Once this is established, his conclusion that the third man is guilty is valid. But if there is a fourth man who might have committed the murder, the argument is not sound. In everyday life, indirect arguments are subject to doubt, because not all alternatives are considered. But in mathematics and many other logical inquiries, indirect argument is often necessary.

A special case of indirect argument is known under the name *reductio ad absurdum*. For example, suppose we had two statements, "A is true" and "B is true," and we wished to prove "C is true." We might proceed: Let us assume that C is false and consider together the three statements "A is true," "B is true," "C is false." If we could show that this produces a contradiction, then we should know that "C is false" led to a contradiction and thus that C must be true. This is the method of *reductio ad absurdum*, which finds frequent use in mathematical proof.

A simple example is the proof that no largest integer exists. Let us assume that this is false and that a largest integer exists. Let us call it N and consider the quantity $N + 1$. It is an integer, for any integer plus 1 is an integer; and obviously it is greater than N. Then our assumption that a largest integer exists has led to a contradiction. Thus we have proved that no largest integer exists by a *reductio ad absurdum* argument.

A simple argument consists of three parts, the premises, the conclusion, and the deduction. The premises may be true or false. The conclusion may be true or false. The deduction may be valid or invalid. Sometimes we are inclined to believe that the premises must be true because we know that the conclusion is true. But this does not follow. In fact, from a false premise, with perfectly valid reasoning, we may obtain either a true or a false conclusion. We write the following table of possibilities, where T means true, F false, V valid, and IV invalid:

Premises	T	F	F	T	T	F	F
Deduction	V	V	V	IV	IV	IV	IV
Conclusions	T	T	F	T	F	T	F

We notice that this table has every possible combination except premise T, deduction V, and conclusion F. This means that we cannot obtain a false conclusion from true premises and valid reasoning. We can give examples of all seven combinations in the table. At the end of the Junior Prom when the students are tired from dancing, we might have the following argument where one of the premises is false, the reasoning valid, and the conclusion true: The students have been studying, and whenever they study they become tired; hence they are tired.

We may conclude just two possibilities from our table:

1. If the premises are true and the reasoning is valid, our conclusion is true.

2. If the conclusion is false, either a premise is false, or the reasoning is not valid, or both.

EXERCISES

Discuss the arguments used in Prob. 1-11.

1. Whenever it is going to rain, my rheumatism bothers me. My rheumatism bothers me. Hence it is going to rain.

2. Whenever it is going to rain, my rheumatism bothers me. My rheumatism does not bother me. Hence it is not going to rain.

3. He is a citizen of Chicago. Every citizen of Chicago is a citizen of Illinois. Every citizen of Illinois is a citizen of the United States. Hence he is a citizen of the United States.

4. Patchpants is the bravest of tailors. All tailors are men. Hence Patchpants is the bravest of men.

5. "If anyone has failed to study hard, he'll flunk this quiz." John studied hard. He will pass.

6. If Roosevelt is elected, grass will grow in the streets. (Campaign claim, 1932 election.) Grass did not grow in the streets. Hence Roosevelt was not elected.

7. I know he doesn't love me, for men never tell the truth to a girl, and he told me he loves me.

8. Bigamy is a crime. The Mormon religion permitted bigamy. Hence the Mormon religion permitted crime.

9. If a Republican is elected president, prices will rise. A Democrat is elected. Hence prices will not rise.

10. No state can exist unless its citizens exist. Hence no state can survive for two centuries.

11. A good man does not inflict pain. But a dentist inflicts pain. Hence a dentist is not a good man.

12. Find an advertisement in a newspaper or magazine giving a nonvalid argument.

??????????? PROBLEM JUST FOR FUN ???????????

Mary, Jane, and Violet belong to the same history class. If Mary is present, Jane and Violet are either both present or both absent. If Violet is present, Mary is present. Name all the possibilities under which Jane is absent.

???????????????? JUST FOR FUN ????????????????

5. Paradoxes

The dictionary defines paradox as "a statement essentially absurd and false." The paradox has had a long and interesting history, for man has always been intrigued with the dilemma of a seemingly self-contradictory statement.

As a simple example, suppose I say, "I am now lying." Let us consider that this statement is true. Then I am lying when I say it and thus I must not be lying. Hence my statement is false. On the other hand, let us consider the original statement false. Then I am stating a truth when I say, "I am now lying," and the statement is true. Here we have the typical paradox. Our statement gets us into difficulties no matter whether we consider it true or false.

EXERCISES

Analyze the following paradoxes and dilemmas.

1. The barber says, "I shave all men who do not shave themselves." Who shaves the barber?

2. Every rule has an exception.

3. Everything has a cause other than itself. God is the first cause.

4. Let us consider the class of all classes each of which does not contain itself as a member. Is this class a member of itself or not?

5. Protagoras gave his pupil Euathlus legal training, guaranteeing his training by the agreement that he should pay for it if and only if he won his first court case. When Euathlus failed to practice law at all, Protagoras brought suit against him. Protagoras argued before the court, "If I win this case, Euathlus must pay me by order of the court. If I lose it, he must pay me by the terms of our agreement. But I must win or lose this case; in either case he must pay me." But Euathlus showed he had profited by his training and argued in reply, "If I lose this case, the terms of our agreement say I do not have to pay, for I will have lost my first case. On the other hand, if I win, the court will decree that I do not have to pay. In either case I do not have to pay."

??????????? PROBLEM JUST FOR FUN ???????????

Three wise men were tested for their reasoning skill by being blindfolded and having a finger rubbed on each of their foreheads, after being told that one or more would have smudges on their foreheads. Actually, all three were given smudges. They were told to tap once if they saw one or more spots on removing the blindfold and to tap twice if they decided that there was a spot on their own forehead. When the blindfolds were removed, all three tapped once. After a pause, one man tapped twice. What was his reasoning?

???????????????? JUST FOR FUN ????????????????

Appendix

TABLE I. Powers and Roots

Squares and Cubes — Square Roots and Cube Roots

No.	Sq.	Sq. Root	Cube	Cube Root	No.	Sq.	Sq. Root	Cube	Cube Root
1	1	1.000	1	1.000	**51**	2,601	7.141	132,651	3.708
2	4	1.414	8	1.260	**52**	2,704	7.211	140,608	3.733
3	9	1.732	27	1.442	**53**	2,809	7.280	148,877	3.756
4	16	2.000	64	1.587	**54**	2,916	7.348	157,464	3.780
5	25	2.236	125	1.710	**55**	3,025	7.416	166,375	3.803
6	36	2.449	216	1.817	**56**	3,136	7.483	175,616	3.826
7	49	2.646	343	1.913	**57**	3,249	7.550	185,193	3.849
8	64	2.828	512	2.000	**58**	3,364	7.616	195,112	3.871
9	81	3.000	729	2.080	**59**	3,481	7.681	205,379	3.893
10	100	3.162	1,000	2.154	**60**	3,600	7.746	216,000	3.915
11	121	3.317	1,331	2.224	**61**	3,721	7.810	226,981	3.936
12	144	3.464	1,728	2.289	**62**	3,844	7.874	238,328	3.958
13	169	3.606	2,197	2.351	**63**	3,969	7.937	250,047	3.979
14	196	3.742	2,744	2.410	**64**	4,096	8.000	262,144	4.000
15	225	3.873	3,375	2.466	**65**	4,225	8.062	274,625	4.021
16	256	4.000	4,096	2.520	**66**	4,356	8.124	287,496	4.041
17	289	4.123	4,913	2.571	**67**	4,489	8.185	300,763	4.062
18	324	4.243	5,832	2.621	**68**	4,624	8.246	314,432	4.082
19	361	4.359	6,859	2.668	**69**	4,761	8.307	328,509	4.102
20	400	4.472	8,000	2.714	**70**	4,900	8.367	343,000	4.121
21	441	4.583	9,261	2.759	**71**	5,041	8.426	357,911	4.141
22	484	4.690	10,648	2.802	**72**	5,184	8.485	373,248	4.160
23	529	4.796	12,167	2.844	**73**	5,329	8.544	389,017	4.179
24	576	4.899	13,824	2.884	**74**	5,476	8.602	405,224	4.198
25	625	5.000	15,625	2.924	**75**	5,625	8.660	421,875	4.217
26	676	5.099	17,576	2.962	**76**	5,776	8.718	438,976	4.236
27	729	5.196	19,683	3.000	**77**	5,929	8.775	456,533	4.254
28	784	5.292	21,952	3.037	**78**	6,084	8.832	474,552	4.273
29	841	5.385	24,389	3.072	**79**	6,241	8.888	493,039	4.291
30	900	5.477	27,000	3.107	**80**	6,400	8.944	512,000	4.309
31	961	5.568	29,791	3.141	**81**	6,561	9.000	531,441	4.327
32	1,024	5.657	32,768	3.175	**82**	6,724	9.055	551,368	4.344
33	1,089	5.745	35,937	3.208	**83**	6,889	9.110	571,787	4.362
34	1,156	5.831	39,304	3.240	**84**	7,056	9.165	592,704	4.380
35	1,225	5.916	42,875	3.271	**85**	7,225	9.220	614,125	4.397
36	1,296	6.000	46,656	3.302	**86**	7,396	9.274	636,056	4.414
37	1,369	6.083	50,653	3.332	**87**	7,569	9.327	658,503	4.431
38	1,444	6.164	54,872	3.362	**88**	7,744	9.381	681,472	4.448
39	1,521	6.245	59,319	3.391	**89**	7,921	9.434	704,969	4.465
40	1,600	6.325	64,000	3.420	**90**	8,100	9.487	729,000	4.481
41	1,681	6.403	68,921	3.448	**91**	8,281	9.539	753,571	4.498
42	1,764	6.481	74,088	3.476	**92**	8,464	9.592	778,688	4.514
43	1,849	6.557	79,507	3.503	**93**	8,649	9.644	804,357	4.531
44	1,936	6.633	85,184	3.530	**94**	8,836	9.695	830,584	4.547
45	2,025	6.708	91,125	3.557	**95**	9,025	9.747	857,375	4.563
46	2,116	6.782	97,336	3.583	**96**	9,216	9.798	884,736	4.579
47	2,209	6.856	103,823	3.609	**97**	9,409	9.849	912,673	4.595
48	2,304	6.928	110,592	3.634	**98**	9,604	9.899	941,192	4.610
49	2,401	7.000	117,649	3.659	**99**	9,801	9.950	970,299	4.626
50	2,500	7.071	125,000	3.684	**100**	10,000	10.000	1,000,000	4.642

TABLE II. Four-place Trigonometric Functions

Degrees	Sine	Tangent	Cotangent	Cosine	
0°00′	.0000	.0000	......	1.0000	90°00′
10	.0029	.0029	343.77	1.0000	50
20	.0058	.0058	171.89	1.0000	40
30	.0087	.0087	114.59	1.0000	30
40	.0116	.0116	85.940	.9999	20
50	.0145	.0145	68.750	.9999	10
1°00′	.0175	.0175	57.290	.9998	89°00′
10	.0204	.0204	49.104	.9998	50
20	.0233	.0233	42.964	.9997	40
30	.0262	.0262	38.188	.9997	30
40	.0291	.0291	34.368	.9996	20
50	.0320	.0320	31.242	.9995	10
2°00′	.0349	.0349	28.636	.9994	88°00′
10	.0378	.0378	26.432	.9993	50
20	.0407	.0407	24.542	.9992	40
30	.0436	.0437	22.904	.9990	30
40	.0465	.0466	21.470	.9989	20
50	.0494	.0495	20.206	.9988	10
3°00′	.0523	.0524	19.081	.9986	87°00′
10	.0552	.0553	18.075	.9985	50
20	.0581	.0582	17.169	.9983	40
30	.0610	.0612	16.350	.9981	30
40	.0640	.0641	15.605	.9980	20
50	.0669	.0670	14.924	.9978	10
4°00′	.0698	.0699	14.301	.9976	86°00′
10	.0727	.0729	13.727	.9974	50
20	.0756	.0758	13.197	.9971	40
30	.0785	.0787	12.706	.9969	30
40	.0814	.0816	12.251	.9967	20
50	.0843	.0846	11.826	.9964	10
5°00′	.0872	.0875	11.430	.9962	85°00′
10	.0901	.0904	11.059	.9959	50
20	.0929	.0934	10.712	.9957	40
30	.0958	.0963	10.385	.9954	30
40	.0987	.0992	10.078	.9951	20
50	.1016	.1022	9.7882	.9948	10
6°00′	.1045	.1051	9.5144	.9945	84°00′
10	.1074	.1080	9.2553	.9942	50
20	.1103	.1110	9.0098	.9939	40
30	.1132	.1139	8.7769	.9936	30
40	.1161	.1169	8.5555	.9932	20
50	.1190	.1198	8.3450	.9929	10
7°00′	.1219	.1228	8.1443	.9925	83°00′
10	.1248	.1257	7.9530	.9922	50
20	.1276	.1287	7.7704	.9918	40
30	.1305	.1317	7.5958	.9914	30
40	.1334	.1346	7.4287	.9911	20
50	.1363	.1376	7.2687	.9907	10
8°00′	.1392	.1405	7.1154	.9903	82°00′
	Cosine	*Cotangent*	*Tangent*	*Sine*	*Degrees*

TABLE II. Four-place Trigonometric Functions.—(Continued)

Degrees	*Sine*	*Tangent*	*Cotangent*	*Cosine*	
8°00′	.1392	.1405	7.1154	.9903	82°00′
10	.1421	.1435	6.9682	.9899	50
20	.1449	.1465	6.8269	.9894	40
30	.1478	.1495	6.6912	.9890	30
40	.1507	.1524	6.5606	.9886	20
50	.1536	.1554	6.4348	.9881	10
9°00′	.1564	.1584	6.3138	.9877	81°00′
10	.1593	.1614	6.1970	.9872	50
20	.1622	.1644	6.0844	.9868	40
30	.1650	.1673	5.9758	.9863	30
40	.1679	.1703	5.8708	.9858	20
50	.1708	.1733	5.7694	.9853	10
10°00′	.1736	.1763	5.6713	.9848	80°00′
10	.1765	.1793	5.5764	.9843	50
20	.1794	.1823	5.4845	.9838	40
30	.1822	.1853	5.3955	.9833	30
40	.1851	.1883	5.3093	.9827	20
50	.1880	.1914	5.2257	.9822	10
11°00′	.1908	.1944	5.1446	.9816	79°00′
10	.1937	.1974	5.0658	.9811	50
20	.1965	.2004	4.9894	.9805	40
30	.1994	.2035	4.9152	.9799	30
40	.2022	.2065	4.8430	.9793	20
50	.2051	.2095	4.7729	.9787	10
12°00′	.2079	.2126	4.7046	.9781	78°00′
10	.2108	.2156	4.6382	.9775	50
20	.2136	.2186	4.5736	.9769	40
30	.2164	.2217	4.5107	.9763	30
40	.2193	.2247	4.4494	.9757	20
50	.2221	.2278	4.3897	.9750	10
13°00′	.2250	.2309	4.3315	.9744	77°00′
10	.2278	.2339	4.2747	.9737	50
20	.2306	.2370	4.2193	.9730	40
30	.2334	.2401	4.1653	.9724	30
40	.2363	.2432	4.1126	.9717	20
50	.2391	.2462	4.0611	.9710	10
14°00′	.2419	.2493	4.0108	.9703	76°00′
10	.2447	.2524	3.9617	.9696	50
20	.2476	.2555	3.9136	.9689	40
30	.2504	.2586	3.8667	.9681	30
40	.2532	.2617	3.8208	.9674	20
50	.2560	.2648	3.7760	.9667	10
15°00′	.2588	.2679	3.7321	.9659	75°00′
10	.2616	.2711	3.6891	.9652	50
20	.2644	.2742	3.6470	.9644	40
30	.2672	.2773	3.6059	.9636	30
40	.2700	.2805	3.5656	.9628	20
50	.2728	.2836	3.5261	.9621	10
16°00′	.2756	.2867	3.4874	.9613	74°00′
	Cosine	*Cotangent*	*Tangent*	*Sine*	*Degrees*

TABLE II. Four-place Trigonometric Functions.—(Continued)

Degrees	*Sine*	*Tangent*	*Cotangent*	*Cosine*	
16°00′	.2756	.2867	3.4874	.9613	74°00′
10	.2784	.2899	3.4495	.9605	50
20	.2812	.2931	3.4124	.9596	40
30	.2840	.2962	3.3759	.9588	30
40	.2868	.2994	3.3402	.9580	20
50	.2896	.3026	3.3052	.9572	10
17°00′	.2924	.3057	3.2709	.9563	73°00′
10	.2952	.3089	3.2371	.9555	50
20	.2979	.3121	3.2041	.9546	40
30	.3007	.3153	3.1716	.9537	30
40	.3035	.3185	3.1397	.9528	20
50	.3062	.3217	3.1084	.9520	10
18°00′	.3090	.3249	3.0777	.9511	72°00′
10	.3118	.3281	3.0475	.9502	50
20	.3145	.3314	3.0178	.9492	40
30	.3173	.3346	2.9887	.9483	30
40	.3201	.3378	2.9600	.9474	20
50	.3228	.3411	2.9319	.9465	10
19°00′	.3256	.3443	2.9042	.9455	71°00′
10	.3283	.3476	2.8770	.9446	50
20	.3311	.3508	2.8502	.9436	40
30	.3338	.3541	2.8239	.9426	30
40	.3365	.3574	2.7980	.9417	20
50	.3393	.3607	2.7725	.9407	10
20°00′	.3420	.3640	2.7475	.9397	70°00′
10	.3448	.3673	2.7228	.9387	50
20	.3475	.3706	2.6985	.9377	40
30	.3502	.3739	2.6746	.9367	30
40	.3529	.3772	2.6511	.9356	20
50	.3557	.3805	2.6279	.9346	10
21°00′	.3584	.3839	2.6051	.9336	69°00′
10	.3611	.3872	2.5826	.9325	50
20	.3638	.3906	2.5605	.9315	40
30	.3665	.3939	2.5386	.9304	30
40	.3692	.3973	2.5172	.9293	20
50	.3719	.4006	2.4960	.9283	10
22°00′	.3746	.4040	2.4751	.9272	68°00′
10	.3773	.4074	2.4545	.9261	50
20	.3800	.4108	2.4342	.9250	40
30	.3827	.4142	2.4142	.9239	30
40	.3854	.4176	2.3945	.9228	20
50	.3881	.4210	2.3750	.9216	10
23°00′	.3907	.4245	2.3559	.9205	67°00′
10	.3934	.4279	2.3369	.9194	50
20	.3961	.4314	2.3183	.9182	40
30	.3987	.4348	2.2998	.9171	30
40	.4014	.4383	2.2817	.9159	20
50	.4041	.4417	2.2637	.9147	10
24°00′	.4067	.4452	2.2460	.9135	66°00′
	Cosine	*Cotangent*	*Tangent*	*Sine*	*Degrees*

TABLE II. Four-place Trigonometric Functions.—(Continued)

Degrees	*Sine*	*Tangent*	*Cotangent*	*Cosine*	
24°00′	.4067	.4452	2.2460	.9135	66°00′
10	.4094	.4487	2.2286	.9124	50
20	.4120	.4522	2.2113	.9112	40
30	.4147	.4557	2.1943	.9100	30
40	.4173	.4592	2.1775	.9088	20
50	.4200	.4628	2.1609	.9075	10
25°00′	.4226	.4663	2.1445	.9063	65°00′
10	.4253	.4699	2.1283	.9051	50
20	.4279	.4734	2.1123	.9038	40
30	.4305	.4770	2.0965	.9026	30
40	.4331	.4806	2.0809	.9013	20
50	.4358	.4841	2.0655	.9001	10
26°00′	.4384	.4877	2.0503	.8988	64°00′
10	.4410	.4913	2.0353	.8975	50
20	.4436	.4950	2.0204	.8962	40
30	.4462	.4986	2.0057	.8949	30
40	.4488	.5022	1.9912	.8936	20
50	.4514	.5059	1.9768	.8923	10
27°00′	.4540	.5095	1.9626	.8910	63°00′
10	.4566	.5132	1.9486	.8897	50
20	.4592	.5169	1.9347	.8884	40
30	.4617	.5206	1.9210	.8870	30
40	.4643	.5243	1.9074	.8857	20
50	.4669	.5280	1.8940	.8843	10
28°00′	.4695	.5317	1.8807	.8829	62°00′
10	.4720	.5354	1.8676	.8816	50
20	.4746	.5392	1.8546	.8802	40
30	.4772	.5430	1.8418	.8788	30
40	.4797	.5467	1.8291	.8774	20
50	.4823	.5505	1.8165	.8760	10
29°00′	.4848	.5543	1.8040	.8746	61°00′
10	.4874	.5581	1.7917	.8732	50
20	.4899	.5619	1.7796	.8718	40
30	.4924	.5658	1.7675	.8704	30
40	.4950	.5696	1.7556	.8689	20
50	.4975	.5735	1.7437	.8675	10
30°00′	.5000	.5774	1.7321	.8660	60°00′
10	.5025	.5812	1.7205	.8646	50
20	.5050	.5851	1.7090	.8631	40
30	.5075	.5890	1.6977	.8616	30
40	.5100	.5930	1.6864	.8601	20
50	.5125	.5969	1.6753	.8587	10
31°00′	.5150	.6009	1.6643	.8572	59°00′
10	.5175	.6048	1.6534	.8557	50
20	.5200	.6088	1.6426	.8542	40
30	.5225	.6128	1.6319	.8526	30
40	.5250	.6168	1.6212	.8511	20
50	.5275	.6208	1.6107	.8496	10
32°00′	.5299	.6249	1.6003	.8480	58°00′
	Cosine	*Cotangent*	*Tangent*	*Sine*	*Degrees*

TABLE II. Four-place Trigonometric Functions.—(Continued)

Degrees	*Sine*	*Tangent*	*Cotangent*	*Cosine*	
32°00′	.5299	.6249	1.6003	.8480	58°00′
10	.5324	.6289	1.5900	.8465	50
20	.5348	.6330	1.5798	.8450	40
30	.5373	.6371	1.5697	.8434	30
40	.5398	.6412	1.5597	.8418	20
50	.5422	.6453	1.5497	.8403	10
33°00′	.5446	.6494	1.5399	.8387	57°00′
10	.5471	.6536	1.5301	.8371	50
20	.5495	.6577	1.5204	.8355	40
30	.5519	.6619	1.5108	.8339	30
40	.5544	.6661	1.5013	.8323	20
50	.5568	.6703	1.4919	.8307	10
34°00′	.5592	.6745	1.4826	.8290	56°00′
10	.5616	.6787	1.4733	.8274	50
20	.5640	.6830	1.4641	.8258	40
30	.5664	.6873	1.4550	.8241	30
40	.5688	.6916	1.4460	.8225	20
50	.5712	.6959	1.4370	.8208	10
35°00′	.5736	.7002	1.4281	.8192	55°00′
10	.5760	.7046	1.4193	.8175	50
20	.5783	.7089	1.4106	.8158	40
30	.5807	.7133	1.4019	.8141	30
40	.5831	.7177	1.3934	.8124	20
50	.5854	.7221	1.3848	.8107	10
36°00′	.5878	.7265	1.3764	.8090	54°00′
10	.5901	.7310	1.3680	.8073	50
20	.5925	.7355	1.3597	.8056	40
30	.5948	.7400	1.3514	.8039	30
40	.5972	.7445	1.3432	.8021	20
50	.5995	.7490	1.3351	.8004	10
37°00′	.6018	.7536	1.3270	.7986	53°00′
10	.6041	.7581	1.3190	.7969	50
20	.6065	.7627	1.3111	.7951	40
30	.6088	.7673	1.3032	.7934	30
40	.6111	.7720	1.2954	.7916	20
50	.6134	.7766	1.2876	.7898	10
38°00′	.6157	.7813	1.2799	.7880	52°00′
10	.6180	.7860	1.2723	.7862	50
20	.6202	.7907	1.2647	.7844	40
30	.6225	.7954	1.2572	.7826	30
40	.6248	.8002	1.2497	.7808	20
50	.6271	.8050	1.2423	.7790	10
39°00′	.6293	.8098	1.2349	.7771	51°00′
10	.6316	.8146	1.2276	.7753	50
20	.6338	.8195	1.2203	.7735	40
30	.6361	.8243	1.2131	.7716	30
40	.6383	.8292	1.2059	.7698	20
50	.6406	.8342	1.1988	.7679	10
40°00′	.6428	.8391	1.1918	.7660	50°00′
	Cosine	*Cotangent*	*Tangent*	*Sine*	*Degrees*

TABLE II. Four-place Trigonometric Functions.—(Continued)

Degrees	*Sine*	*Tangent*	*Cotangent*	*Cosine*	
40°00′	.6428	.8391	1.1918	.7660	50°00′
10	.6450	.8441	1.1847	.7642	50
20	.6472	.8491	1.1778	.7623	40
30	.6494	.8541	1.1708	.7604	30
40	.6517	.8591	1.1640	.7585	20
50	.6539	.8642	1.1571	.7566	10
41°00′	.6561	.8693	1.1504	.7547	49°00′
10	.6583	.8744	1.1436	.7528	50
20	.6604	.8796	1.1369	.7509	40
30	.6626	.8847	1.1303	.7490	30
40	.6648	.8899	1.1237	.7470	20
50	.6670	.8952	1.1171	.7451	10
42°00′	.6691	.9004	1.1106	.7431	48°00′
10	.6713	.9057	1.1041	.7412	50
20	.6734	.9110	1.0977	.7392	40
30	.6756	.9163	1.0913	.7373	30
40	.6777	.9217	1.0850	.7353	20
50	.6799	.9271	1.0786	.7333	10
43°00′	.6820	.9325	1.0724	.7314	47°00′
10	.6841	.9380	1.0661	.7294	50
20	.6862	.9435	1.0599	.7274	40
30	.6884	.9490	1.0538	.7254	30
40	.6905	.9545	1.0477	.7234	20
50	.6926	.9601	1.0416	.7214	10
44°00′	.6947	.9657	1.0355	.7193	46°00′
10	.6967	.9713	1.0295	.7173	50
20	.6988	.9770	1.0235	.7153	40
30	.7009	.9827	1.0176	.7133	30
40	.7030	.9884	1.0117	.7112	20
50	.7050	.9942	1.0058	.7092	10
45°00′	.7071	1.0000	1.0000	.7071	45°00′
	Cosine	*Cotangent*	*Tangent*	*Sine*	*Degrees*

TABLE III. Compound Interest: $(1 + r)^n$

Amount of One Dollar Principal at Compound Interest after n Years

n	1½%	2%	2½%	3%	4%	5%	6%
1	1.0150	1.0200	1.0250	1.0300	1.0400	1.0500	1.0600
2	1.0302	1.0404	1.0506	1.0609	1.0816	1.1025	1.1236
3	1.0457	1.0612	1.0769	1.0927	1.1249	1.1576	1.1910
4	1.0614	1.0824	1.1038	1.1255	1.1699	1.2155	1.2625
5	1.0773	1.1041	1.1314	1.1593	1.2167	1.2763	1.3382
6	1.0934	1.1262	1.1597	1.1941	1.2653	1.3401	1.4185
7	1.1098	1.1487	1.1887	1.2299	1.3159	1.4071	1.5036
8	1.1265	1.1717	1.2184	1.2668	1.3686	1.4775	1.5938
9	1.1434	1.1951	1.2489	1.3048	1.4233	1.5513	1.6895
10	1.1605	1.2190	1.2801	1.3439	1.4802	1.6289	1.7908
11	1.1779	1.2434	1.3121	1.3842	1.5395	1.7103	1.8983
12	1.1956	1.2682	1.3449	1.4258	1.6010	1.7959	2.0122
13	1.2136	1.2936	1.3785	1.4685	1.6651	1.8856	2.1329
14	1.2318	1.3195	1.4130	1.5126	1.7317	1.9799	2.2609
15	1.2502	1.3459	1.4483	1.5580	1.8009	2.0789	2.3966
16	1.2690	1.3728	1.4845	1.6047	1.8730	2.1829	2.5404
17	1.2880	1.4002	1.5216	1.6528	1.9479	2.2920	2.6928
18	1.3073	1.4282	1.5597	1.7024	2.0258	2.4066	2.8543
19	1.3270	1.4568	1.5987	1.7535	2.1068	2.5270	3.0256
20	1.3469	1.4859	1.6386	1.8061	2.1911	2.6533	3.2071
21	1.3671	1.5157	1.6796	1.8603	2.2788	2.7860	3.3996
22	1.3876	1.5460	1.7216	1.9161	2.3699	2.9253	3.6035
23	1.4084	1.5769	1.7646	1.9736	2.4647	3.0715	3.8197
24	1.4295	1.6084	1.8087	2.0328	2.5633	3.2251	4.0489
25	1.4509	1.6406	1.8539	2.0938	2.6658	3.3864	4.2919
26	1.4727	1.6734	1.9003	2.1566	2.7725	3.5557	4.5494
27	1.4948	1.7069	1.9478	2.2213	2.8834	3.7335	4.8223
28	1.5172	1.7410	1.9965	2.2879	2.9987	3.9201	5.1117
29	1.5400	1.7758	2.0464	2.3566	3.1187	4.1161	5.4184
30	1.5631	1.8114	2.0976	2.4273	3.2434	4.3219	5.7435
31	1.5865	1.8476	2.1500	2.5001	3.3731	4.5380	6.0881
32	1.6103	1.8845	2.2038	2.5751	3.5081	4.7649	6.4534
33	1.6345	1.9222	2.2589	2.6523	3.6484	5.0032	6.8406
34	1.6590	1.9607	2.3153	2.7319	3.7943	5.2533	7.2510
35	1.6839	1.9999	2.3732	2.8139	3.9461	5.5160	7.6861
36	1.7091	2.0399	2.4325	2.8983	4.1039	5.7918	8.1473
37	1.7348	2.0807	2.4933	2.9852	4.2681	6.0814	8.6361
38	1.7608	2.1223	2.5557	3.0748	4.4388	6.3855	9.1543
39	1.7872	2.1647	2.6196	3.1670	4.6164	6.7048	9.7035
40	1.8140	2.2080	2.6851	3.2620	4.8010	7.0400	10.2857
41	1.8412	2.2522	2.7522	3.3599	4.9931	7.3920	10.9029
42	1.8688	2.2972	2.8210	3.4607	5.1928	7.7616	11.5570
43	1.8969	2.3432	2.8915	3.5645	5.4005	8.1497	12.2505
44	1.9253	2.3901	2.9638	3.6715	5.6165	8.5572	12.9855
45	1.9542	2.4379	3.0379	3.7816	5.8412	8.9850	13,7646
46	1.9835	2.4866	3.1139	3.8950	6.0748	9.4343	14.5905
47	2.0133	2.5363	3.1917	4.0119	6.3178	9.9060	15.4659
48	2.0435	2.5871	3.2715	4.1323	6.5705	10.4013	16.3939
49	2.0741	2.6388	3.3533	4.2562	6.8333	10.9213	17.3775
50	2.1052	2.6916	3.4371	4.3839	7.1067	11.4674	18.4202

TABLE IV. Compound Discount: $1/(1 + r)^n$

Present Value of One Dollar Due at the End of n Years

n	1½%	2%	2½%	3%	4%	5%	6%
1	.985 22	.980 39	.97561	.97087	.96154	.95238	.94340
2	.970 66	.961 17	.95181	.94260	.92456	.90703	.89000
3	.956 32	.942 32	.92860	.91514	.88900	.86384	.83962
4	.942 18	.923 85	.90595	.88849	.85480	.82270	.79209
5	.928 26	.905 73	.88385	.86261	.82193	.78353	.74726
6	.914 54	.887 97	.86230	.83748	.79031	.74622	.70496
7	.901 03	.870 56	.84127	.81309	.75992	.71068	.66506
8	.887 71	.853 49	.82075	.78941	.73069	.67684	.62741
9	.874 59	.836 76	.80073	.76642	.70259	.64461	.59190
10	.861 67	.820 35	.78120	.74409	.67556	.61391	.55839
11	.848 93	.804 26	.76214	.72242	.64958	.58468	.52679
12	.836 39	.788 49	.74356	.70138	.62460	.55684	.49697
13	.824 03	.773 03	.72542	.68095	.60057	.53032	.46884
14	.811 85	.757 88	.70773	.66112	.57748	.50507	.44230
15	.799 85	.743 01	.69047	.64186	.55526	.48102	.41727
16	.788 03	.728 45	.67362	.62317	.53391	.45811	.39365
17	.776 39	.714 16	.65720	.60502	.51337	.43630	.37136
18	.764 91	.700 16	.64117	.58739	.49363	.41552	.35034
19	.753 61	.686 43	.62553	.57029	.47464	.39573	.33051
20	.742 47	.672 97	.61027	.55368	.45639	.37689	.31180
21	.731 50	.659 78	.59539	.53755	.43883	.35894	.29416
22	.720 69	.646 84	.58086	.52189	.42196	.34185	.27751
23	.710 04	.634 16	.56670	.50669	.40573	.32557	.26180
24	.699 54	.621 72	.55288	.49193	.39012	.31007	.24698
25	.689 21	.609 53	.53939	.47761	.37512	.29530	.23300
26	.679 02	.597 58	.52623	.46369	.36069	.28124	.21981
27	.668 99	.585 86	.51340	.45019	.34682	.26785	.20737
28	.659 10	.574 37	.50088	.43708	.33348	.25509	.19563
29	.649 36	.563 11	.48866	.42435	.32065	.24295	.18456
30	.639 76	.552 07	.47674	.41199	.30832	.23138	.17411
31	.630 31	.541 25	.46511	.39999	.29646	.22036	.16425
32	.620 99	.530 63	.45377	.38834	.28506	.20987	.15496
33	.611 82	.520 23	.44270	.37703	.27409	.19987	.14619
34	.602 77	.510 03	.43191	.36604	.26355	.19035	.13791
35	.593 87	.500 03	.42137	.35538	.25342	.18129	.13011
36	.585 09	.490 22	.41109	.34503	.24367	.17266	.12274
37	.576 44	.480 61	.40107	.33498	.23430	.16444	.11579
38	.567 92	.471 19	.39128	.32523	.22529	.15661	.10924
39	.559 53	.461 95	.38174	.31575	.21662	.14915	.10306
40	.551 26	.452 89	.37243	.30656	.20829	.14205	.09722
41	.543 12	.444 01	.36335	.29763	.20028	.13528	.09172
42	.535 09	.435 30	.35448	.28896	.19257	.12884	.08653
43	.527 18	.426 77	.34584	.28054	.18517	.12270	.08163
44	.519 39	.418 40	.33740	.27237	.17805	.11686	.07701
45	.511 71	.410 20	.32917	.26444	.17120	.11130	.07265
46	.504 15	.402 15	.32115	.25674	.16461	.10600	.06854
47	.496 70	.394 27	.31331	.24926	.15828	.10095	.06466
48	.489 36	.386 54	.30567	.24200	.15219	.09614	.06100
49	.482 13	.378 96	.29822	.23495	.14634	.09156	.05755
50	.475 00	.371 53	.29094	.22811	.14071	.08720	.05429

TABLE V. Amount of an Annuity

Amount of An Annuity of One Dollar per Year after n Years

n	1½%	2%	2½%	3%	4%	5%	6%
1	1.0000	1.0000	1.0000	1.0000	1.0000	1.0000	1.0000
2	2.0150	2.0200	2.0250	2.0300	2.0400	2.0500	2.0600
3	3.0452	3.0604	3.0756	3.0909	3.1216	3.1525	3.1836
4	4.0909	4.1216	4.1525	4.1836	4.2465	4.3101	4.3746
5	5.1523	5.2040	5.2563	5.3091	5.4163	5.5256	5.6371
6	6.2296	6.3081	6.3877	6.4684	6.6330	6.8019	6.9753
7	7.3230	7.4343	7.5474	7.6625	7.8983	8.1420	8.3938
8	8.4328	8.5830	8.7361	8.8923	9.2142	9.5491	9.8975
9	9.5593	9.7546	9.9545	10.1591	10.5828	11.0266	11.4913
10	10.7027	10.9497	11.2034	11.4639	12.0061	12.5779	13.1808
11	11.8633	12.1687	12.4835	12.8078	13.4864	14.2068	14.9716
12	13.0412	13.4121	13.7956	14.1920	15.0258	15.9171	16.8699
13	14.2368	14.6803	15.1404	15.6178	16.6268	17.7130	18.8821
14	15.4504	15.9739	16.5190	17.0863	18.2919	19.5986	21.0151
15	16.6821	17.2934	17.9319	18.5989	20.0236	21.5786	23.2760
16	17.9324	18.6393	19.3802	20.1569	21.8245	23.6575	25.6725
17	19.2014	20.0121	20.8647	21.7616	23.6975	25.8404	28.2129
18	20.4894	21.4123	22.3863	23.4144	25.6454	28.1324	30.9057
19	21.7967	22.8406	23.9460	25.1169	27.6712	30.5390	33.7600
20	23.1237	24.2974	25.5447	26.8704	29.7781	33.0660	36.7856
21	24.4705	25.7833	27.1833	28.6765	31.9692	35.7193	39.9927
22	25.8376	27.2990	28.8629	30.5368	34.2480	38.5052	43.3923
23	27.2251	28.8450	30.5844	32.4529	36.6179	41.4305	46.9958
24	28.6335	30.4219	32.3490	34.4265	39.0826	44.5020	50.8156
25	30.0630	32.0303	34.1578	36.4593	41.6459	47.7271	54.8645
26	31.5140	33.6709	36.0117	38.5530	44.3117	51.1135	59.1564
27	32.9867	35.3443	37.9120	40.7096	47.0842	54.6691	63.7058
28	34.4815	37.0512	39.8598	42.9309	49.9676	58.4026	68.5281
29	35.9987	38.7922	41.8563	45.2189	52.9663	62.3227	73.6398
30	37.5387	40.5681	43.9027	47.5754	56.0849	66.4388	79.0582
31	39.1018	42.3794	46.0003	50.0027	59.3283	70.7608	84.8017
32	40.6883	44.2270	48.1503	52.5028	62.7015	75.2988	90.8898
33	42.2986	46.1116	50.3540	55.0778	66.2095	80.0638	97.3432
34	43.9331	48.0338	52.6129	57.7302	69.8579	85.0670	104.1838
35	45.5921	49.9945	54.9282	60.4621	73.6522	90.3203	111.4348
36	47.2760	51.9944	57.3014	63.2759	77.5983	95.8363	119.1209
37	48.9851	54.0343	59.7339	66.1742	81.7022	101.6281	127.2681
38	50.7199	56.1149	62.2273	69.1594	85.9703	107.7095	135.9042
39	52.4807	58.2372	64.7830	72.2342	90.4091	114.0950	145.0585
40	54.2679	60.4020	67.4026	75.4013	95.0255	120.7998	154.7620
41	56.0819	62.6100	70.0876	78.6633	99.8265	127.8398	165.0477
42	57.9231	64.8622	72.8398	82.0232	104.8196	135.2318	175.9505
43	59.7920	67.1595	75.6608	85.4839	110.0124	142.9933	187.5076
44	61.6889	69.5027	78.5523	89.0484	115.4129	151.1430	199.7580
45	63.6142	71.8927	81.5161	92.7199	121.0294	159.7002	212.7435
46	65.5684	74.3306	84.5540	96.5015	126.8706	168.6852	226.5081
47	67.5519	76.8172	87.6679	100.3965	132.9454	178.1194	241.0986
48	69.5652	79.3535	90.8596	104.4084	139.2632	188.0254	256.5645
49	71.6087	81.9406	94.1311	108.5406	145.8337	198.4267	272.9584
50	73.6828	84.5794	97.4843	112.7969	152.6671	209.3480	290.3359

TABLE VI. Present Value of an Annuity

Present Value of One Dollar per Year for n Years

n	1½%	2%	2½%	3%	4%	5%	6%
1	.9852	.9804	.9756	.9709	.9615	.9524	.9434
2	1.9559	1.9416	1.9274	1.9135	1.8861	1.8594	1.8334
3	2.9122	2.8839	2.8560	2.8286	2.7751	2.7232	2.6730
4	3.8544	3.8077	3.7620	3.7171	3.6299	3.5460	3.4651
5	4.7826	4.7135	4.6458	4.5797	4.4518	4.3295	4.2124
6	5.6972	5.6014	5.5081	5.4172	5.2421	5.0757	4.9173
7	6.5982	6.4720	6.3494	6.2303	6.0021	5.7864	5.5824
8	7.4859	7.3255	7.1701	7.0197	6.7327	6.4632	6.2098
9	8.3605	8.1622	7.9709	7.7861	7.4353	7.1078	6.8017
10	9.2222	8.9826	8.7521	8.5302	8.1109	7.7217	7.3601
11	10.0711	9.7868	9.5142	9.2526	8.7605	8.3064	7.8869
12	10.9075	10.5753	10.2578	9.9540	9.3851	8.8633	8.3838
13	11.7315	11.3484	10.9832	10.6350	9.9856	9.3936	8.8527
14	12.5434	12.1062	11.6909	11.2961	10.5631	9.8986	9.2950
15	13.3432	12.8493	12.3814	11.9379	11.1184	10.3797	9.7122
16	14.1313	13.5777	13.0550	12.5611	11.6523	10.8378	10.1059
17	14.9076	14.2919	13.7122	13.1661	12.1657	11.2741	10.4773
18	15.6726	14.9920	14.3534	13.7535	12.6593	11.6896	10.8276
19	16.4262	15.6785	14.9789	14.3238	13.1339	12.0853	11.1581
20	17.1686	16.3514	15.5892	14.8775	13.5903	12.4622	11.4699
21	17.9001	17.0112	16.1845	15.4150	14.0292	12.8212	11.7641
22	18.6208	17.6580	16.7654	15.9369	14.4511	13.1630	12.0416
23	19.3309	18.2922	17.3321	16.4436	14.8568	13.4886	12.3034
24	20.0304	18.9139	17.8850	16.9355	15.2470	13.7986	12.5504
25	20.7196	19.5235	18.4244	17.4131	15.6221	14.0939	12.7834
26	21.3986	20.1210	18.9506	17.8768	15.9828	14.3752	13.0032
27	22.0676	20.7069	19.4640	18.3270	16.3296	14.6430	13.2105
28	22.7267	21.2813	19.9649	18.7641	16.6631	14.8981	13.4062
29	23.3761	21.8444	20.4535	19.1885	16.9837	15.1411	13.5907
30	24.0158	22.3965	20.9303	19.6004	17.2920	15.3725	13.7648
31	24.6461	22.9377	21.3954	20.0004	17.5885	15.5928	13.9291
32	25.2671	23.4683	21.8492	20.3888	17.8736	15.8027	14.0840
33	25.8790	23.9886	22.2919	20.7658	18.1476	16.0025	14.2302
34	26.4817	24.4986	22.7238	21.1318	18.4112	16.1929	14.3681
35	27.0756	24.9986	23.1452	21.4872	18.6646	16.3742	14.4982
36	27.6607	25.4888	23.5563	21.8323	18.9083	16.5469	14.6210
37	28.2371	25.9695	23.9573	22.1672	19.1426	16.7113	14.7368
38	28.8051	26.4406	24.3486	22.4925	19.3679	16.8679	14.8460
39	29.3646	26.9026	24.7303	22.8082	19.5845	17.0170	14.9491
40	29.9158	27.3555	25.1028	23.1148	19.7928	17.1591	15.0463
41	30.4590	27.7995	25.4661	23.4124	19.9931	17.2944	15.1380
42	30.9941	28.2348	25.8206	23.7014	20.1856	17.4232	15.2245
43	31.5212	28.6616	26.1664	23.9819	20.3708	17.5459	15.3062
44	32.0406	29.0800	26.5038	24.2543	20.5488	17.6628	15.3832
45	32.5523	29.4902	26.8330	24.5187	20.7200	17.7741	15.4558
46	33.0565	29.8923	27.1542	24.7754	20.8847	17.8801	15.5244
47	33.5532	30.2866	27.4675	25.0247	21.0429	17.9810	15.5890
48	34.0426	30.6731	27.7732	25.2667	21.1951	18.0772	15.6500
49	34.5247	31.0521	28.0714	25.5017	21.3415	18.1687	15.7076
50	34.9997	31.4236	28.3623	25.7298	21.4822	18.2559	15.7619

TABLE VII. Common Logarithms, $N = 10^x$

x Values Are Given in the Table for Values of N Indicated at the Side and Top

N	0	1	2	3	4	5	6	7	8	9
1.0	0000	0043	0086	0128	0170	0212	0253	0294	0334	0374
1.1	0414	0453	0492	0531	0569	0607	0645	0682	0719	0755
1.2	0792	0828	0864	0899	0934	0969	1004	1038	1072	1106
1.3	1139	1173	1206	1239	1271	1303	1335	1367	1399	1430
1.4	1461	1492	1523	1553	1584	1614	1644	1673	1703	1732
1.5	1761	1790	1818	1847	1875	1903	1931	1959	1987	2014
1.6	2041	2068	2095	2122	2148	2175	2201	2227	2253	2279
1.7	2304	2330	2355	2380	2405	2430	2455	2480	2504	2529
1.8	2553	2577	2601	2625	2648	2672	2695	2718	2742	2765
1.9	2788	2810	2833	2856	2878	2900	2923	2945	2967	2989
2.0	3010	3032	3054	3075	3096	3118	3139	3160	3181	3201
2.1	3222	3243	3263	3284	3304	3324	3345	3365	3385	3404
2.2	3424	3444	3464	3483	3502	3522	3541	3560	3579	3598
2.3	3617	3636	3655	3674	3692	3711	3729	3747	3766	3784
2.4	3802	3820	3838	3856	3874	3892	3909	3927	3945	3962
2.5	3979	3997	4014	4031	4048	4065	4082	4099	4116	4133
2.6	4150	4166	4183	4200	4216	4232	4249	4265	4281	4298
2.7	4314	4330	4346	4362	4378	4393	4409	4425	4440	4456
2.8	4472	4487	4502	4518	4533	4548	4564	4579	4594	4609
2.9	4624	4639	4654	4669	4683	4698	4713	4728	4742	4757
3.0	4771	4786	4800	4814	4829	4843	4857	4871	4886	4900
3.1	4914	4928	4942	4955	4969	4983	4997	5011	5024	5038
3.2	5051	5065	5079	5092	5105	5119	5132	5145	5159	5172
3.3	5185	5198	5211	5224	5237	5250	5263	5276	5289	5302
3.4	5315	5328	5340	5353	5366	5378	5391	5403	5416	5428
3.5	5441	5453	5465	5478	5490	5502	5514	5527	5539	5551
3.6	5563	5575	5587	5599	5611	5623	5635	5647	5658	5670
3.7	5682	5694	5705	5717	5729	5740	5752	5763	5775	5786
3.8	5798	5809	5821	5832	5843	5855	5866	5877	5888	5899
3.9	5911	5922	5933	5944	5955	5966	5977	5988	5999	6010
4.0	6021	6031	6042	6053	6064	6075	6085	6096	6107	6117
4.1	6128	6138	6149	6160	6170	6180	6191	6201	6212	6222
4.2	6232	6243	6253	6263	6274	6284	6294	6304	6314	6325
4.3	6335	6345	6355	6365	6375	6385	6395	6405	6415	6425
4.4	6435	6444	6454	6464	6474	6484	6493	6503	6513	6522
4.5	6532	6542	6551	6561	6571	6580	6590	6599	6609	6618
4.6	6628	6637	6646	6656	6665	6675	6684	6693	6702	6712
4.7	6721	6730	6739	6749	6758	6767	6776	6785	6794	6803
4.8	6812	6821	6830	6839	6848	6857	6866	6875	6884	6893
4.9	6902	6911	6920	6928	6937	6946	6955	6964	6972	6981
5.0	6990	6998	7007	7016	7024	7033	7042	7050	7059	7067
5.1	7076	7084	7093	7101	7110	7118	7126	7135	7143	7152
5.2	7160	7168	7177	7185	7193	7202	7210	7218	7226	7235
5.3	7243	7251	7259	7267	7275	7284	7292	7300	7308	7316
5.4	7324	7332	7340	7348	7356	7364	7372	7380	7388	7396
N	0	1	2	3	4	5	6	7	8	9

TABLE VII. Common Logarithms.—(Continued)

x Values Are Given in the Table for Values of N Indicated at the Side and Top

N	0	1	2	3	4	5	6	7	8	9
5.5	7404	7412	7419	7427	7435	7443	7451	7459	7466	7474
5.6	7482	7490	7497	7505	7513	7520	7528	7536	7543	7551
5.7	7559	7566	7574	7582	7589	7597	7604	7612	7619	7627
5.8	7634	7642	7649	7657	7664	7672	7679	7686	7694	7701
5.9	7709	7716	7723	7731	7738	7745	7752	7760	7767	7774
6.0	7782	7789	7796	7803	7810	7818	7825	7832	7839	7846
6.1	7853	7860	7868	7875	7882	7889	7896	7903	7910	7917
6.2	7924	7931	7938	7945	7952	7959	7966	7973	7980	7987
6.3	7993	8000	8007	8014	8021	8028	8035	8041	8048	8055
6.4	8062	8069	8075	8082	8089	8096	8102	8109	8116	8122
6.5	8129	8136	8142	8149	8156	8162	8169	8176	8182	8189
6.6	8195	8202	8209	8215	8222	8228	8235	8241	8248	8254
6.7	8261	8267	8274	8280	8287	8293	8299	8306	8312	8319
6.8	8325	8331	8338	8344	8351	8357	8363	8370	8376	8382
6.9	8388	8395	8401	8407	8414	8420	8426	8432	8439	8445
7.0	8451	8457	8463	8470	8476	8482	8488	8494	8500	8506
7.1	8513	8519	8525	8531	8537	8543	8549	8555	8561	8567
7.2	8573	8579	8585	8591	8597	8603	8609	8615	8621	8627
7.3	8633	8639	8645	8651	8657	8663	8669	8675	8681	8686
7.4	8692	8698	8704	8710	8716	8722	8727	8733	8739	8745
7.5	8751	8756	8762	8768	8774	8779	8785	8791	8797	8802
7.6	8808	8814	8820	8825	8831	8837	8842	8848	8854	8859
7.7	8865	8871	8876	8882	8887	8893	8899	8904	8910	8915
7.8	8921	8927	8932	8938	8943	8949	8954	8960	8965	8971
7.9	8976	8982	8987	8993	8998	9004	9009	9015	9020	9025
8.0	9031	9036	9042	9047	9053	9058	9063	9069	9074	9079
8.1	9085	9090	9096	9101	9106	9112	9117	9122	9128	9133
8.2	9138	9143	9149	9154	9159	9165	9170	9175	9180	9186
8.3	9191	9196	9201	9206	9212	9217	9222	9227	9232	9238
8.4	9243	9248	9253	9258	9263	9269	9274	9279	9284	9289
8.5	9294	9299	9304	9309	9315	9320	9325	9330	9335	9340
8.6	9345	9350	9355	9360	9365	9370	9375	9380	9385	9390
8.7	9395	9400	9405	9410	9415	9420	9425	9430	9435	9440
8.8	9445	9450	9455	9460	9465	9469	9474	9479	9484	9489
8.9	9494	9499	9504	9509	9513	9518	9523	9528	9533	9538
9.0	9542	9547	9552	9557	9562	9566	9571	9576	9581	9586
9.1	9590	9595	9600	9605	9609	9614	9619	9624	9628	9633
9.2	9638	9643	9647	9652	9657	9661	9666	9671	9675	9680
9.3	9685	9689	9694	9699	9703	9708	9713	9717	9722	9727
9.4	9731	9736	9741	9745	9750	9754	9759	9763	9768	9773
9.5	9777	9782	9786	9791	9795	9800	9805	9809	9814	9818
9.6	9823	9827	9832	9836	9841	9845	9850	9854	9859	9863
9.7	9868	9872	9877	9881	9886	9890	9894	9899	9903	9908
9.8	9912	9917	9921	9926	9930	9934	9939	9943	9948	9952
9.9	9956	9961	9965	9969	9974	9978	9983	9987	9991	9996
N	0	1	2	3	4	5	6	7	8	9

TABLE VIII. Values of the Exponential Functions e^x and e^{-x}

x	e^x	e^{-x}
.05	1.051	.951
.10	1.105	.905
.15	1.162	.861
.20	1.221	.819
.25	1.284	.779
.30	1.350	.741
.35	1.419	.705
.40	1.492	.670
.45	1.568	.638
.50	1.649	.606
.6	1.822	.549
.7	2.014	.497
.8	2.226	.449
.9	2.460	.407
1.0	2.718	.368
1.1	3.004	.333
1.2	3.320	.301
1.3	3.669	.272
1.4	4.055	.247
1.5	4.482	.223
1.6	4.953	.202
1.7	5.474	.183
1.8	6.050	.165
1.9	6.686	.150
2.0	7.389	.135
2.1	8.166	.122
2.2	9.025	.111
2.3	9.974	.100
2.4	11.023	.091
2.5	12.182	.082
3.0	20.086	.050
3.5	33.115	.030
4.0	54.598	.018
4.5	90.017	.011
5.0	148.413	.0067
5.5	244.692	.0041
6.0	403.429	.0025
6.5	665.14	.0015
7.0	1096.6	.0009
7.5	1808.0	.0006
8.0	2981.0	.0003
9.0	8103.1	.0001
10.0	22026.0	.00005

Index

G

H

I

J

K

L

M

N

O

P

Q

R

S

T

V

W

Answers to Odd-numbered Problems

Page 4

1. *a.* $\frac{5}{8}$, 0.625; *c.* $\frac{5}{4}$, 1.25; *e.* $\frac{1}{8}$, 0.125
2. *a.* 87.5%; *c.* $66\frac{2}{3}$%; *e.* $16\frac{2}{3}$%
3. 1930: 32% concrete, 12% bituminous, 56% gravel
1935: 10% concrete, 46% bituminous, 44% gravel
1940: 7% concrete, 72% bituminous, 21% gravel
1945: 3% concrete, 82% bituminous, 15% gravel

Pages 19–20

3. $T = 102.3°$C., $P = 781$ mm.

Pages 24–25

1. 20 ft. **3.** 4.692 lb. **5.** 18.60 lb. copper, 12.60 lb. zinc
7. 420, 300 **9.** 270 acres

Pages 29–30

1. $A = kd^2$ **3.** $I = \dfrac{k}{d^2}$ **5.** $V = 6{,}545\frac{5}{11}$ cu. ft.
7. $h = 100$ ft. **9.** $A = 8.57$ grams **11.** $d = 91\frac{41}{49}$ ft.; $132\frac{12}{49}$ ft

Pages 31–32

1. $A = kLW$ **3.** $F = \frac{4}{9}$ lb. **5.** $t = 250\frac{5}{27}$ sec.

Pages 40–41

1. $W = 2S$ **3.** $V = \frac{2}{3}T + 182$ **5.** $C = \frac{1}{50}N + 130$

Page 43

1. $y = -3x$ **3.** $y = \dfrac{6x + 11}{7}$ **5.** $x = 5$
7. $y = \dfrac{(y_1 - y_2)}{(x_1 - x_2)}x + \dfrac{(x_2y_1 - x_1y_2)}{(x_2 - x_1)}$

Page 47

1. 7 Cokes **3.** \$1.93 **5.** $S = \$(25{,}000 + 500n)$
7. \$325 **9.** 225 lb.

Pages 48–49

1. \$3,250 **3.** 52, 8 **5.** 16, 18, 20
7. 3 classical, 7 modern **9.** $4{,}927\frac{37}{69}$ cu. ft.

Page 51

1. 80 cents, 40 cents **3.** 60 by 95 ft.
5. 13 magazines, 77 newspapers **7.** 50 lb. of each
9. 96 **11.** 60 cents **13.** 15, 17
15. 9 cents a pound for flour, 10 cents a pound for sugar

Page 53

1. 250 cc. **3.** 100 lb. of each **5.** \$4,545.45
7. 30 boys **9.** 42 yr., 12 yr.

Pages 54–55

1. 2 hr. **3.** $1\frac{2}{7}$ hr. **5.** 3:20 P.M.
7. $4\frac{1}{2}$ mi./hr., $5\frac{1}{2}$ mi./hr. **9.** 4 mi./hr.

Page 56

1. $6\frac{2}{3}$ hr. **3.** $2\frac{5}{8}$ hr. **5.** 25 days, $16\frac{2}{3}$ days
7. $6\frac{32}{33}$ hr. **9.** \$22.50 **11.** $3\frac{13}{17}$ qt.

Pages 61–62

1. $s = 16.1t^2$, positive values of t **3.** $t = 0.00015625f^2$, 0.01891 sec., 0.0049 sec.
5. $S = 12.57d^2$

Pages 65–66

1. 21, 22 **3.** 10 by 24 ft. **5.** 7 by 8 ft.
7. 4 ft. **9.** 3 **11.** 30 vases
13. 12 by 5 by 10 ft. **15.** 2.8 hr., 6.8 hr.

Page 69

1. $h = -16t^2 + 64t$; 64 ft.; approx. 0.3 sec. or 3.7 sec.

Page 75

1. 5.87 ft. **3.** 20 ft. **5.** 153.9 ft.

Page 77

1. 60 ft. **3.** 51°20′, 12.5 ft. **5.** 238,464 mi.

Page 84

1. $\sin B = b/c$, $\cos B = a/c$, $\tan B = b/a$
3. $\begin{cases} \sin R = r/q, \cos R = p/q, \tan R = r/q \\ \sin P = p/q, \cos P = r/q, \tan P = q/r \end{cases}$

Pages 89–90

1. 346.4 ft., 400 ft.
3. Frontages on Primrose Path are 253.88 ft., 230.8 ft., 184.64 ft., 115.4 ft.; the respective depths are 126.94 ft., 242.34 ft., 334.66 ft., 392.36 ft.
5. 13.86 ft., 16 ft. **7.** 138.6 ft. **9.** 13.86 ft. up and 8 ft. out
11. 692.84 ft. **13.** 4.10 mi. **15.** 1,636.9 yd.

Page 93

5. 48.05 ft. **7.** 11.08 ft., 17.23 ft.

Pages 97–98

1. 40°40′ **3.** 2°20′ **5.** 773.4 ft., 798.7 ft.
7. 53°10′ **9.** 6.2 mi. north, 16.9 mi. west **11.** 90.4 mi.
13. 41°50′, 8.94 ft. **15.** 15,577 ft.
17. 3°30′, 2,000 ft. from the closer church

Pages 106–107

1. 136.4 ft. **3.** 53°10′, 36°50′, 24,000 sq. ft. **5.** 50°40′, 25°40′
6. 29.87 mi. **7.** 8°20′ north of west **9.** 10.4 mi.

Page 114

1. *a.* 0.5000; *c.* −0.9397; *e.* −0.866; *g.* −0.577; *i.* 0.364
2. *a.* 138°40′, 221°20′; *c.* 26°30′, 206°30′; *e.* 224°30′, 315°30′
3. 997.7 ft. **5.** 79°30′

Pages 120–121

4. *a.* 1, 720°; *c.* 5, 1,080°; *e.* 1, 720°

Pages 123–124

1. $437.23 **3.** $247.83 **5.** 0.03%
7. 4,308 bricks **9.** $13.20, $9.90 **11.** $3.15 per yd.
13. Impossible

Pages 125–126

1. $15, $515 **3.** 1 1/14 yr. **5.** $1,428.57
7. $1.07 per hundred **9.** 6% **11.** $6,400
13. 3.3% **15.** 2.17%

Pages 129–130

1. $6,312.50 **3.** $6,334 **5.** $17,553.09
7. $2,737.20 **9.** $2,710.35

Page 132

1. $9,824.16 **3.** $398.56

Pages 133–134

1. Schedule of payments:

Year	*Principal outstanding at beginning of year*	*Interest at 4%*	*Payment*	*Principal repaid*
1	$5,000.00	$200.00	$616.46	$416.46
2	4,583.54	183.35	616.46	433.11
3	4,150.43	166.02	616.46	450.44
4	3,699.99	148.00	616.46	468.46
5	3,231.53	129.27	616.46	487.19
6	2,744.34	109.78	616.46	506.68
7	2,237.66	89.51	616.46	526.95
8	1,710.71	68.43	616.46	548.03
9	1,162.68	46.51	616.46	569.95
10	592.73	23.71	616.46	592.75

3. $441.50 **5.** 1½% per month **7.** $41.25
9. $192.36 per year., $589.10

Page 136

1. *a.* 27; *c.* 4; *e.* 16; *g.* 81

2. *a.* 3^3; *c.* 2^5; *e.* 7^2; *g.* 10^2

3. *a.* a^{13}; *c.* x^7; *e.* a^7; *g.* 10^2

4. *a.* $\frac{10^3 \cdot 10^3}{10^2} = 10^4 = 10{,}000$

c. $\frac{3^3 \cdot 3^2}{3^4} = 3^1 = 3$

e. $\frac{2^4 \cdot 2^3 \cdot 2^2}{2^5} = 2^4 = 16$

Pages 138–139

1. $x^{-4} = \frac{1}{x^4}$ **3.** 1 **5.** a^6

7. a^2 **9.** $2^4 = 16$ **11.** 1

13. $b^{-3} = \frac{1}{b^3}$ **15.** $10^{-1} = 1/10 = 0.1$ **17.** x^2

19. a^3

Page 142

1. *a.* 7.3×10^{-4}; *c.* 3.5×10^{-3}; *e.* 6.8×10^{-9}; *g.* 6.87×10^{11}; *i.* 3.620×10^3
2. *a.* 56,300; *c.* 0.0000000000000000000000046; *e.* 0.000000832; *g.* 3,270,000; *i.* 0.00143
3. 6.696×10^8 mi./hr. **5.** 2.33×10^{23} molecules per gram

Page 143

1. $10^{3.8645}$ **3.** $10^{2.4281}$ **5.** $10^{0.2380}$
7. $10^{-2.2660}$ **9.** $10^{-1.1643}$

Page 144

1. 673 **3.** 4,630 **5.** 0.00803
7. 0.0485 **9.** 6.73

Page 145

1. 65,400 **3.** 0.180 **5.** 5,140

Page 153

1. 329.8, 2,436.4 **3.** $1,822 **5.** $15,050
7. *a.* 29.92 in.; *b.* 27.08 in.; *c.* 9.96 in.; *d.* 4.04 in.
9. 0.247 gram, 0.111 gram

Page 158

1. *a.* $\frac{1}{6}$; *b.* $\frac{1}{4}$; *c.* $\frac{1}{7}$ (approx.) **3.** *a.* $\frac{1}{8}$; *b.* $\frac{1}{8}$; *c.* $\frac{3}{8}$
5. $\frac{1}{2}$

Page 160

1. *a.* $\frac{1}{10}$; *b.* $\frac{1}{2}$; *c.* $\frac{3}{10}$; *d.* $\frac{1}{4}$ **3.** $\frac{1}{2}$
5. *a.* $\frac{1}{36}$; *c.* $\frac{1}{12}$; *e.* $\frac{5}{36}$; *g.* $\frac{5}{36}$; *i.* $\frac{1}{12}$ **7.** *a.* $\frac{1}{216}$; *b.* $\frac{1}{36}$; *c.* $\frac{7}{72}$

Page 163

1. 8 **3.** 504 **5.** 60
7. 12 **9.** 30,240

Pages 166–167

1. 151; 200; 1,680; 720 **3.** *ab, ba, ca, ac, bc, cb* **5.** $\frac{15!}{5!} = 10{,}897{,}286{,}400$
7. 24, 24 **9.** 48 **11.** 362,880

Page 168

1. 59,875,200 **3.** 24 **5.** 100,800

Pages 170–171

1. 12,650; 120; 35; 1; 1 **3.** 10 **5.** 66
7. 120 **9.** 10 **11.** $C_{52,13} = \frac{52!}{39!13!} = 635{,}013{,}559{,}600$
13. 27,720 **15.** 720

Page 172

1. 33/66,640 **3.** *a.* $\frac{65}{253}$; *b.* $\frac{195}{506}$

Page 175

1. $\frac{1}{8}$ **3.** $\frac{5}{16}$ **5.** $\frac{33}{95}$

Page 176

1. $1.25 **3.** Yes **5.** At 2 cents he loses, at 1 cent he wins

Pages 178–179

1. 0.232 or 23.2% **3.** 0.305 or 30.5% **5.** 4,412; 3,682; 2,470; 117

Page 183

1. *a.* 36; *c.* 21
2. *a.* 5.5; *c.* 14.5

Pages 185–186

1. $\bar{x} = 46.8$, $\sigma_x = 17.05$
3. $\bar{x} = 70.77$, $\sigma_x = 14.34$

Page 196

Prob. 1, p. 193: mean = 11.8, mode = 15, median = 13.3
(NOTE: The answers will vary depending on the interpretation as to what constitutes a word.)
Prob. 4, p. 194: mean = 3.89, mode = 4, median = 4
Prob. 5, p. 194: mean = 11.595, mode = 11.40, median = 11.60

Page 197

1. Prob. 1, p. 193: $\sigma_x = 5.18$; Prob. 4, p. 194: $\sigma_x = 1.47$; Prob. 5, p. 194: $\sigma_x = 0.406$

Pages 206–207

1. 50%
3. 0.928
5. *a.* 86.6%; *b.* 0.3%; *c.* 0.788 or 78.8%; *d.* 143.3 lb. to 147.7 lb.; *e.* 150.2 lb.

Pages 213–214

1. The interval becomes wider
3. 1,140 mi.
5. No, since the 95% confidence interval has $d = 2.35$

Page 220

1. XLIV
3. CCLIX
5. XLII
7. CCCXC
9. CCXIV

Page 224

1. 56
3. 143
5. 162
7. 1,060

Page 226

1. 177
3. 1100; 110; 30; 22
5. 1111101
7. 1000111
9. 1100011

Page 230

1. 3, 5, 17, 257
3. 2, 3, 5, 7, 11, 13, 17, 19, 23, 29, 31, 37, 41, 43, 47, 53, 59, 61, 67, 71, 73
5. Several different answers are possible, such as

$40 = 37 + 3 = 29 + 11 = 23 + 17$
$42 = 37 + 5 = 29 + 13 = 23 + 19$
$44 = 41 + 3 = 37 + 7 = 31 + 13$
$46 = 43 + 3 = 41 + 5 = 29 + 17$
$48 = 43 + 5 = 41 + 7 = 29 + 19$
$50 = 47 + 3 = 43 + 7 = 37 + 13$

Page 231

1. 6, 28

Page 234

1. $23 = 2^3 + 2^3 + 1^3 + 1^3 + 1^3 + 1^3 + 1^3 + 1^3 + 1^3$
All other numbers up to 50 may be expressed as the sum of less than 9 cubes.

Pages 242–243

1. $V = 16$, $A = 24$, $R = 10$
3. $V = 8$, $A = 12$, $R = 6$
5. $V = 6$, $A = 12$, $R = 8$
7. $V - A + 1 = 2$, therefore $V = A + 1$

Page 248

1. Yes, but not ending at the same point, *e.g.*, remove bridge BC.

3. This may be done in several ways if two bridges are closed, *e.g.*, bridges AB and CD.

5. Not possible even beginning and ending at different points, for corresponding network contains three points of order 5 and one of order 9.

Page 251

1. $V = 4$, $A = 8$, $R = 4$
3. $V = 9$, $A = 17$, $R = 6$

Page 255

1. The top pair (1) is an example of such a map covering the entire torus.
The bottom pair (2) is an example of such a map covering only part of the torus.

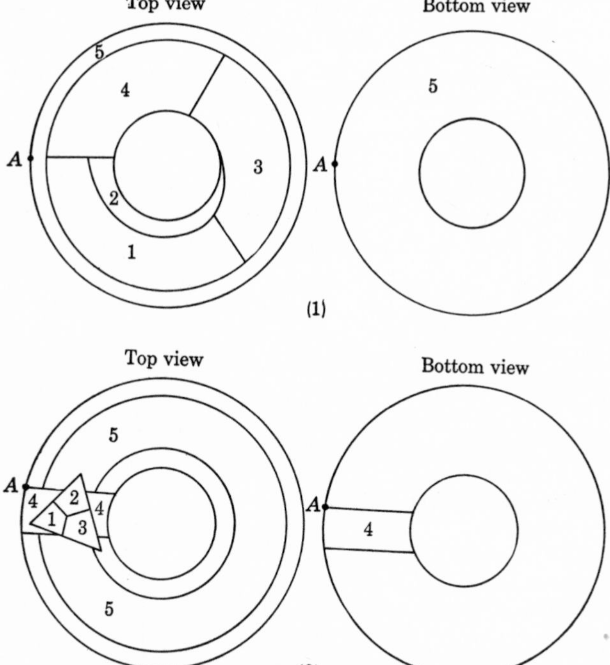

3. The Möbius band is opened out, such as

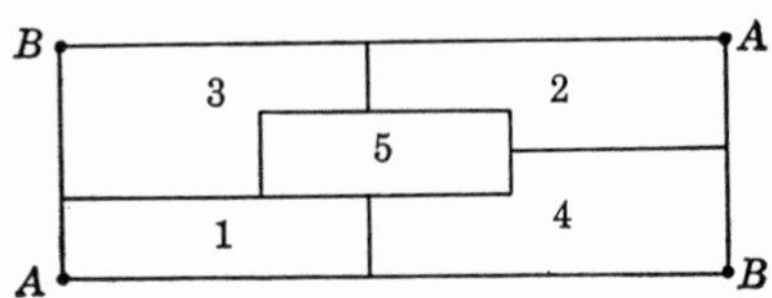

5.

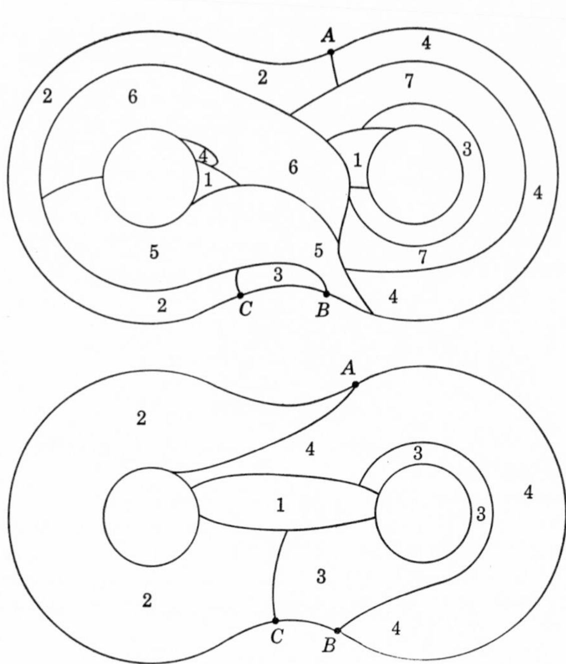

6. The six regions on a Möbius strip.

A
6
4
3
5
4
1
1
2
A